Applied Experimental Psychology

HUMAN FACTORS IN ENGINEERING DESIGN

ALPHONSE CHAPANIS
ASSISTANT PROFESSOR OF PSYCHOLOGY
WENDELL R. GARNER
DIRECTOR, PSYCHOLOGICAL LABORATORY
INSTITUTE FOR COOPERATIVE RESEARCH
CLIFFORD T. MORGAN
PROFESSOR OF PSYCHOLOGY AND
CHAIRMAN OF THE DEPARTMENT

All at The Johns Hopkins University

NEW YORK · JOHN WILEY & SONS, INC.
LONDON · CHAPMAN & HALL, LTD. · 1949

Preface

FOR YEARS EXPERIMENTAL PSYCHOLOGISTS HAVE WORKED DILIGENTLY IN academic laboratories studying man's capacities to perceive, to work, and to learn. Only very slowly, however, have the facts and methods which they have assembled been put to use in everyday life. A particularly glaring gap in modern technology, both industrial and military, is the lack of human engineering—engineering of machines for human use and engineering of human tasks for operating machines. Motion-and-time engineers have been at work for years on many of these problems, but the experimental psychologist is also needed for his fundamental knowledge of human capacities and his methods of measuring human performance.

The recent war put the spotlight on this gap. The war needed, and produced, many complex machines, and it taxed the resources of both the designer and operator in making them practical for human use. The war also brought together psychologists, physiologists, physicists, design engineers, and motion-and-time engineers to solve some of these problems. Though much of their work began too late to do any real good, it has continued on a rather large scale into the peace.

Today, there are many groups busy with research on man–machine problems. They use different names to describe the work in its various aspects: biotechnology, biomechanics, psychoacoustics, human engineering, applied psychophysics, engineering psychology, and systems research. Other names might also be appropriate and may appear in the future. In casting about for a title for this book, we tried to select one that would describe the subject matter without the restrictive connotations attaching to some of the names mentioned above. *Applied Experimental Psychology* seemed best to fill these requirements, because the traditional data and subject matter of experimental psychology are fundamental to this field. Throughout the book, we have also used the terms engineering psychology and human engineering in talking about this subject matter. But whatever the name, the objective is the same—to develop, through fundamental research and applied tests, a science that can deal adequately with the design and operation of machines for human use.

Engineering psychology, being a young field, has no textbooks. One cannot even compile a short bibliography that will give a reasonably complete view of the field. In addition to our research effort in this field, we are still in the stage of compiling information and methods from all sorts of places: from textbooks of experimental psychology, physiology, physics, and motion-and-time engineering; from the journals of these professions; and from many previously classified reports which have not yet seen the light of day. As a consequence, we who are doing research in engineering psychology are hampered by a lack of well-compiled reference material, and we have a hard time telling our potential customers, the design engineers, what we are about.

We therefore jumped at an invitation to give a series of lectures on engineering psychology to the postgraduate engineering students at the Naval Postgraduate School, Annapolis. This series of lectures—delivered in the spring of 1947—let us tell a large group of well-selected engineering officers what engineering psychology is about. It also forced us to make the first attempt at digging out and compiling information for ourselves and our colleagues in the field. These lectures were subsequently printed in a classified Naval report, and their favorable reception among workers in the field encouraged us to rewrite and expand them into this book.

One of the favorable comments we heard time and again about the printed lectures was that they were understandable. We were academics talking about technical psychological matters to an engineering audience. For this reason, we had made deliberate efforts to use small words instead of big ones; short direct sentences instead of long indirect ones; and colloquial expressions instead of academic and technical phrases. It was and is our conviction that the rigor of scientific writing need not be sacrificed in writing to students. This book has much the flavor of our lectures. We are not writing to you; we are talking to you. You will find, however, that although we may say things in an easy fashion the data and concepts we talk about are just as complicated and precise as in more academic textbooks.

For us, then, this book is an adventure—an adventure into a new field of applied science and an adventure into a new style of textbook writing.

We owe our thanks to several people who, in one way or another, have helped us see this job to completion. Dr. Fillmore H. Sanford edited and rewrote much of the original lectures before they were given at Annapolis. Although he is not directly responsible for the material in this book, his influence can be seen in these pages.

Anyone who has ever written a book knows the myriad details—illustrations, references, acknowledgments, indexing, and general supervision—that must be attended to. Miss Helene L. Kuhn has taken care of these details for us, and we are most grateful to her.

Mrs. Marion R. Chapanis and Mrs. Patricia W. Levering were primarily responsible for the typing of the manuscript.

Finally, we owe special thanks to Mr. John Spurbeck and his staff in the illustration department at The Johns Hopkins University for his meticulous work in preparing most of the figures used here.

Acknowledgments and thanks are also due the following for permission to use the figures indicated: J. D. Coakley, Figure 11; P. M. Fitts, Figures 126 and 127; H. Fletcher and W. A. Munson, Figure 94; W. F. Grether, Figure 138; W. F. Grether and A. C. Williams, Jr., Figure 62; W. E. Kappauf, W. M. Smith, and C. W. Bray, Figures 60 and 61; K. D. Kryter, Figure 103; J. C. R. Licklider, Figures 109, 110, and 111; G. A. Miller, Figures 106, 107, and 108; E. G. Shower and R. Biddulph, Figure 99; S. S. Stevens and H. Davis, Figure 98; the Acoustical Society of America, Figures 94, 99, 103, 109, and 110; and the American Psychological Association and the *Psychological Bulletin*, Figures 106, 107, and 108.

A. CHAPANIS
W. R. GARNER
C. T. MORGAN

Baltimore, Maryland
February 1949

Contents

Contents

1. *Introduction*

IN WRITING THIS BOOK, THE AUTHORS HAD THREE OBJECTIVES IN MIND. The first is definition. What does *Applied Experimental Psychology* mean? What subject matter does the title cover, and in what area is the subject matter most useful? This first chapter attempts to provide a general definition of the field, even though we must recognize that a complete definition is possible only after the entire book has been read or at least skimmed.

The second objective is to introduce the reader to the most important experimental and statistical techniques in this field. Two chapters, therefore, are concerned solely with problems of methodology because there are some new techniques that are helpful in handling experimental problems in this field, and they are not too well known. Furthermore, the statistical methodology used in an experiment is more than a tool; it is a way of thinking rigorously about quantitative data. This "way of thinking" is particularly important for the scientist in this field.

The third and most important objective is to provide an introduction to the many facts that have been accumulated in this area during the past several years. The bulk of the book is, of course, devoted to this objective. Some of the facts we discuss are specific in the sense that they can be applied only in restricted situations; others are of a general nature and will be useful in many different situations. More time will be spent on general facts because of their greater usefulness, but, when general facts are not available in discussing a particular problem, we shall offer specific facts.

WHAT IS APPLIED EXPERIMENTAL PSYCHOLOGY?

Perhaps a good way to begin a general definition of the field is to mention some of the many names that have been used to describe the subject matter. The newness of the field has led to the use of many different terms, none of which seems to express all possible shades of meaning adequately. We have chosen to call it *Applied Experimental*

Psychology for reasons we shall explain below. Other terms that have been used, however, are engineering psychology, human engineering, biomechanics, psychological problems in equipment design, the human factor in equipment design, applied psychophysics, and psychotechnology. Any of these terms could, with various degrees of precision, be used to describe the subject matter of this book. We shall frequently use many of these terms interchangeably. Particularly, we feel that the term *engineering psychology* is synonymous with applied experimental psychology and shall frequently use it as an equivalent term.

Psychology. These many terms in themselves give some idea of our interests and point of view. In the first place, this field is psychological—it is concerned with the behavior of human beings. It is concerned, however, with only certain kinds of behavior—the behavior of human beings while working with machines or instruments. We want to know about the abilities and capacities of man because we want to know how well he can work with different kinds of machines.

Design of instruments. But the applied experimental psychologist is also concerned with instruments and machines with which human beings work. His interest here, however, is in those characteristics of the machine which determine how well a man can use them. Is the machine designed in such a way that it can be used most efficiently by an operator? Can a better machine be designed—better in the sense that it can be used more easily? These are questions about the machine, but they are questions which have to do with the operation of the instrument or machine by human beings.

Man–machine relations. Perhaps the best way of stating the whole problem is to say that we, as applied experimental psychologists, are interested in the interrelation between men and machines. We want to know the best way to design a machine so that a human being can use it. How should the dials be constructed and arranged? How should the controls be designed, so that the normal human being can use them easily and accurately? How should equipments be arranged in a group?

Our interest in the design of machines for human use runs the full gamut of machine complexity—from the design of single instruments to the design of complete systems of machines which must be operated with some degree of coordination. In Chapter 5, for example, we consider some of the factors which determine how fast and accurately a single dial can be read. This is a relatively simple machine unit. But in Chapter 12, we discuss principles of the arrangement of whole units of equipments into a single integrated work area. Some of these systems—radar systems, for example—may involve groups of ten or more extremely complex machines with ten or more men working together as a team.

AN HISTORICAL APPROACH

No new branch of science suddenly springs from nowhere to become a full-fledged member of the scientific world. Science grows, and usually its growth can be traced. In the case of experimental psychology, or engineering psychology, there are three quite distinct lines of development which have led to the present status of this science. One of these developments stems from the engineering sciences; the other two have their roots in the history of psychology.

TIME-AND-MOTION ENGINEERING

One of the scientific developments that has led to the growth of engineering psychology is time-and-motion study. Time-and-motion study grew out of the engineering sciences, and the people who started it were engineers. There is a general distinction made between time studies and motion studies, in theory at least, although in practice it is often difficult to separate them.

Time study. The time relations of motions and sequences of motion are the particular concern of time studies. The primary effort here has been to find out the best working rate in order to set the base rate on which pay should be scaled. Credit for the beginning of time study usually goes to Frederick W. Taylor, who made the first time studies in the machine shop about 1881. At present some industries use time study methods in determining wage rates. Unfortunately, people have often made the too ready assumption that the primary function of a time engineer is to get more work for less money out of the worker. That is not necessarily so.

Motion study. Credit for the development of motion study is usually given to Frank B. Gilbreth, an engineer, and his psychologist wife, Lillian M. Gilbreth. Motion study, unlike time study, is concerned primarily with the manipulations or movements which a human operator must make in performing any job. It usually consists of an analysis of those movements in an attempt to get at the best way of doing a particular job by studying the various possible ways it can be done. Several techniques have been developed from motion study, some of which have been very useful to us. But we shall see more of these techniques in Chapter 12.

Job simplification. Frequently, the time-and-motion engineer has been able to assume that the machine is already there and that his task is simply to determine the individual's best way of operating the machine. Sometimes this assumption of the prior existence and status of the machine has been necessary, and at other times it has been convenient. Nevertheless, many such engineers have realized that often the machine or the job arrangement is ill designed for the capabilities of the human operator. They have frequently found it necessary to change the machine or the job, instead of trying to make the behavior of the worker conform to characteristics that really do not match his capabilities. When they make such changes, they have become interested in some of the same kinds of problems that we, as applied experimental psychologists, are concerned with.

PERSONNEL SELECTION

One root of applied experimental psychology, then, goes back into time-and-motion engineering. Personnel selection, a second historical influence, comes from psychology.

Human similarities and differences. It could be said that psychologists, in terms of their interests, fall into two general groups. Some are interested in human similarities, whereas others are interested mainly in human differences. Those concerned with similarities try to find out what the *average* person can see, feel, hear, or do under various circumstances. To such psychologists, the fact that all people are not precisely alike is simply an inconvenience. Those who work with human differences, however, consider *variability* as the problem. These two emphases have led to two different developments in psychology. The emphasis on human differences has given us the field of personnel selection as we know it today.

Intelligence selection. From its official birth until the turn of the century, psychology was primarily a science of individual similarities. Individual differences were not considered much of a problem until a psychologist named Cattell became interested in the way people differ in reaction time, in the ability to see, hear, smell, move, and solve problems. Work on human differences developed strongly during the First World War when large numbers of people became available for testing. As a result of the work during the First World War, intelligence testing became a firmly established technique.

Development of tests. The science of individual differences got the impetus it needed during the First World War, and psychologists did a tremendous amount of work on problems of personnel selection between the two wars. Industry began to use tests more and more. New tests were devised, tried out, revised, found good, and put to use. There were performance tests and paper-and-pencil tests, ability tests and interest tests, long tests, short tests, big tests, and little tests. Almost any one of them, if properly used, could be shown to have some useful selective function.

Selection of operators. The development of selection techniques stressed another aspect of the general problem of human beings working with machines. This branch of psychology developed because it was recognized that there is a best man for every kind of job, and that there is a best job for every kind of man. Some people can do some jobs better than others, and how well a man can do one job does not necessarily determine how well he can do another.

Selection versus designed jobs. There is no denying the very great significance of selection procedures. In studying and doing something about the human being in his working environment, personnel selection has been of outstanding importance. In *Applied Experimental Psychology*, however, we are not primarily interested in that aspect of the problem. We are not so much interested in selecting a particular man for the job as we are in designing the job so that the average man can perform efficiently.

Limits of selection. We have decided not to present any systematic treatment of selection techniques, partly because this field is highly specialized and there are already many excellent books on that subject. But there is another reason for our emphasis on the design of the machine rather than the selection of the man. Selection of personnel can be profitable only when there is a reasonable number of people to select from—people who have the right abilities and capabilities. Many modern machines have become so complicated that no amount of selection will make it possible to get more out of the machine. When machines become so complex that none or only a very few people can work with them satisfactorily, selection is of no help. It is necessary then to turn our attention to some of the basic problems of human limitations and to study the machine in the light of these limitations.

EXPERIMENTAL PSYCHOLOGY

The third development leading to applied experimental psychology is experimental psychology itself. Before we describe the interests and activities of the experimental psychologist, it might be well to point out that there are various kinds of psychology.

Nonexperimental psychologists. Just as there are different kinds of engineers—electrical, civil, mechanical, chemical, and so forth—so psychologists are divided into various specializations. Some psychologists have a primary interest in personality and abnormal psychology. When they are particularly interested in the treatment of abnormal cases, they are called *clinical* psychologists.

Another kind of psychologist we have already mentioned is the *personnel* psychologist, who is interested in the selection of people for various jobs. Still another kind is interested in the social interaction of human beings, or the behavior of groups of humans. These *social* psychologists work with such things as public-opinion polls, scales for measuring attitudes, propaganda devices, group morale, and racial prejudice. There are also those interested in educational problems, who are called *educational* psychologists.

Experimental psychologists. There are many other kinds of psychological specialists, but our interest is in *experimental* psychology, which is the oldest form of psychology. The usual date given for the birth of experimental psychology (at least in the laboratory) is 1879. This date like most such dates is not exact but indicates the general time when experimental psychology began to be a specialized science. In the past the experimental psychologist has been interested primarily in the behavior of the normal man—man as a perceiver and a doer— in vision, hearing, tactual sensitivity, motor behavior, and learning. He has worked mostly in university laboratories, since there were very few other places where he could apply his interests. With increased technical knowledge in other fields, however, and with increasingly technical machines, the interests of experimental psychologists became of practical importance and were put to use. Knowledge about the average human being's capabilities is now being applied in the design of instruments, and we have called this application *applied experimental psychology.*

Incidentally, it should be clear that many different types of psychologists do experiments. The name *experimental* started out to distinguish psychologists who were interested in an experimental science from those who were philosophically inclined. The name stuck to people interested in certain kinds of behavior, although since then many other psychologists have become experimental. But engineering psychology stems most directly from experimental psychology, not from the other types.

WARTIME DEVELOPMENTS

Although applied experimental psychology started at the turn of the century, scientific studies in this field during the next 40 years were rather few in number. The big impetus came during World War II when most psychologists were forced out of the academic laboratory and began to do much more practical research. The demands made during this war were so great that they could not be ignored. It was really during this time that experimental psychology merged with time-and-motion engineering to produce what we have called applied experimental psychology.

Human limitations. This last war gave new importance to many things that were not important before. It imposed new demands on machines and on the men who operate these machines. New machines were developed, and these new machines made life more complicated for the man who had to operate them. Something had to be done to make man more efficient—or, to change our perspective 180 degrees, to make the machines more efficient. Often the machine did not do what was expected of it, only because of the limitations of the humans who operated it.

We can make a machine that will do almost anything, given enough time and enough engineers. But man has limits to his development, at least as far as we can see it. When we think how much a single radar can do in a small fraction of a second, and then realize by comparison that even the simplest form of reaction for a human being requires about a fifth of a second, we realize what we are up against. Machines that demand superhuman performance will fail, and jobs that push man beyond the limits of his skill, speed, sensitivity, and endurance will not be done.

Physiological limitations. The human limitations that we have run up against are of two kinds—physiological and psychological. We have developed modern aircraft so rapidly, for example, that we are now worried about not only whether a man can fly it but also whether he can live in it. With the tremendous speeds now being obtained in modern aircraft, the purely physiological limitations of the human organism become a cardinal consideration for designers and engineers —if they want the aircraft to be flown and returned.

Psychological limitations. But we are more concerned with the psychological limitations, which we meet more frequently. Our problem is often: What can a man bear and still work? We are now reaching the point where, because of human limitations, better and better equipment does not necessarily insure better and better performance.

Even now it is surprising to remember that not until 1934 was anything done about the design of an airplane from the point of view of the individual who has to fly it, even though considerable attention was devoted to the selection of the pilots. The reasons for this are now easy to see. In the first place, the airplane of early days was fairly slow; it had only a few simple controls and instruments; and it did not fly very high. Second, there were only a few airplanes but many pilots to fly them. Selection procedures could thus work fairly well.

But during succeeding years the need for greater numbers of pilots arose. In order to get these pilots selection standards had to be lowered. In addition, the next few years produced revolutionary new aircraft, that flew so high and so fast and were so complex that many months of training were required for an ordinary man to learn to fly them. So not only were more pilots needed, but also the airplane had become more complicated. Both these factors changed the emphasis from selection of the pilot to better psychological design of the airplane.

Electronic instruments. Aircraft were not the only machines that began to tax human limitations. The electronic equipment—radio communications systems, radar, sonar—which became so common during the war imposed new problems for the human operator. Many of these instruments, in their entirety, were so complex that it was almost impossible to get the most out of the machine. The full potentialities of radar, for example, lagged far behind physical developments because human operators could not master the complex operation of this machine system. We had to worry about such things as a new kind of visual signal—very small and not very bright. In sonar we had to worry about the limits of hearing. The communications equipment likewise had its own special problems.

Historically, then, much of experimental psychology was first applied during the war—because it had to be. Science had gotten so far ahead in physical developments that something had to be done about the human beings. Physical developments had begun to reach their limits, because human beings could not operate the machines efficiently after they were built. The job of the experimental psychologist was to worry about designing these instruments so that human beings could operate them and get the most out of them.

SCIENCE AND APPLIED EXPERIMENTAL PSYCHOLOGY

In order to bring this subject into a little better perspective, it might be well to discuss for a moment the nature of science and its applications. Science can be approached from a fundamental or an applied point of view, and in *Applied Experimental Psychology* we are interested in both points of view. We are interested both in the acquisition of basic knowledge and in the application of that knowledge to engineering problems.

FUNDAMENTAL SCIENCE

Fundamental science is sometimes called "pure" science, and its general purpose is to determine basic relationships among phenomena. Scientists, for example, have been interested in discovering the basic relations among voltage, resistance, and current flow in electric circuits; the relationships among atoms in various sorts of chemical elements; the effect of extreme variations in temperature on human behavior; and so on.

Controlled experiments. The emphasis of fundamental science is on discovery rather than on application. Fundamental scientists are research people, who spend their time accumulating information, usually by controlled experiments. Traditionally, the controlled experiment is arranged so that all factors are held constant except the one being investigated. Then that factor is systematically varied, and the result of that variation on just one other factor is measured. What is varied is called the independent variable, and what is measured is called the dependent variable. When the experiment is done, we know the relation between two phenomena—the independent and dependent variables. If we like, that relationship can be stated in mathematical terms, in a graph, or in a table.

In practice, of course, experiments are not always that simple. Actually sometimes, several things are varied all at once, but, when we are done, it is still necessary to know about the relation between just two things at a time. The experimental techniques for getting information this way can get quite complicated; some of them are discussed in Chapter 3.

Scientific laws. After the scientist has assembled many specific relationships or facts, he attempts to catalog and sort them into meaningful groups and then to deduce from these many observations and relations some scientific laws or generalizations which describe all the relationships. A famous example of this sort is Newton's universal law of gravitation.

Generality of scientific laws. An important thing to remember about scientific laws is that they really are general: they apply to any relevant situation. From basic scientific laws we can make many predictions about specific things. Newton's law, for example, accounts for the rise and fall of tides, the behavior of falling bodies, and the motion of the planets. These laws are general, and they do not change with time.

We can summarize the approach of the fundamental or pure scientist, then, as follows: (*a*) He makes many systematic observations on whatever he is interested in, (*b*) he collects and arranges his data, (*c*) he pores over these data with the idea of hitting upon (*d*) some generalization which, he at least hopes, will describe once and for all the general phenomena he has been studying.

Efficiency of general laws. In any new area of science, such as engineering psychology, we look for these general relations. We look for them because they are the most efficient way of summarizing our knowledge of the field. Also, when experiments are done in such a way as to provide general laws, the acquiring of knowledge is more efficient. General laws apply to many things. Specific relations apply only to the circumstances under which the relations were obtained.

APPLIED SCIENCE

But the scientist's job has not ended when the scientific laws are established. Science becomes of practical value only when these facts or principles are applied. There are, in general, two kinds of applications of fundamental science.

Applied research. In the first place, the *techniques* of science—the research methods—can be used to find out specific information about specific things, if scientific laws do not predict what will happen in a particular instance. For example, we might want to determine which of two instruments is better in terms of an operator's ability to use them. We do a little experiment—called a test—and use the techniques of science to answer our immediate question.

Design. The second application of science involves the use of basic knowledge in the design or evaluation of equipments and machines or systems of equipment. For example, if we have the basic information about the way human arms and legs work, we can probably do a better job of designing radar or aircraft controls. Basic information about visual acuity can be used in designing new instrument dials. This putting to use of basic science provides many problems of its own.

APPLICATIONS OF ENGINEERING PSYCHOLOGY

In order to make this discussion more specific, we shall point out several ways in which experimental psychology can be applied to engineering problems. Some of these applications are essentially applied research; others involve engineering and development.

1. Appraisals. One very practical application is the testing of new equipment designs. A new design may be appraised by either comparing it to existing equipment or making a logical analysis of its characteristics. That is to say, we may be interested only in the relative value of the instrument, in which case we simply make a test comparing two or more instruments. On the other hand, if we want some absolute appraisal, we can rate the instrument in terms of its conformity to known principles of design.

2. Optimal methods of work. Another application involves the determination of optimal methods of work with equipment that is already available. It is the classical time-and-motion approach. This kind of work is practical and immediately applicable. Sometimes research is needed; at other times a time-and-motion analysis may prove sufficient.

3. Design of instruments. This is a development-engineering problem. After certain basic relations are determined, these principles are put to use in the design of new equipments. We have already stressed the importance of this type of work.

4. Design of tasks. With this type of work we should be able to classify certain kinds of jobs and to establish certain principles for the classification of such jobs. In this way jobs can be made more efficient. This application is different from that involving optimal methods of work in that here we are interested in the design of the job before the machines are decided on. The design of the job involves the design and arrangement of the equipment with which a man works; we do not assume that the equipment is already there and must be used as is. The equipment is part of the total job.

5. Design of systems. Last, but not least, we would like to determine the overall design of systems of equipment and systems of men operating the equipment. This is the problem of the coordination of

machines with other machines, or men with men, when several people
have to work together. It is not only the most difficult application
but also, often, the most important.

ORGANIZATION OF THE BOOK

Before we go on to the main sections of *Applied Experimental Psychology,* we should like to say a word about the topical organization.
In the next two chapters we take up specific problems of measurement
and experimental design. In the application of engineering psychology, it is often as necessary to know the techniques as it is to know
the facts. Remember that one of the chief applications of experimental psychology involves performing tests and appraising equipment. The little statistics that we give here are useful in that type of
problem. Furthermore, an understanding of the methodology of psychological research is necessary, because frequently it is impossible to
understand the conclusions of a particular research problem until we
know how the research was done. The generality of the conclusions
reached from research are often limited by the methodology. The
chapters on statistics, then, should give you a better appreciation of
the later factual content.

The next seven chapters (4 through 10) deal with problems of sensation and perception. You can think of these as the input to the
human operator. We are concerned with such problems as how a man
sees and how he hears; how to arrange dials, and how to design communications equipment. In general, how does a worker get the information he needs to do his work accurately and efficiently?

Then we have two chapters specifically on the problems of the output of a man. We are concerned here with what we call a man's
motor behavior and with the design of the equipment he manipulates
and uses. We discuss such things as the construction of cranks and
knobs and the arrangement of the work instruments.

In Chapters 13 and 14 we discuss some of the problems that are not
directly concerned with equipment design but that nevertheless determine the efficiency of the workingman. For example, problems of
fatigue are discussed in Chapter 13 and problems of heat and ventilation in Chapter 14.

SELECTED REFERENCES

1. BARNES, R. M. *Motion and time study* (3d Ed.). New York: John Wiley, 1949.
2. FITTS, P. M. Psychological research on equipment design in the AAF. *Amer. Psychologist,* 1947, **2,** 93–98.
3. KAPPAUF, W. E. History of psychological studies of the design and operation of equipment. *Amer. Psychologist,* 1947, **2,** 83–86.
4. STEVENS, S. S. Machines cannot fight alone. *Amer. Scientist,* 1946, **34,** 389–400.
5. TAYLOR, F. V. Psychology at the Naval Research Laboratory. *Amer. Psychologist,* 1947, **2,** 87–92.

2. A Little Statistics

THE PURPOSE OF THIS CHAPTER IS TO INTRODUCE SOME ELEMENTARY statistical concepts and formulas. It is obviously impossible to do a very thorough job in a short chapter, and at best this can only serve as an introduction to the field. This chapter has two objectives: (*a*) to provide a common basis for understanding some of the statistical terms that will keep cropping up in the research data throughout the rest of the book, and (*b*) to serve as a background for some statistical ideas that have special importance in the investigation of man–machine relationships. The latter techniques are discussed in Chapter 3.

Statistics and everyday life. The man in the street has very little use for statistics, or so he thinks, and if you were to ask him about it he would probably tell you that statistics is some "highfalutin" kind of mathematics that has very little to do with everyday life. Even some research workers will tell you that they never need or use statistics. Actually this is about as sensible as saying that we do not need numbers to get along in our present world. Anyone who owns insurance is subscribing to one of the most complex statistical plans ever devised by man. Production charts are statistical charts. The fact that men tend to be taller and heavier than women is a statistical fact. Inspection procedures in industry make use of statistical sampling methods. Even our belief that the sun will rise tomorrow is an expression of our faith in statistical probabilities. So, whether we like it or not, statistics surround us constantly in our everyday life. We cannot get along without them. The problem is one of deciding what kind of statistics we need for our own particular jobs.

The uses of statistics. There are two principal uses of statistics. The first is to summarize and describe large masses of data. This kind of statistical analysis is called descriptive statistics. The second is to interpret and make forecasts about events that have not yet happened. This is sometimes called sampling, interpretive, or predictive statistics. We shall present examples of both types of statistics. It is important to point out, however, that descriptive statistics are usually pretty straightforward. There is very little to argue about in descriptive statistics since, after all, they merely describe and summarize a set of data. Most of the hot statistical arguments are concerned with sampling or interpretive statistics, and it is in this branch of analysis that we find some really bad "boners."

DESCRIPTIVE STATISTICS

The value of statistics in summarizing and describing sets of data can be demonstrated by working through the following example. A quality control statistician was assigned to study a production line manufacturing bushings. The specifications called for an outside diameter of 2.0000 inches with tolerances of ±0.0032 inch. In order to determine whether a process is under control, the statistician needs actual measurements; counts of the number of items which pass a go–no-go gage do not yield enough information. An inspector was provided to obtain these measurements, and he recorded the outside diameters of every tenth bushing that came along the production line. Two hundred such measurements, made to the nearest 0.0001 inch, are shown in Table 1. You will probably agree that it is pretty hard to make much sense of the data when they are presented in this way. About all you can tell is that the bushings varied from 1.9943 to 2.0056 inches and that there were only five bushings which were exactly 2.0000 inches in size.

DISTRIBUTIONS IN TABULAR AND GRAPHIC FORM

Frequency distributions. The first thing a statistician usually does with data like these is to arrange and group them numerically in a way which can be more easily understood. He constructs what is known as a *frequency distribution* (Table 2). Since individual measurements are usually not important by themselves, he makes the data more compact by squeezing them into *classes*. The seventh class from the top, for example, contains all measurements between 2.0023 and 2.0027 inches, inclusive. Eight bushings fall into this category. The next lower class contains all measurements (11 in all) between 2.0018 and 2.0022 inches, inclusive.

By grouping the data into a frequency distribution, we have both gained and lost something. We have lost the ability to identify individual measurements (for example, we can no longer tell from Table 2 how big the 27th bushing was), but this kind of information is seldom of much value anyway. What appears to be a more serious loss is that we cannot identify the precise value of any individual measure-

TABLE 1. OUTSIDE DIAMETERS OF 200 BUSHINGS MEASURED TO THE NEAREST
0.0001 INCH

2.0039	1.9956	2.0026	2.0004	2.0005
2.0014	1.9996	1.9994	1.9977	2.0023
1.9980	2.0025	2.0043	2.0004	1.9989
2.0000	2.0028	1.9954	1.9974	1.9992
1.9973	1.9994	2.0009	2.0033	2.0005
1.9996	1.9998	2.0026	2.0031	2.0034
2.0010	1.9995	1.9976	2.0009	1.9991
1.9999	1.9979	1.9983	1.9972	1.9998
2.0003	1.9968	2.0013	2.0007	2.0041
2.0037	2.0012	1.9985	2.0018	1.9987
2.0021	2.0008	2.0014	2.0000	2.0016
2.0006	2.0015	1.9971	2.0020	2.0046
1.9976	1.9988	2.0021	1.9990	2.0039
1.9978	1.9975	1.9988	2.0008	1.9986
2.0006	1.9984	2.0005	1.9948	2.0023
1.9943	2.0022	1.9985	1.9964	2.0005
1.9993	1.9967	2.0006	2.0008	1.9959
2.0016	1.9958	2.0056	1.9982	1.9999
1.9970	1.9996	1.9997	2.0009	1.9979
2.0005	1.9991	1.9989	2.0017	1.9993
2.0001	1.9997	1.9989	2.0020	1.9969
2.0049	2.0010	1.9981	2.0002	2.0001
1.9997	1.9963	1.9990	2.0031	1.9984
1.9992	1.9997	2.0000	2.0003	2.0027
2.0035	2.0002	1.9999	2.0016	2.0022
1.9998	1.9995	1.9997	1.9978	2.0007
1.9998	2.0009	2.0029	1.9996	2.0011
2.0012	1.9984	2.0033	1.9990	2.0013
2.0019	1.9992	2.0025	2.0002	1.9999
1.9981	1.9970	2.0011	2.0015	2.0013
2.0007	1.9985	1.9982	1.9980	2.0001
2.0000	1.9995	1.9984	2.0050	2.0003
2.0001	2.0010	1.9988	2.0008	1.9987
1.9983	2.0005	2.0028	1.9991	1.9993
2.0023	2.0004	2.0001	1.9989	1.9983
2.0015	1.9986	1.9993	2.0006	1.9982
1.9975	2.0010	2.0019	2.0000	1.9966
2.0030	1.9995	1.9987	1.9979	1.9999
1.9991	2.0019	1.9994	2.0017	2.0003
2.0018	2.0012	2.0015	1.9990	1.9996

TABLE 2. FREQUENCY DISTRIBUTION OF THE DATA IN TABLE 1

Class limits, inches from to	Actual midpoints	Coded midpoints	Frequency, numbers of bushings
(1)	(2)	(3)	(4)
2.0053–2.0057	2.0055	22	1
2.0048–2.0052	2.0050	21	2
2.0043–2.0047	2.0045	20	2
2.0038–2.0042	2.0040	19	3
2.0033–2.0037	2.0035	18	5
2.0028–2.0032	2.0030	17	6
2.0023–2.0027	2.0025	16	8
2.0018–2.0022	2.0020	15	11
2.0013–2.0017	2.0015	14	14
2.0008–2.0012	2.0010	13	17
2.0003–2.0007	2.0005	12	20
1.9998–2.0002	2.0000	11	22
1.9993–1.9997	1.9995	10	21
1.9988–1.9992	1.9990	9	18
1.9983–1.9987	1.9985	8	15
1.9978–1.9982	1.9980	7	12
1.9973–1.9977	1.9975	6	7
1.9968–1.9972	1.9970	5	6
1.9963–1.9967	1.9965	4	4
1.9958–1.9962	1.9960	3	2
1.9953–1.9957	1.9955	2	2
1.9948–1.9952	1.9950	1	1
1.9943–1.9947	1.9945	0	1

ment. We can no longer tell what the eight measurements were like in the seventh class. They might all have been 2.0023 inches, or 2.0024 inches, or there might have been one of 2.0023 inches, three of 2.0024 inches, and four of 2.0027 inches. As we shall see later, however, this is not really so serious as it looks.

In exchange for the loss of identity of individual measurements, we have gained quite a bit. The frequency distribution in Table 2 gives us much more information than we could get from the unarranged data. We can see at a glance that most of the bushings had outside diameters very close to the one called for in the specifications. Twenty-two of the 200 bushings (11 percent) were within ±0.0002 inch; 63 of the 200 bushings (31.5 percent) were within ±0.0007 inch; and 23 of the 200 (11.5 percent) fell outside the tolerances allowed. Our first statistical transformation—the construction of a frequency distribution—has been a big help in enabling us to see at a glance the general nature of our data.

The normal curve. We can show something more about our data by plotting them in what is called a *histogram* (Figure 1). Now it becomes apparent that most measurements are grouped around a central value, that they gradually tail off towards the ends in both directions from the center, and that they are symmetrically distributed. Many kinds of biological, psychological, and even physical measurements follow this pattern. The smooth bell-shaped curve drawn in

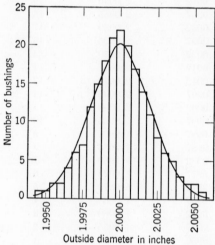

Fig. 1. Histogram of the 200 bushing measurements in Tables 1 and 2.

Figure 1 is the model for data of this kind. It has been variously called the *normal curve, normal probability curve, normal curve of error, Gaussian curve,* and many other names. Data fall into a normal curve when the things being measured are caused by a large number of factors each of which operates according to chance. Many of our statistical procedures—and quality control procedures as well—rest on the assumption that the measurements concerned are normally distributed.

Other normal distributions. This notion of normal distributions is such an important one that we ought to look at some other examples. Shown in Figure 2 is a distribution of 428 errors in range obtained with a modern radar. Radar operators ranged on a series of targets whose distances were accurately known by independent measurement. A range error is the difference between the range reported by the radar operator and the true range of the target. Notice the characteristic symmetrical nature of the data.

Other distributions of this sort have been published by Pearson [5] on (a) tensile-strength measurements of cement–mortar briquettes made of a particular brand of cement, (b) the life span of electric light bulbs operated at rated voltage, and (c) the ash content of samples of coal obtained over a 5-year period. Of a somewhat different sort are some data reported by Campbell and Lovell [1] on 72 independent laboratory ratings of the octane number of the *same* fuel. When the 72 octane

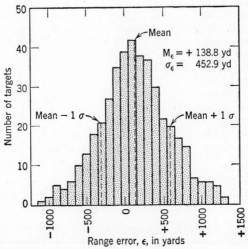

Fig. 2. Histogram of 428 errors in range obtained with a modern radar. Each measurement is the difference between the range reported by the radar operator and the true range of the target.

ratings were plotted they also came very close to a normal distribution.

Measurements of human characteristics are almost all normally distributed. This is definitely true of most physical measurements, such as height, weight, visual acuity, or strength of grip, and is probably true of complex psychological functions as well. Intelligence, reaction time, learning ability, mechanical ability, and many other human traits are usually assumed to be normally distributed.

Skewed distributions. Not *all* distributions turn out to be normal, as are those discussed so far. Another type of distribution the statistician finds fairly frequently is the *skewed distribution*. In a skewed distribution the measurements are grouped around a central value, and they decrease towards the ends in both directions just as in a normal distribution. But the skewed distribution differs from a normal one

TABLE 3. ANNUAL SALARIES OF 132 INSTRUCTORS AND PROFESSORS AT
UNIVERSITY X

Class limits from to	Actual midpoints	Coded midpoints	Frequency, f
(1)	(2)	(3)	(4)
$9,500–$9,999	$9,750	14	1
9,000– 9,499	9,250	13	1
8,500– 8,999	8,750	12	1
8,000– 8,499	8,250	11	2
7,500– 7,999	7,750	10	2
7,000– 7,499	7,250	9	3
6,500– 6,999	6,750	8	5
6,000– 6,499	6,250	7	7
5,500– 5,999	5,750	6	8
5,000– 5,499	5,250	5	12
4,500– 4,999	4,750	4	25
4,000– 4,499	4,250	3	31
3,500– 3,999	3,750	2	19
3,000– 3,499	3,250	1	10
2,500– 2,999	2,750	0	5

		Total	132
		Mean Salary	$4,818.18
		Median Salary	$4,520.00

in this important respect: The measurements are not symmetrically
distributed. The salary data in Table 3 and Figure 3 are a good
illustration. Most professors earn salaries between $4,000 and $4,499.
The five lowest-paid instructors earn salaries between $2,500 and
$2,999. But on the high side salaries go up nearly to $10,000. The
difference between the salaries of the highest-paid professor and the
most typical professor is much greater than the difference between the
lowest-paid instructor and the most typical professor. The distribution, in short, tails off much more slowly on the high side than it does
on the low side. It is said to be positively skewed. If the distribution stretched out longer toward the low values than toward the high
ones, it would be negatively skewed.

Variation the rule rather than the exception. We have provided
these illustrations to show that variation in almost anything we measure is the rule rather than the exception. No matter how much a producer may strive for uniformity, there will always be some fluctuations
in the quality of his product. It may not always be apparent, because
most inspection procedures operate on a go–no-go principle. If none
of a series of items is rejected, you might get the idea that the items

are all the same. This is not true. It merely means that the variations in the product are less than certain arbitrary tolerances. But the variations are there just the same.

The fact of psychological variability provides the basis for most psychological testing programs. If everyone could learn just as well as his neighbor, or if everyone had the same amount of natural mechanical "sense" as his neighbor, there would be no point to giving psychological tests. But human differences are so great that it is

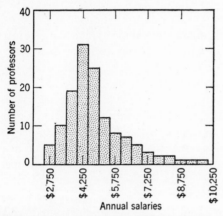

Fig. 3. Histogram of the annual salaries of 132 instructors and professors at University X.

often very profitable to select those individuals who have more of these abilities. Training time and accident rates can often be decreased and production increased markedly by selecting certain kinds of individuals for certain jobs.

MEASURES OF CENTRAL TENDENCY

The arithmetic mean. One of the first and simplest kinds of statistics we can compute for a batch of data is a measure of central tendency. An *average* is such a measure. It is used so commonly that many people hardly realize that this is the first step in statistical analysis. An average is a single number near the center of a distribution which can be used to typify or represent the whole group of data. The simplest kind of average—and what most people mean when they say average—is the *arithmetic mean*. Its formula is

$$M = \frac{\Sigma X}{N} \tag{1}$$

X represents any one of our measurements, Σ (the capital Greek letter sigma) means "the sum of," and N is the total number of observations. To calculate the mean of the data in Table 1, we add up all the bushing measurements and divide by 200. Thus:

$$M = \frac{2.0039 + 2.0014 + 1.9980 + \cdots + 1.9996}{200}$$

$$= \frac{400.0078}{200} = 2.00004 \text{ inches}$$

The mean bushing diameter, rounded off to the nearest ten-thousandth of an inch, is thus equal to 2.0000 inches. This tells us that, on the average, this production line produced bushings that were exactly what the specifications called for.

Short-cut calculation of the mean. The method we used to calculate the mean may become quite tedious when the number of measurements is as large as in this case. When the data are grouped in a frequency distribution it is possible to make use of a short cut which greatly simplifies the computation. This short-cut method makes one assumption, that all of the cases in any class are located at the midpoint of the class. There is, of course, some loss in accuracy in making this assumption, but the loss is extremely small and, for most practical purposes, insignificant. In this example we use the same formula 1 as before, except that we assume that every case in each class falls at the midpoints given in column 2 of Table 2. Thus:

$$M = \frac{2.0055 + 2.0050 + 2.0050 + 2.0045 + \cdots + 1.9945}{200}$$

$$= \frac{\left\{ \begin{array}{l} (1)(2.0055) + (2)(2.0050) + (2)(2.0045) \\ \quad + (3)(2.0040) + \cdots + (1)(1.9945) \end{array} \right\}}{200}$$

$$= \frac{400.0100}{200} = 2.00005$$

The mean value obtained is almost exactly the same as the mean obtained by the more laborious but exact method.

Even with this method our computations are still tedious because the numbers are so big. We can make this calculation much simpler by coding the midpoints of the class intervals as was done in column 3 of Table 2. Coding makes no additional assumptions and involves no loss in accuracy. In this case, it involves subtracting 1.9945 from each midpoint and dividing the difference by 0.0005. The coded midpoints are now much smaller numbers and easier to work with. The only thing that needs to be remembered is that we must correct the final coded answer to get the true mean. To correct the coded mean value we must perform the opposite kinds of arithmetic operations in the reverse order; that is, we must first *multiply* the coded mean by 0.0005 and then *add* 1.9945. We shall use the symbol M' to refer to the mean calculated with coded values and M to refer to the mean calculated with actual values. Our computation procedure is exactly as before.

$$M' = \frac{(1)(22) + (2)(21) + (2)(20) + (3)(19) + \cdots + (1)(1) + (1)(0)}{200}$$

$$M' = \frac{2220}{200} = 11.10$$

$$M = [(0.0005)(M')] + 1.9945 = [(0.0005)(11.10)] + 1.9945$$

$$= 0.00555 + 1.9945 = 2.00005$$

This is exactly the same answer we get by doing the computations with the actual midpoints.

The median. The mean is a very stable measure and so is usually the preferred measure of central tendency for most statistical computations. In badly skewed distributions, however, the mean may not be representative, or typical, of the data because it is weighted too heavily by extreme values. In such cases another measure of central tendency, the median, is frequently used instead. Thus, the mean salary in Table 3 turns out to be $4,818.18. You will probably agree that this seems a little high for these data. The median is more appropriate because it is the point in a distribution which divides the values in half. Thus, the median salary is $4,520. Exactly half the professors earn more than this amount; half earn less.

Since, by definition, the median divides the distribution exactly in half, the median salary is that of the 66th highest-paid professor. Sixty-five professors earn $4,499 or less, so that the median must be more than $4,500. In this case, it is computed by interpolation to be:

$$\text{med} = \$4,500 + \tfrac{1}{25}(500) = \$4,520$$

This computation can be checked by working in the reverse direction. Forty-two professors earn $5,000 or more. The salary of the 66th one, by interpolation, is $2\tfrac{4}{25}$ths of $500 less than that. Thus:

$$\text{med} = \$5,000 - \tfrac{24}{25}(500) = \$4,520$$

The median bushing size for the data of Table 2 is 2.0000 inches, which is exactly the same as the mean value. It is characteristic of normally or nearly normally distributed data that the mean and median are nearly identical.

A measure of skewness. The difference between the mean and median of a set of scores forms the basis for one measure of skewness of distributions. If the mean and median are very much alike, the distribution is probably normal. If they are very much different, the chances are that the distribution is skewed. Since we cannot consider this problem in greater detail here, the interested reader should consult the textbooks mentioned later for a more complete discussion of these techniques. For our purposes, it is important only to note that when a median is reported in experimental data the reason is probably that the distribution is skewed.

MEASURES OF DISPERSION

After he has calculated an appropriate measure of central tendency, the statistician usually wants to have some measure of dispersion to tell him how closely the data are grouped around the measure of central tendency. A mean or median is not enough, because it is possible to have two distributions with identical means but with widely different amounts of dispersion. The data in both distributions in Figure 4 have the same means and medians and the same numbers of observations. But the data in the tall slender distribution are much more consistent—the industrial statistician would say that they indicate better control—than the data in the other distribution.

Range. A simple measure of dispersion is the *range* of values encountered, that is, the difference between the highest and lowest values. In Table 1, for example, the bushing data varied from 1.9943 to 2.0056 inches—a range of 0.0113 inch. As a quickly computed simple measure of dispersion the range is a fairly useful statistic. It is not a particularly stable one, however, because (a) it is dependent on only extreme values which might easily vary considerably, and (b) it is based on only two measures—it does not take into account the other 198 measurements in Table 1. If our extreme values had been 1.9950 and 2.0050 inches—as they might easily have been—the range would be only 0.0100 inch.

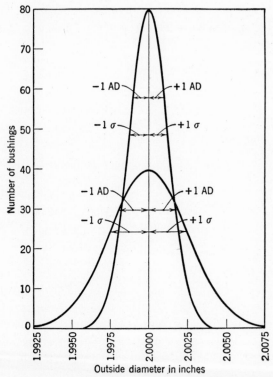

Fɪɢ. 4. Two frequency distributions with identical means but with different amounts of dispersion.

Average deviation. A commonly used measure of dispersion which is more stable than the range is the average deviation. It tells us how much, on the average, all our measurements deviate from the mean. Its equation is

$$AD = \frac{\Sigma \left| X - M_x \right|}{N} \tag{2}$$

The two vertical bars in this equation mean that we use the absolute deviation of each measurement from the mean without regard to its sign. We are interested, in short, in how far off the individual measures are from the mean, regardless of whether each measure is greater or less than the mean. For the ungrouped data in Table 1, the average deviation is found by subtracting each score from the mean and computing the mean of the differences, algebraic signs being ignored. Thus:

$$AD = \frac{\left\{ \begin{array}{l} |\ 2.0039 - 2.0000\ | + |\ 2.0014 - 2.0000\ | \\ \ \ + |\ 1.9980 - 2.0000\ | + \cdots + |\ 1.9996 - 2.0000\ | \end{array} \right\}}{200}$$

$$= \frac{0.0039 + 0.0014 + 0.0020 + \cdots + 0.0004}{200}$$

$$= \frac{0.3150}{200} = 0.00158$$

For the grouped data in Table 2, the average deviation, computed with midpoint values, is

$$AD = \frac{\left\{ \begin{array}{l} 1\ |\ 2.0055 - 2.0000\ | + 2\ |\ 2.0050 - 2.0000\ | \\ \ \ + 2\ |\ 2.0045 - 2.0000\ | + \cdots + 1\ |\ 1.9945 - 2.0000\ | \end{array} \right\}}{200}$$

$$= \frac{0.3140}{200} = 0.00157$$

Notice that we lost virtually nothing in accuracy by using our short-cut computation method. Using coded midpoint values also gives us identical results, provided we use the coded mean in our computations and remember to correct for it later. Thus:

$$AD' = \frac{\left\{ \begin{array}{l} 1\ |\ 22 - 11.1\ | + 2\ |\ 21 - 11.1\ | \\ \ \ + 2\ |\ 20 - 11.1\ | + 3\ |\ 19 - 11.1\ | + \cdots \end{array} \right\}}{200}$$

$$= \frac{630.2}{200} = 3.151$$

$$AD = (0.0005)(AD') = (0.0005)(3.151) = 0.00158$$

Standard deviation. By far the most common and useful measure of dispersion is the *standard deviation*, symbolized by the small Greek letter σ. (Although quality control and other statisticians frequently refer to the standard deviation by its Greek name, sigma, the reader will realize that this can very easily be confused with the capital letter which means "the sum of.") The standard deviation is a considerably more stable measure than the average deviation and has some other valuable properties which we will discover later. Its formula is

$$\sigma = \sqrt{\frac{\Sigma(X - M)^2}{N}} \tag{3}$$

To use it for the data of Table 1 we get

$$\sigma = \sqrt{\frac{\left\{\begin{array}{l} (2.0039 - 2.0000)^2 + (2.0014 - 2.0000)^2 \\ + (1.9980 - 2.0000)^2 + \cdots + (1.9996 - 2.0000)^2 \end{array}\right\}}{200}}$$

$$= 0.00202$$

Short-cut computation of the standard deviation. Formula 3 is very difficult to use because it involves 200 subtractions and 200 numbers to be squared. Statisticians more frequently use the following formula which, although it looks more formidable, is actually much simpler:

$$\sigma = \sqrt{\frac{N\Sigma X^2 - (\Sigma X)^2}{N^2}} \tag{4}$$

Formula 4 is exactly equivalent to formula 3, as any statistician would be glad to prove to you. Both will give the same answer. Let us look at what the various symbols mean. N is still the number of measures, that is, 200. ΣX^2 is the sum of all the measures squared, that is, $(2.0039)^2 + (2.0014)^2 + (1.9980)^2 + \cdots + (1.9996)^2$. $(\Sigma X)^2$ is the squared sum of all the values, that is, $(2.0039 + 2.0014 + 1.9980 + \cdots + 1.9996)^2$. Now we can see that formula 4 has eliminated 200 separate $(X - M)$ subtractions and that the (ΣX) quantity is already available from our computation of the mean. As applied to Table 1,

$$\sigma = \sqrt{\frac{200(800.03201262) - (400.0078)^2}{40,000}} = 0.00202$$

This same formula 4 works equally well with data arranged in a frequency distribution. Using the coded midpoints in Table 2, ΣX^2 is equal to $(1)(22)^2 + (2)(21)^2 + (2)(20)^2 + (3)(19)^2 + \cdots + (1)(0)^2$, or 27,884. ΣX, we found, in our computation of the mean using coded values, to be 2,220. As before, we must be sure to correct our coded standard deviation by a factor of 0.0005. Thus:

$$\sigma' = \sqrt{\frac{200(27,884) - (2,220)^2}{40,000}} = 4.026$$

$$\sigma = (0.0005)(\sigma') = (0.0005)(4.026) = 0.00201$$

Even though we used midpoints instead of actual values, the standard deviation is practically identical to the value obtained by direct computation.

The use of a standard deviation. Having computed a standard deviation, we are now in a position to ask: What good is it? One obvious answer is that it tells us how widely dispersed our data are. The smaller the standard deviation, the more closely are the data grouped around the mean value. In addition to this, however, the standard deviation gives the statistician some fairly precise information about the way the data are dispersed in a normal distribution. Using special tables of the normal curve, the statistician can predict that about 68.3 percent of the data will fall between the mean and one standard deviation above and below the mean. About 95.4 percent of the data will fall between the mean and two standard deviations above and below it, while 3 σ's above and below the mean include 99.7 percent of the cases.

Let us see how this works out in our bushing example. With a mean of 2.0000 and a σ of 0.0020, we should expect to find about 68 percent, or 136 bushings, with outside diameters between 2.0020—(2.0000 + 0.0020)—and 1.9980—(2.0000 − 0.0020)—inches. By actual count, there are 141. Similarly we should expect to find about 95 percent, or 190 bushings, with outside diameters between 2.0040—[2.0000 + (2 × 0.0020)]—and 1.9960—[2.0000 − (2 × 0.0020)]—inches. By actual count there are 188. Finally, we should expect to find about 99.7 percent, or 199 bushings, with outside diameters between 2.0060 —[2.0000 + (3 × 0.0020)]—and 1.9940—[2.0000 − (3 × 0.0020)]— inches. Actually all 200 cases fall within these limits.

Tables of the normal curve are worked out so that the statistician can predict percentages other than those given above. The middle 50 percent of the cases in a normal distribution, for example, fall between the mean and plus or minus 0.6745 σ's. Thus we can expect 100 bushings with diameters between 2.0013 and 1.9987. Actually there were 104. Although these predictions are not perfect, they are very close and the standard deviation helps the statistician to "size up" the data in a normal distribution with reasonable accuracy.

A MEASURE OF RELATIONSHIP

Correlation. So far we have been discussing statistics for describing sets of measurements that vary along some single scale, for example, length, error in yards, and height. Frequently, however, we are interested in describing the *relationship* between measurements on one kind of scale and those on some other kind of scale. Height and weight are a good example. Just by looking at people you can tell that there is a relationship between height and weight: As a general rule, taller people weigh more than shorter people. But you can also tell that the relationship is not perfect. Some persons who are 5 feet tall weigh more than others who are 6 feet tall. How good is the relationship? That is what a correlation measures—the strength of the relationship between measurements of one kind with those of another kind.

An industrial example. Correlations have their place in industrial and engineering work too. In dealing with metal products, for example, specifications frequently state that the metal samples shall have a certain strength. But in order to test the strength of the samples, many of them must be destroyed. The producer will be ahead if he can find some kind of test that (*a*) is related to strength and (*b*) does not destroy the sample.

An industrial engineer faced with this problem decided to investigate the relationship between the tensile strength of aluminum die castings and the hardness of the samples as measured by Rockwell's E. His decision was made on the basis of a general observation that the harder castings didn't seem to break as easily as the softer ones. Measurements on a sample of 20 castings are shown in Table 4 and

TABLE 4. THE HARDNESS AND TENSILE STRENGTH OF 20 ALUMINUM DIE CASTINGS

Hardness, Rockwell's E	Tensile strength, pounds per square inch	Hardness, Rockwell's E	Tensile strength, pounds per square inch
62	31,300	64	24,950
78	36,250	80	33,150
85	32,200	90	34,600
70	28,750	96	39,100
54	27,550	85	36,350
53	22,850	57	25,700
70	35,400	45	24,500
78	29,850	61	27,550
49	27,400	69	31,650
43	21,550	72	32,450

Figure 5. It is easy to see from Figure 5 that there is some relationship here. The five castings with hardness ratings of 80 or more have tensile strengths of 32,200 pounds per square inch or greater; the six castings with hardness ratings of 57 or less have tensile strengths of 27,550 pounds per square inch or less. But the relationship is not per-

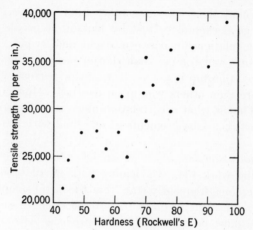

F‍IG. 5. The relationship between the hardness and tensile strength of the 20 aluminum die castings listed in Table 4.

fect. It is impossible to draw a single straight line through all of the points. How good is the relationship?

Calculating a correlation coefficient. The coefficient of correlation r is a single number that tells us the degree of correlation between sets of paired measurements. Its formula is

$$r = \frac{\Sigma(X - M_x)(Y - M_y)}{N\sigma_x\sigma_y} \tag{5}$$

In practice, the statistician uses another formula which looks a lot more complicated but is actually simpler to use. It is

$$r = \frac{N\Sigma XY - \Sigma X\Sigma Y}{\sqrt{[N\Sigma X^2 - (\Sigma X)^2][N\Sigma Y^2 - (\Sigma Y)^2]}} \tag{6}$$

Formula 6 is mathematically identical to formula 5. Since we have two sets of measurements here, we are using X to refer to one of them, the hardness ratings, and Y to the other, the tensile strengths.

The only new term which formula 6 introduces is ΣXY. In Table 4 this is equal to $(62 \times 31,300) + (78 \times 36,250) + \cdots + (72 \times 32,450)$, or 42,266,250. Inserting the proper numbers into formula 6 gives us

$$r = \frac{(20 \times 42,266,250) - (1,361 \times 603,100)}{\sqrt{(20 \times 96,989) - (1,361)^2}\sqrt{(20 \times 18,640,810,000) - (603,100)^2}}$$

$$= \frac{24,505,900}{28,190,167} = +0.869$$

What does the correlation coefficient mean? Having computed a correlation, we are now in a position to ask: What does it mean? Correlation coefficients vary from +1.00 through 0 to −1.00. A zero correlation means that there is no relationship between the two sets of scores (see Figure 6). The higher the coefficient, the closer the relationship. Thus, an *r* of 0.80 indicates a closer relationship than one of 0.40. But the coefficients do not, unfortunately, tell you the amount of relationship directly. The co-efficients are not percentages, and an *r* of 0.80 is not twice as much as one of 0.40. The amount of relationship between sets of data is indicated better by r^2. A correlation of 0.707 ($r^2 = 0.50$) is thus twice as close as one of 0.50 ($r^2 = 0.25$).

Positive and negative coefficients of the same numerical value are equally good. An *r* of −0.80 indicates as much correlation as one of +0.80. The sign merely tells us the direction of the relationship. A positive correlation means that the scores in one variable increase as the scores in the other increase. Thus, as the hardness of the die castings increased, the tensile strength increased. But, if we had

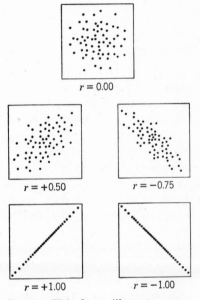

Fig. 6. This figure illustrates correlation coefficients of various amounts.

correlated the thickness of optical lenses against the amount of light transmitted, we would find a negative correlation. The thicker the lens, the less light gets through. You can get some idea about the closeness of an *r* from the samples in Figure 6.

Correlation and causation. Many people think that a high correlation between two variables means that one causes the other. This is not so at all. Just because there is a high correlation between the hardness and tensile strengths of the 20 die castings, we are not justified in saying that variations in hardness *cause* variations in tensile strength. Nor can we say that variations in tensile strength produce or cause variations in hardness. Variations in hardness and tensile strength may both be the result of other factors in the manufacturing process, for example, quenching—the rate at which the castings are cooled, variations in pressure applied to the mold, variations in the composition of the alloy, or variations in the mechanics of pouring.

Similarly, the fact that height is correlated with weight among people does not mean that one causes the other. Variations in both height and weight are caused by variations in our genetic inheritance, nutrition, disease, and the like. A correlation, in short, merely tells us that two sets of measurements or scores tend to vary in unison. This does not mean that a correlation has no practical importance. We will show what we can do with one later.

SUMMARY

Thus far we have taken a quick look at three kinds of elementary statistical concepts: measures of central tendency, measures of variability, and correlation. In one example, we started with a heterogeneous collection of 200 data and saw how the statistician can take data of this sort, arrange them, compress them, and calculate a few simple statistics to represent the whole batch. If you have followed this development, it should be clear that only three simple items of information are necessary to describe the large set of measurements we had. These are: (1) The data are normally distributed, (2) the mean is equal to 2.0000 inches, and (3) the standard deviation is equal to 0.0020 inch. Knowing these three simple things, the statistician can predict with surprising accuracy the original form of the data.

In the correlation example, we saw that one simple number—the correlation coefficient—can give the statistician a pretty good idea about the amount of relationship between two sets of scores.

This discussion by no means exhausts the gamut of descriptive statistics available to the statistician. There are many more for describing normally distributed data and still others for data that do not fall into this pattern, that is, that are skewed in one way or another. But perhaps this will serve to emphasize the importance of statistics in handling and working with experimental data.

STATISTICAL INFERENCE

For all their importance in describing data, statistics serve a much more useful function in enabling us to make predictions about data we have not collected. It is this aspect of statistics that the experimenter and quality control statistician are primarily interested in. Not only are they interested in the measurements of 200 bushings taken from the production line, but they would also like to be able to predict what the measurements would be like if they sampled a lot more under the same conditions.

Population and sample. This problem of prediction may be rephrased in a slightly different way. Given a sample of data, can we predict the characteristics of the *population,* or *universe,* from which this sample was taken? In this sense, a population refers to a large collection of measurements all having a common character, or characteristic. A population is a logical class of units having something in common. It may be the heights of all males in the United States, all errors in range obtained with a particular radar, or, in our example, the outside diameters of all bushings coming from a production line. Rarely, however, can we ever measure all the units in a population. We have to take samples from these populations and use these samples to predict the characteristics of the population.

Fortunately for us, mathematicians have demonstrated that we can make fairly accurate predictions about a population if we have a *random* sample of data from it. Taking a random sample of males in the United States, medical statisticians can predict with fairly good results how the heights of all men in the United States are distributed. Given a random sample of bushings, the industrial statistician can predict with surprising accuracy what the whole batch will be like: what the average outside diameter will be, how many will pass inspection tolerances, and so on.

Standard error of the mean. Suppose that we have a normally distributed population of measurements and that we draw repeated random samples of size N from this population. Because of minor random fluctuations from sample to sample we could hardly expect the means of our successive samples to agree exactly. If we took enough samples, however, we would find that the means of the samples formed a normal distribution with a mean and standard deviation all their own. The standard deviation of this distribution of sample means is called the standard error of a mean and is equal to

$$SE_M = \frac{\sigma_{\text{pop}}}{\sqrt{N}} \tag{7}$$

where σ_{pop} is the standard deviation of measures in the population and N is the number of measures in the sample.

Population variability. The formula for the standard error of a mean contains a term that we cannot measure directly, namely, σ_{pop}. Fortunately, the calculus of probability has shown that this value can

be estimated with considerable accuracy from the standard deviation
of a sample drawn from the population. If σ_S is the standard deviation of the sample, then,

$$\sigma_{\text{pop}} = \sigma_S \sqrt{\frac{N}{N-1}} \tag{8}$$

When the number of cases in our sample is very large, the term $\frac{N}{N-1}$
is very close to 1.0 and may be ignored. With a large number of cases,
for example, over 100, the population variability on the average can
be estimated directly from the sample variability. For our example,
therefore,

$$SE_M = \frac{0.00202}{\sqrt{200}} = 0.000143$$

The use of the standard error of a mean. Now let us see how we
can use the standard error. Since it is really a standard deviation we
can use it exactly as we use a standard deviation. Our best estimate
of the mean of the population is 2.0000 inches. In short, the mean of
one sample is our best prediction of the means of future samples and
of the mean of the population. But we should probably be very much
surprised if the mean of another 200 measurements came out to be
exactly 2.0000 inches. The data exhibit so much variability and so
many random fluctuations that future samples of such data could
hardly be expected to give the same results. The problem then becomes: How far off can we expect the mean of another sample to be
from this one? Or: Within what limits can we reasonably expect the
mean of the new data to occur?

If we were to take a large number of sets of 200 bushings under the
same conditions we used originally, we would expect 68.3 percent of
the means of these future samples to fall between the mean and plus-
or-minus 1 *SE*, that is, between 1.99986 and 2.00014 inches. About 95
percent of the means would fall between 1.99972 and 2.00028 inches
and virtually all of them (99.7 percent) between 1.99958 and 2.00042
inches.

This information can be translated into probabilities. The chances
are a little better than 2 in 3 (68 in 100) that the mean of another set
of 200 data will be between 1.99986 and 2.00014 inches. The chances
are about 19 in 20 (95 in 100) that the mean of another set will be
between 1.99972 and 2.00028 inches, and we can be almost certain
(chances are 997 in 1,000) that the mean will lie between 1.99958 and

2.00042 inches. These are also our best predictions of the mean of the population. If the mean of our sample is 2.0000 inches and the standard error 0.00014, we can be practically certain that the mean of the population is between 1.99958 and 2.00042 inches. The chances are 50–50 that the mean of the population is between 1.99991 and 2.00009 inches (2.0000 ± 0.6745 × 0.00014).

The difference between two means. This type of technique provides us with a method for evaluating the significance of the difference between two means. If a sample of 200 measurements from another production line gave us a mean of 2.0005 inches and a standard deviation of 0.0019 inch, we might question whether the two samples were really drawn from the same population. Could we, by chance, get two samples with means as widely different as 2.0005 and 2.0000? This question can be answered by this formula:

$$t = \frac{\text{diff}_{(M_1 - M_2)}}{SE_{\text{diff}}} \qquad (9)$$

where

$$SE_{\text{diff}} = \sqrt{SE^2_{M_1} + SE^2_{M_2}} \qquad (10)$$

The standard error of the mean of our first sample is 0.000143 inch; of our second sample,

$$\sigma_{M_2} = \frac{0.0019}{\sqrt{200}} = 0.000134 \text{ inch}$$

The standard error of the difference is

$$\sigma_{\text{diff}} = \sqrt{(0.000143)^2 + (0.000134)^2} = 0.000196$$

and

$$t = \frac{M_1 - M_2}{SE_{\text{diff}}} = \frac{0.0005}{0.000196} = 2.5$$

This ratio can then be evaluated by recourse to probability tables, and we discover that the chances are less than 1 in 100 that we could have obtained a difference as large as this by chance. In this situation, the industrial statistician would be justified in looking for some source of variation in the manufacturing process which made the sample of the second production line significantly different from that of the first.

The role of the experimenter in statistics. This solution brings up a very important problem in statistical analysis. The statistician's answers always come out in terms of probabilities. He can do no better. It is up to the experimenter or engineer to decide whether this is satisfactory. If we were experimenting with the tolerable dose of a drug, we might not be satisfied unless the risk of a fatality decreased to 1 in 1,000. If, on the other hand, we are concerned with the probability of getting defective pieces in a lot of manufactured items, we might be satisfied with much lower probabilities, for example, 1 in 10. With tolerances such as these, we would expect to find, on the average, only 1 lot in every 10 which failed to meet specifications. The point is that these risks are things which the experimenter or consumer, not the statistician, must set. For most experimental work, however, it seems to be generally agreed that differences are significant if they could occur by chance less than 5 percent of the time (chances 1 in 20). A difference is regarded as highly significant if such a difference could occur only once in 100 times by chance (probability = 1 percent, or 0.01).

The common sense of statistics. Even though we cannot give the derivations of these formulas, we should note that they agree with certain common-sense ideas. Look at formulas 8 and 9, for example. The probability that a difference is significant is dependent on (*a*) the size of the difference. This is a reasonable kind of notion, because it says, in effect: The greater the difference, the more confidence we can place in it. Then, too, the probability is related to (*b*) the number of cases we have. This also is a reasonable idea: If the difference is constant in size, we feel more certain of that difference with the greater number of observations. Finally, the significance of a difference is related to (*c*) the amount of variability in the data. The smaller the amount of overlapping of scores, the more confident we feel about the difference.

Statistics, then, provide a technique for taking a lot of common-sense ideas about data and putting them on sound mathematical foundations. The experimenter who does not use or thinks he does not have to use statistics is constantly having to guess at the meaning of his data. If he finds a difference between two sets of data, he estimates the significance of the difference on an intuitive basis. Statistics give us a procedure for rigorously analyzing the data according to well-known laws of probability.

The use of correlations in predicting. Correlations can also be useful for predictive purposes. Figure 7 is a schematic diagram of the correlation between the hardness and tensile strength of die castings. Along the right-hand edge of this figure is the normal distribution *A* of tensile strengths that we would get if we were to plot the tensile strength of a very large number of castings without regard to their hardness. If the foundry foreman came up to the statistician and said, "Here is a casting. What is your best guess about its tensile strength?" the statistician's best estimate would be that it had a tensile strength equal to the mean of this distribution. But the strength could have a value anywhere along that distribution. The size of this distribution, in short, is a measure of the possible error the statistician might make in his prediction if he knew nothing more about the specimen.

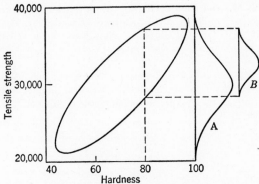

Fig. 7. This diagram illustrates how a correlation reduces the possible error in predicting the tensile strength of an aluminum die casting if the hardness of the casting is known.

But suppose an inspector measured the hardness of the casting and reported that it had a value of 80. Now, what is the statistician's best estimate of the tensile strength of the casting? Knowing the magnitude and form of the correlation, he can reduce his error of estimate considerably. He can predict that the tensile strength of the casting will almost certainly lie within the confines of the smaller distribution *B* shown at the far right. We can also see from Figure 6 that, the higher the correlation, the greater is the reduction in the possible error of prediction. The little distribution *B* gets smaller as the correlation increases.

Other textbooks on statistics. This is about as far as we can go in our discussion of basic statistics. It is important to emphasize again that this is an introduction to a statistical way of thinking. It is by no means a complete treatment even of those statistics that are discussed. There is no table, for example, of the areas under the normal curve—that highly important table which enables us to make the probability predictions we have been talking about. But if you have followed this discussion you should have a pretty good idea about how the statistician works and what some of his terms mean. If you are interested in learning more about them and do not have a good mathematical background, you will find the texts by Freeman [2] and McNemar [4] very useful. If you have studied elementary calculus, you will probably find Hoel's book [3] more to your liking.

SELECTED REFERENCES

1. CAMPBELL, J. M., and LOVELL, W. G.   Application of statistical concepts to the knock-rating problem. *J. Soc. Automot. Engrs.,* 1938, **43**, 421–426.
2. FREEMAN, H. A. *Industrial statistics.* New York: John Wiley, 1946.
3. HOEL, P. G. *Introduction to mathematical statistics.* New York: John Wiley, 1947.
4. McNEMAR, Q. *Psychological statistics.* New York: John Wiley, 1949.
5. PEARSON, E. S.   A survey of the uses of statistical method in the control and standardization of the quality of manufactured products. *J. Roy. Statist. Soc.,* 1933, **96**, 21–60.

3. The Use of Statistics

IN WORKING WITH MAN–MACHINE SYSTEMS IT IS NOT ALWAYS POSSIBLE to maintain the degree of control the scientist would like to have. For instance, if we were doing an experiment on board ship, the skipper might not cooperate completely when, for experimental purposes, it became desirable to have a heavy cruiser stand on beam's end while we did a 10-minute study of a radar scope. Similarly, if a quality control statistician were trying to track down sources of error in a manufacturing process, it might be uneconomical to close down production so that he could do a controlled experiment. In such instances the experimenter must resort to statistical methods for obtaining the answers.

Controlling errors in systems. In addition to the economic considerations that hamper the experimenter, various important factors in a system may escape deliberate manipulation. There are usually many sources of error in most man–machine systems, and the experimenter who wants to study a particular kind of error frequently finds that he cannot control all the other errors while he does his experiment. When operators read target locations from a radar, for example, the investigator discovers that not only are there human errors in these readings but also the radar itself comes with some built-in errors. The final range reading of a target, as given by the operator, is a combination of two sources of error: the operator's own error in locating, identifying, and reading the target location, and the inherent error of the instrument itself. Unfortunately, both kinds of errors happen at the same time. We may be interested only in the operator's errors, but we cannot make the radar perfect while we do our experiment.

Human errors in automatic systems. Even when the machine part of a system is completely automatic, or apparently so, the operator may still introduce some of his own peculiar errors into the quality of the final result or the finished product. Coakley,[4] for example, made

a study of the weights of stockings manufactured by automatic knit-
ting machines operated by different workers. The operator's task was
merely to pull certain levers at certain times. The time of pulling
these levers was determined automatically as the machine completed
each stage of its task. It is hard to see how an operator could add to
or subtract from the number of stitches or the number of courses knit
into a stocking. Yet, when the same machine, using the same yarn,
with the same adjustments, was run by different operators, the distributions of weights of stockings came out differently! In general, these
variations were found to arise from relatively simple causes such as
the order in which the operator used the controls, the way he set the
controls, and the way he stretched and inspected the hose during knit-
ting.

What is the true value? In evaluating many types of complex man–
machine systems, the statistician frequently finds himself up against
another problem: He has difficulty measuring the errors of the system
because he cannot find out what the true values are. Let us illustrate
what we mean by using a radar example. The ideal method for measuring the accuracy of a radar and its operator would be to make use
of a series of targets whose distances from the radar are very accurately known. To be sure that we give the radar a fair test and to
avoid the possibility that the radar operator will memorize the positions of some of the targets, we should have a large number of targets,
50 or more. The targets should be located in all directions from the
radar, they should be at distances of 2 to 100 miles, and their distances should be known to within a few yards. But the expense of
setting up such an ideal testing range is so great that substitute
methods have to be used.

Instead of using a testing range, we might compare the ranges reported from one radar with those from another radar. But any radar
that is used as a standard has *its* own error—usually of unknown size.
We can be sure that we will get discrepancies between the two radars.
But the real problem is: How much of the error is in the test radar,
and how much is in the one being used as a standard?

To get around these difficulties we might use an electronic device for
producing artificial targets. The output of such a gadget can be fed
into the radar to produce targets which appear quite realistic. But
the problem is still not solved, because we will find that the target
generating system has *its* own peculiar errors which interact with the
errors in the radar circuits.

The whole problem, then, boils down to this: How can we measure the accuracy of the information a man gets from a radar when we know that (*a*) the radar has its own errors, (*b*) the man contributes some of his own errors, and (*c*) the standard (either another radar or a target simulator) against which we compare the radar and operator has *its* own error?

How do we calibrate an instrument? Although you might not have thought about it, this problem has a rough parallel in the field of precision instrumentation. Thus, in speaking about thermometers, one writer (Behar [2]) states: "Since there is no such thing as absolute accuracy in the instrumental measurement of magnitude such as temperature, and since the function of a measuring instrument is to assign to a measured magnitude a numerical value, that is, a mathematically-usable quantity, it follows that 'accuracy' is the relation between the true value (of the magnitude) and the obtained value (of the quantity). The true value, of course, is a quantity obtained by means of a 'more accurate' instrument which has been certified by means of 'still more accurate' instruments defining the International Temperature Scale." The relative sizes of the errors involved in the use of precision instruments and in the use of radar are very different, of course. But the two problems are similar in terms of the basic ideas involved.

How is it possible to sort out and evaluate the sources of error in systems that involve such complex interrelationships? The rest of this chapter is concerned primarily with the answer to this question.

KINDS OF ERRORS

Constant and Variable Errors

Because people use the word "error" in many different ways, it is necessary to look closely at the kinds of errors systems may exhibit. In their research, psychologists have frequently made a distinction between (*a*) constant errors and (*b*) variable errors. A constant error is the difference between the average of a large series of measurements and the true, or expected, value. A variable error is measured by some statistical quantity that defines the dispersion, or spread, of the individual measurements.

Constant and variable errors in rifle shooting. We can illustrate this distinction between constant and variable errors by a fairly simple example. In contests between expert riflemen, each man shoots a series of practice rounds. Shown in Figure 8 are the patterns shot by two riflemen, *A* and *B*. In general, rifleman *A* placed his shots around the

central area. We would say that he had no constant error. Rifleman
B, on the other hand, has a rather large constant error. The average
position of his ten shots is far from the center.

The variable errors for these two riflemen are measured by the
spread of the individual shots on the target. Rifleman *A*, for example,
is an inconsistent shot. Although his sights appear to be accurately
aligned on the target, he shows a great deal of unsteadiness. We would

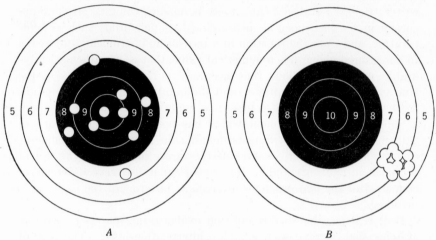

A   B

Fig. 8. Here are two target patterns shot by riflemen *A* and *B*. *A* has no constant
error but large variable errors. *B* has a large constant error but small variable
errors. (After Chapanis, 1949)

say that he makes large variable errors. Rifleman *B*, on the other
hand, is an extremely consistent shot. His variable errors are very
small, even though he has a large constant error.

Constant and variable errors in instrumentation. This distinction
between the two kinds of errors is found also in the field of accurate
instrumentation. Thus, Behar [2] states: ". . . intrinsic accuracy im-
plies other measuring properties, because its determination involves a
more or less complete calibration, in the course of which it may be
found that the error varies not only for different true values, but for
the same true value when successive measurements are made."

Another writer in this field (Schlink [7]) states: "The third important factor to determine in the calibration of a measuring instrument
is that of variance, which is defined as the range, at any given value
of the measured quantity, of variation in reading which may be ex-
hibited by the instrument under repeated application of the same value

of the quantity being measured, after a steady reading has been attained, the environment remaining unchanged. This quantity . . . may also be called the range of uncertainty of indication in that it represents the range within which the readings may be expected to lie when all causes of variation save those inherent in the instrument are eliminated."

Constant and variable errors in radar. The radar problem turns out to be very similar to the shooting problem even though we have increased the complexity of the machinery involved. A radar operator takes a sight on a distant target. He reports a range for the target. Let us call these ranges R_O, that is, range obtained from the radar. If the true range of the target is R_T, the error of measurement ϵ is $R_O - R_T$. The subtraction is always carried out in this order. This means that an error may be minus, that is, the radar range is short of the true range, or plus, the radar range is greater than the true range.

In general, if the errors of the radar system and the operator are variable and if the radar set is calibrated, the discrepancy between the radar range and the true range will average around zero. This means that the obtained range will be too great as often as it is too short. If we took enough range readings from the radar set, the mean obtained range should be a very close approximation to the true range. The plus errors and the minus errors would cancel themselves out. If the average error did not come out to zero but to 500 yards, for example, we would have discovered what is known as a constant error in the radar system. Note that we calculate the mean range error by using equation 1 discussed in the last chapter. Instead of the quantity X used in that equation, however, we substitute the quantity ϵ. And we must remember to take the sign of each error into account; that is, we must add the errors algebraically.

In the radar example there is a true range for every target. But in the bushing example used in Chapter 2, we do not have a "true" value. There is instead an expected value to aim for—the diameter of 2.0000 inches called for by the specifications. If the average outside diameter of the bushing had turned out to be 2.0010 inches, there would be a constant error of +0.0010 inch.

Constant errors in quality control work. In quality control work,[9] the average value tells the statistician whether the process is "centered" satisfactorily. A constant error, in our terminology, means that control is at the wrong level. Control is at too high a level if the constant error is positive; that is, the average is higher than that called for by the specifications. Control is at too low a level if the constant error is negative; that is, the average is lower than what the specifications called for.

Measuring variable errors. Although it is important to identify and measure the constant errors in systems, it is much more important to study the variable errors. Engineers use the maximum limits of the errors obtained as a measure of the variable errors of the instrument. In the quotation from Schlink cited previously, for example, the variance of a measuring instrument is defined as the range * of variation in readings that results when the same quantity is measured over and over. Although the range of errors is an easy quantity to compute, it is not a satisfactory measure of the variable errors in a system. We mentioned in Chapter 2 some of the reasons why this is so. Statisticians usually prefer to use the standard deviation as a measure of variable errors. In quality control work, a manufacturing process is said to be "controlled" if the variations of the items around the average are small. This is another way of saying that the standard deviation of the measurements is small. A controlled manufacturing process, therefore, produces items with a high degree of uniformity.

Using constant and variable errors in production. Distributions of variable errors in industrial applications are not seen very often, because inspection is usually on a go–no-go basis. But the variability is there, nonetheless, and, if you understand the principle of the thing, you can occasionally put this information to practical use. Alger,[1] for instance, gives an example in which 15 percent of frequency relays were being rejected because they fell outside the tolerances allowed in specifications. Plotting a distribution of the measurements showed that all the rejections were on the high side. A shift in the calibration setting of the machines, that is, changing the mean of the distribution, reduced the rejections to a trivial amount without any design or manufacturing change. We can see how this worked by looking at the situation schematically in Figure 9. Shifting the average, without changing the variability of the units, reduced the rejects from 15 percent to only 2.8 percent.

Measuring constant and variable errors together. For some purposes, it is convenient to have a measure of the constant and variable errors together. This, apparently, is what instrument makers mean by the limit of error. It is the maximum error we get in calibrating an instrument when we make no distinction between the constant and variable errors of the instrument. Thus, Behar [2] states: ". . . The

---

* The word "range" in this connotation refers to the statistical quantity mentioned in Chapter 2.

intrinsic accuracy of an instrument is the resultant of its measuring properties. It usually is expressed in terms of the *limit of error,* defined by the Scientific Apparatus Makers of America as 'the maximum error by which the readings of an instrument will depart from true values.' "

Since the limit of error is dependent on only one value—the most deviant error in a series of measurements—and is subject to the same

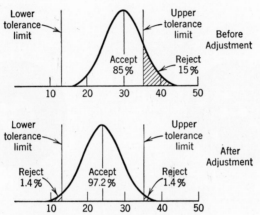

Fɪɢ. 9. This is a distribution of production units with a high proportion of rejects (above). Shifting the calibration setting of the machines, that is, changing the mean of the distribution, reduced the rejects greatly (below). (After Chapanis, 1949)

objections we raised in Chapter 2 with regard to the range, we shall define a new measure $_0\sigma$ as the root-mean-square of the errors around the zero error, that is, around the true value. $_0\sigma$ is equal to the square root of the second moment of the series of measurements. It is another kind of standard deviation and is defined by the equation:

$$_0\sigma = [u'_2]^{1/2} = \left[\frac{\Sigma\epsilon^2}{N}\right]^{1/2}$$

Tʜᴇ Rᴇʟᴀᴛɪᴠᴇ Iᴍᴘᴏʀᴛᴀɴᴄᴇ ᴏғ Cᴏɴsᴛᴀɴᴛ ᴀɴᴅ Vᴀʀɪᴀʙʟᴇ Eʀʀᴏʀs

Having defined constant and variable errors, we are in a position to ask: Which are the more important? Let us go back for a moment to the target patterns shot by the two riflemen (Figure 8). At first glance you might say that *B* is a very inaccurate shot. And yet any rifleman will tell you that this is not the case at all. *B* is a much better shot than *A*. The reason is this: The large constant error in the trial shots fired by *B* can be compensated for very easily by simple adjustments in his sights. With suitable corrections in elevation and windage, rifleman *B* will turn in a perfect score (see Figure 10). In rifle shooting, then, constant errors are not the important ones, because they can be very easily corrected by changing the alignment of the sights on the gun. The really important errors are the variable errors. No corrections of the sights on *A*'s gun will make all his shots fall in the center

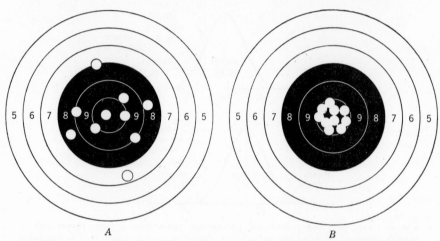

A   *B*

Fɪɢ. 10. These are the same target patterns you saw in Figure 8. Here, however, rifleman *B* has corrected his constant error by changing the alignment of his sights. Note that *A*'s variable errors will not let him get a perfect score. In many cases, variable errors are the better indicators of instability in a man–machine system. (After Chapanis, 1949)

bull. He is inherently much too variable for that. All this is true, of course, provided the constant errors are recognized and corrected. If *B*'s constant error were not corrected, he would get a very low score.

Correcting constant errors in radar. Just as in the shooting example, constant errors in radar systems are less important than variable errors because it is always possible to correct the constant errors. Variable errors are the true indicators of the inherent instability or inaccuracy of a system. The reason for this is easy to see: If operators on a radar *always* read ranges 500 yards short of the true range, we could correct the error by a simple change in the electronic circuits or even in the dials. The real source of difficulty, however, lies in the fact that an operator will give a series of readings, the first of which is 500 yards too short, the next 400 yards too great, the next 1,000 yards too short, and so on. The reduction of these annoying variable errors constitutes one major objective of engineering psychology.

Correcting constant errors in instruments. Corrections for constant errors are also used in the field of precision instrumentation. In the use of certain instruments, constant errors are corrected by data furnished with the instrument. The better grades of fever thermometers used in hospitals are a good example. Each thermometer has been laboratory-tested against accurate standards and is accompanied by a chart (see Table 5) which shows the size of the calibration, or constant, error. The variable errors for such an instrument are usually

TABLE 5. CORRECTIONS FOR CONSTANT ERRORS IN A HIGH-GRADE FEVER
THERMOMETER

These Errors Are Frequently Called Calibration Errors

Reading	Correction
98°	−0.1
102°	+0.1
106°	+0.3

When the correction is +, it must be added to the observed reading, and, when −, subtracted.

very small, indicating great inherent precision or stability. Thus the thermometer that had the constant errors shown in Table 5 was certified to reproduce the same temperature within 0.1° on repeated trials.

Relative importance of constant and variable errors in production. This distinction between the relative importance of constant and variable errors is so significant that we shall look at another example. Coakley [4] measured the weights of stockings made by machines adjusted to manufacture them in sizes 9.5, 10, and 10.5. The distributions he obtained are shown in Figure 11. On the *average*, the size 10.5 stockings were heavier than the size 10, and these, in turn, were heavier than the size 9.5 stockings. But the average weight is not important here. By adjusting the machines, the operator can adjust for any constant error and make stockings heavier or lighter, as he pleases.

The real problem arises from the variable errors. There was so much variability in the weights of stockings that a customer might get some size 9.5 stockings that were heavier than some of the size 10.5; in fact, not even the heaviest size 10.5 stocking was heavier than *all* size 10's. Not only is the customer likely to be dissatisfied because of this variability, but also the manufacturing process is made more difficult because of it. If stockings vary a great deal, it is much harder to match them up into pairs. So here again we see that it is the variable errors that indicate genuine instability in the man–machine relationship.

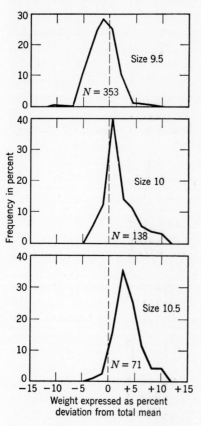

Fig. 11. Here are three distributions of stockings which were supposed to be size 9.5 (top), 10 (center), and 10.5 (bottom). The variable errors are so great that you might buy a 9.5 stocking that is heavier than a size 10.5. (After Coakley, 1947)

THE ACCUMULATION OF ERRORS IN MAN–MACHINE SYSTEMS

There are usually many sources of error which contribute to variability in the final result. We have already mentioned some of these in the early part of this chapter. In the case of radar, for example, some errors arise from the electronic circuits in the radar itself, others from the radar operator. We know that both sources of error are also found in the use of precision measuring instruments. Some errors are due to the instruments themselves. A meter or gage will not always come to rest at precisely the same point on repeated trials. Lag, friction, hysteresis, thermal expansion, and so on contribute to these instrument errors. But there are also some rather large human errors in the use of precision instruments. It is worth pointing out, incidentally, that the human error in using precision gages, micrometers, and calipers, is considerably greater than most supervisors or standards men expect. Lawshe and Tiffin,[6] for example, studied the accuracy and variability of measurements made by 200 inspectors and 45 experienced toolmakers in using such instruments. Their data indicate a surprising amount of human error.

THE ADDITION OF CONSTANT ERRORS

The engineering psychologist, who is faced with the problem of reducing variable errors in man–machine systems, must know how errors accumulate in a system in order that he may go about his task intelligently. The source of error that contributes most to the final variability is obviously the most economical one to tackle. This may seem so obvious that nothing more need be said about it. But there is more to the problem than this, as we shall see.

TABLE 6. AN ILLUSTRATION OF ACCUMULATION OF ERRORS IN MEASUREMENTS OF
THE OUTSIDE DIAMETERS OF BUSHINGS

Bushing number	"True" outside diameter	Error of measurement	Reported outside diameter
1	2.0039	+0.0005	2.0044
2	2.0014	+0.0009	2.0023
3	1.9980	−0.0006	1.9974
4	2.0000	+0.0003	2.0003
5	1.9973	+0.0008	1.9981
6	1.9996	−0.0002	1.9994
7	2.0010	−0.0007	2.0003
8	1.9999	+0.0007	2.0006
9	2.0003	0.0000	2.0003
10	2.0037	−0.0004	2.0033
11	2.0021	−0.0002	2.0023
12	2.0006	0.0000	2.0006
13	1.9976	+0.0001	1.9977
14	1.9978	−0.0001	1.9977
15	2.0006	+0.0006	2.0012
16	1.9943	+0.0002	1.9945
17	1.9993	+0.0004	1.9997
18	2.0016	+0.0002	2.0018
19	1.9970	+0.0003	1.9973
20	2.0005	+0.0003	2.0008
M	1.9998	+0.0002	2.0000
σ	0.00227	0.00042	0.00230

An example of accumulation of error. Let us suppose that the first 20 bushings in Table 1 were measured with such extreme precision that we could be sure of these measurements to the fourth decimal place. They are listed in Table 6 as the "true" outside diameters. Now let us suppose that the inspector made certain errors in measuring these bushings with his vernier micrometer. His errors are shown in the column headed "Error of measurement." The third column of this table gives the algebraic sums of the first two columns—they are the outside diameters of the 20 bushings as finally reported by the inspector. Thus, the first bushing had a true diameter of 2.0039 inches, and the inspector's error in using the micrometer was +0.0005 inch, so that what he actually reported to the statistician was a measurement of 2.0044 inches. Similarly, the second bushing had a true diameter of 2.0014 inches, and the inspector's error in reading the micrometer was +0.0009 inch, so that what he reported to the statistician was a measurement of 2.0023 inches. Now let us examine more closely what has happened.

How constant errors add. The first 20 bushings in Table 6 have a mean diameter of 1.9998 inches; that is, there is a constant error for this sample of −0.0002 inch. On the average, the inspector made a constant error of +0.0002 inch in using his micrometer, that is, he tended to read a little too high. Now look at the average diameter reported to the statistician. It is 2.0000 inches and is exactly equal to the average true diameter of the bushings plus the average error of measurement. Thus, the rule for the accumulation of constant errors in a system is simple enough: They add algebraically.

To pick another example, suppose a radar is miscalibrated so that it reads 20 yards short of the true range; that is, its constant error is −20 yards. Now let us suppose we have a radar operator who, because of the way he aligns the range marker with a target, has a tendency to read 50 yards too high. On the average, he will give us range readings 50 yards too great—his constant error is +50 yards. Put the radar operator together with this particular radar, and we will get range readings which are 30 yards too great, that is, −20 + 50 = +30.

THE ACCUMULATION OF VARIABLE ERRORS

Now let us look at the variable errors in Table 6. If we add the standard deviation of the true measurements (0.00227) to the standard deviation of the inspector's errors (0.00042), we do not get the standard deviation of the reported measurements (0.00230). The sum is 0.00269 and is about 17 percent too big. But notice this: The squares of these standard deviations add up to

$$(0.00227)^2 + (0.00042)^2 = 0.000,005,329$$

And now notice that the square root of this sum is

$$(0.000,005,329)^{1/2} = 0.00231$$

This checks with the standard deviation of the reported measurements within less than 1 percent and would have checked exactly if the correlation between the true measurements and the inspector's errors were exactly zero.

So, when we speak of the accumulation of variable errors, we use the word "accumulation" instead of "addition" for a very good reason. Variable errors do not add directly but according to their squares. Since a standard deviation is a measure of variable error, we cannot add standard deviations of component errors to compute variable errors in systems. We must first square the standard deviations, then add them, and finally extract the square root of the total to get the variable error of the system. The "squared standard deviation" is so important in statistics that it has a name of its own—variance.* The variance is still a measure of variable error, but its meaning is difficult to interpret graphically in the same way that we illustrated the standard deviation. It is best to think of a variance, therefore, as an abstract mathematical quantity that has value for getting an end result.

Formula for the accumulation of variances. Now let us put the information just given into a formula. If we have a man–machine system with several components, $A, B, C, \cdots$, each contributing some amount of error, the variance of the error in the final product or result T turned out by the total system is equal to the following:

$$\sigma^2_T = \sigma^2_{A \pm B \pm C \pm \cdots} \tag{11}$$

$$\sigma^2_T = \sigma^2_A + \sigma^2_B + \sigma^2_C + \cdots$$

$$\pm 2r_{AB}\sigma_A\sigma_B \pm 2r_{AC}\sigma_A\sigma_C \pm 2r_{BC}\sigma_B\sigma_C \pm \cdots \tag{12}$$

This looks like a very complicated formula,† but it is really not so bad when you dissect it. First of all, notice that the last group of terms includes the correlation coefficient r between the component errors. Fortunately, the errors in component parts of man–machine systems are usually uncorrelated—they bear no relationship to each other. This means that the r's are equal to 0, so that we can neglect all those terms involving r's. In Table 6, for example, we have no reason for suspecting that the amount and direction of the error that the

---

* As we have already seen, the term "variance" is also used by instrument makers in a slightly different sense (see p. 42). This confusion of terminology is unfortunate, and the reader should be careful to differentiate between the two meanings. Throughout the rest of the book, the term "variance" is used in the statistical sense to refer to variable errors measured in terms of σ^2.

† The proofs for all these formulas have been worked out by Chapanis.[3] Readers who like to follow mathematical derivations can find them in his article.

inspector makes is related systematically to the random variations in the size of the bushings. If you work out this correlation you find, in fact, that the r is equal to -0.021, which is almost exactly no correlation.

This correlation factor will not always turn out to be zero, of course. It is likely, for instance, that a rough grinding operation on castings would give variable errors related to the variable errors produced by the casting process. The amount of material ground off the casting is probably related to the initial size of the casting. The possibilities of such correlations must be studied for each system separately and require that the statistician have a reasonably good idea of what goes on in the system.

Sum of variances. In the most common case, however, there is no correlation between component errors, so that formula 12 reduces to

$$\sigma^2{}_T = \sigma^2{}_A + \sigma^2{}_B + \sigma^2{}_C + \cdots \tag{13}$$

This formula says that the variance of the error in our complete or total system is equal to the sum of the variances of the error contributed by individual parts of the system. This basic equation does two important things. First, it gives us some extremely useful information about the way errors accumulate in a system, and, second, it enables us to analyze the magnitude of errors in certain parts of our system, if we know certain other errors in the system.

Distribution of machine error. In order to see how errors accumulate in a system, let us assume another realistic example that might arise in a systems analysis with a radar indicator. The upper curve in Figure 12 is a distribution of a thousand errors contributed to the final range readings by the radar itself. These errors include all sources of inherent inaccuracy in the radar system. We have postulated here a standard deviation of 10 yards.

Man and machine error. Now, let us further assume that the human error in operating the radar remote indicator is equal to 20 yards. That is to say, on the average, the operator is twice as inaccurate as the machine. What happens now when we accumulate both sources of error? The resultant error is shown by the lowest curve in Figure 12. If we accumulate both the inherent errors of the machine and the inherent errors of the operator, the resultant variable error is equal to 22.36 yards; that is, $\sqrt{(10)^2 + (20)^2}$. Although this method of accumulating errors in a system may not appear reasonable, a large number of studies at the experimental and mathematical level show it to be true.

Which error is important? This sort of accumulation of errors in a system has extremely important implications. In the first place, we notice that, when we accumulate errors in this way, the machine's

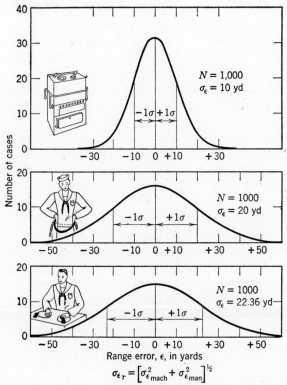

$$\sigma_{\epsilon_T} = \left[\sigma^2_{\epsilon_{\text{mach}}} + \sigma^2_{\epsilon_{\text{man}}}\right]^{\frac{1}{2}}$$

Fig. 12. How random errors accumulate in a man–machine system. Suppose that the standard deviation of machine errors is 10 yards (top curve) and the standard deviation of human errors is 20 yards (middle curve). Because such errors accumulate according to their squares (see formula at the bottom), the final distribution of man–machine errors will have a standard deviation of 22.36 yards. Though the machine variability was 10 yards, it only increases the man variability by 2.36 yards. (After Chapanis, 1949)

errors amount to relatively very little. We have increased the variable error of the man from 20 yards to only 22.36 yards by adding in the error of the machine.

What does this imply as to the kind of problem the investigator should attack? Let us look at the question in this way. If we were able to eliminate completely the inherent error of the machine, we would be reducing the variable error of the final range readings by only 2.36 yards. This means, in short, that we can make our greatest contribution to increasing the accuracy of the man and machine combination not by worrying about the accuracy of the machine, but rather by increasing the inherent accuracy of the operator. We are likely to get more for our money if we concentrate on the man.

The effect of changing variance ratios. In the previous illustration it was assumed that the error of the man alone was twice as great as that of the machine alone. Now, see what happens as we increase this differential. If the variable error of the man is 30 yards and the variable error of the machine is still 10 yards (a ratio of 3 to 1) the variable error of the man and machine is only 31.62 yards. The addition of the machine error to the man error in this case has increased the total error by 1.62 yards, or 5 percent. If the variable error of the man is 50 yards and the error of the machine still 10 yards (a ratio of 5 to 1), the variable error of the man *and* machine is 50.99 yards. In this case, adding the error of the machine to that of the man has increased the total error of the combination by roughly 1 yard, or 2 percent. To state it another way, if we could make a perfect machine for this combination, we would reduce our final variable error by only 2 percent.

Figure 13 shows what percentage of the total variable error is accounted for by the smaller of two component errors. Notice how rapidly this contribution drops off as the difference between the component errors increases, that is, as the ratios in Figure 13 get smaller.

The significance of this example should be clear. Suppose that at one point in a system there is an instrument or an operation that has a low inherent error and in another location in the system there is an operation or instrument that is relatively more inaccurate. It is not economical to attack the operation that has the lower source of error since its contribution to the total or resultant error is much smaller than we might at first suppose. Remember that not the addition of errors but the addition of squares of errors makes up the final result.

Application to instrument design. You can make up your own examples to amplify this accumulation of variances still further. We will give one more illustration that is important for engineering psychology: There is no reason to increase the inherent stability of instruments to the absolute limit if the dials and scales on these instruments are so constructed that a human operator makes large errors in reading them. The following quotation from Schlink [7] is pertinent to this problem: "It is often found that particular measuring instruments are given a sensitivity far higher than warranted in the face of the error obtainable in reading and resulting from the variance present. Similarly, the graduation of instruments is often found to be far closer than the large amount of the variance justifies. Care should be taken in the design of measuring instruments so that the units of graduation

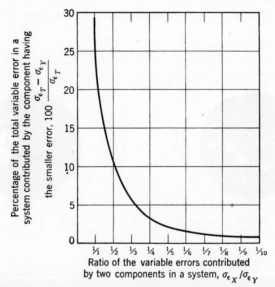

FIG. 13. This shows what percentage of the total variable error in a system is contributed by the smaller of two component sources of error. Notice how rapidly the amount contributed by the smaller source of error drops off as it becomes relatively smaller and smaller. (After Chapanis, 1949)

and the openness of the scale are not out of all proportion to the effective reproducibility of reading possible."

The Accumulation of Constant and Variable Errors

Now let us look at how the constant and variable errors combine in a system. The equation that shows this is

$$_0\sigma_{\epsilon_T} = [M^2_{\epsilon_T} + \sigma^2_{\epsilon_T}]^{1/2} \tag{14}$$

This formula states that the variable error around the zero error or true value is equal to the square root of the squared constant error plus the squared variable error around the constant error. It is very similar to formula 13 which shows how component variable errors accumulate to make up the total variable errors in a system.

Importance of constant and variable errors. This formula is significant because it provides us with a mathematical statement about the
relative importance of the constant and variable errors in a system.
Exactly the same argument that applied to formula 13 holds here. So
long as the constant error, M_{ϵ_T}, is small compared with the variable
error, σ_{ϵ_T}, its contribution to the total error of the system is very small.
A constant error in the system means that the readings will be biased;

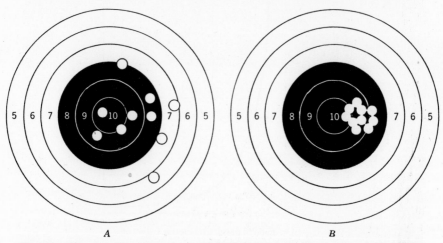

A   B

FIG. 14. These are the same target patterns you saw in Figures 8 and 10. Here,
however, the same small constant error has been added to both patterns. Notice
that the constant error does not change *A*'s score very much because his variable
errors are so large. The same constant error makes a big difference in *B*'s score
because his variable errors are so small. (After Chapanis, 1949)

that is, the average of a large number of readings will be too high or too
low by some amount. But so long as the ratio $M_{\epsilon_T}/\sigma_{\epsilon_T}$ is $\frac{1}{3}$ or less,
the contribution of the constant error to any single reading will, on the
average, be unimportant.

Applications. This conclusion is important for most man–machine
systems, although it is not always generally understood by engineers.
Some of them spend great amounts of money and time in calibrating
equipment, that is, in attempting to eliminate constant errors or calibration errors, without at the same time concerning themselves with
the instability of the equipment as reflected in the variable errors.
Because it is such an important idea to understand, let us see how it
works out in the case of our riflemen. In Figure 14 are the same target patterns shot by the two riflemen, *A* and *B*, that were shown in

Figure 10. Here, however, we have slightly changed the adjustment of the rifle sights on both guns. This is equivalent to adding in a constant error—the same constant error for both riflemen. Notice that this slight error in the adjustment of his rifle sight does not really affect A's score very much. However, this small constant error makes quite a difference in B's score. The reason, we can see, is that the constant error is almost as big as his variable error.

ANALYSIS OF SYSTEMS ERRORS

Although equations 13 and 14 are very helpful in telling us about the relative importance of component errors in a system, they serve a much more useful function in enabling us to measure the amount of error in certain parts of a system when certain other errors are known. Perhaps the best way to demonstrate their usefulness is by specific examples.

RADAR EXAMPLES

Analyzing errors in one kind of radar. One type of problem we mentioned earlier in connection with radar research is that of measuring the variable error of a radar when the true ranges of targets cannot be measured. The solution to this problem can be found if two radar indicators of the same type are used together. Both radars are ranged on the same series of targets. The range report from the first radar R_1 is a combination of the true range of the target R_T plus the error of the radar indicator and its operator ϵ_1. Thus:

$$R_1 = R_T + \epsilon_1 \tag{15}$$

Similarly, a range report from the second radar R_2 is

$$R_2 = R_T + \epsilon_2 \tag{16}$$

Even if we have *only* the range reports from the two radars, we can still discover more about the inherent variability of one radar system by performing a few algebraic manipulations. First, let us find the difference between corresponding range reports from the two radars. Thus:

$$R_1 - R_2 = (R_T + \epsilon_1) - (R_T + \epsilon_2)$$
$$= \epsilon_1 - \epsilon_2 \tag{17}$$

This formula states that when two radars have ranged on the same target, the difference between their range reports is equal to the difference between the errors inherent in the two radars and their operators.

If such differences are obtained on a large number of targets, we may write

$$\sigma_{R_1 - R_2} = \sigma_{\epsilon_1 - \epsilon_2} = [\sigma_{\epsilon_1}{}^2 + \sigma_{\epsilon_2}{}^2]^{1/2} \tag{18}$$

The values on the left of the second equal sign are the ones we know. In this instance, however, it is reasonable to assume that the variable errors of the two radars are of about the same order of magnitude, so that

$$\sigma_\epsilon = \sigma_{\epsilon_1} = \sigma_{\epsilon_2} \tag{19}$$

Thus
$$\sigma_{\epsilon_1 - \epsilon_2} = [2\sigma^2{}_\epsilon]^{1/2} \tag{20}$$

and
$$\sigma_\epsilon = \frac{1}{\sqrt{2}} \sigma_{\epsilon_1 - \epsilon_2} = \frac{1}{\sqrt{2}} \sigma_{R_1 - R_2} \tag{21}$$

This last equation 21 tells us that the variable error of one radar and its operator is equal to the standard deviation of the differences between range reports divided by $\sqrt{2}$. To pick specific numbers, if the σ of the difference between range reports on the two radars is 100 yards, the variable error of the range reports from one radar is 70.7 yards.

It is important to note in this example that it is impossible to determine the magnitude of the constant errors of the two radars. Let us assume, for example, that the mean difference, $M_{R_1 - R_2}$, was -10 yards. This tells us that there is some constant error, either physical or psychological or both, in the operation of one or both of the radars. But we cannot discover the magnitude of the constant error of one radar because one might be off by 100 yards, the other by 90, or one might be off by -30 and the other by -40, and the constant difference would be the same.

Analyzing errors in different kinds of radars. One of the most useful applications of these techniques is an extension of the problem we have just dealt with. It involves the simultaneous determination of the variable error of three *different* radars, each ranging on identical targets which are at unknown distances. By using equation 18 three times, it is possible to set up three simultaneous equations:

$$\sigma_{R_1 - R_2} = [\sigma^2{}_{\epsilon_1} + \sigma^2{}_{\epsilon_2}]^{1/2} \tag{22}$$

$$\sigma_{R_1 - R_3} = [\sigma^2{}_{\epsilon_1} + \sigma^2{}_{\epsilon_3}]^{1/2} \tag{23}$$

$$\sigma_{R_2 - R_3} = [\sigma^2_{\epsilon_2} + \sigma^2_{\epsilon_3}]^{\frac{1}{2}} \tag{24}$$

The quantities to the left of the equal signs are the only ones known, but there are three equations to solve for three unknowns: σ_{ϵ_1}, σ_{ϵ_2}, and σ_{ϵ_3}. Needless to say, the problem is easily solved when set up in this fashion.

Notice in this example that it is no longer necessary to make any assumptions about the variable errors of any of the radars. When only two radars are used, it is necessary that they be the same kind of radar, and it is also necessary to assume that the variable errors of the two radars are of the same order of magnitude (equation 19). Neither of these conditions must be met when three or more radars are used.

Measuring the error of target simulators. The solution to the three-radar problem also provides a solution to the problem of estimating the magnitude of the error contributed by a target generator of some sort. If two radars are operated from the same target generator, we can use the same kinds of simultaneous equations as 22, 23, and 24. The only difference is that the range set into the target generator is substituted for the range reported from one of the radars. Thus, if we let R_G represent the range set into the generator, the equations are:

$$\sigma_{R_G - R_1} = [\sigma^2_{\epsilon_G} + \sigma^2_{\epsilon_1}]^{\frac{1}{2}} \tag{25}$$

$$\sigma_{R_G - R_2} = [\sigma^2_{\epsilon_G} + \sigma^2_{\epsilon_2}]^{\frac{1}{2}} \tag{26}$$

$$\sigma_{R_1 - R_2} = [\sigma^2_{\epsilon_1} + \sigma^2_{\epsilon_2}]^{\frac{1}{2}} \tag{27}$$

Even though we have referred frequently to radar in the last few pages, you should realize that these equations can be used for other kinds of problems. Grubbs [5] and Simon,[8] for example, used equations like 22, 23, and 24 to solve a problem dealing with the measurement of fuse-burning times for ammunition. They found, incidentally, that observers with stop watches can be safely used to time fuses. Even though human reaction times vary from moment to moment, the variance in reaction time was much less than the variance of fuse-burning times so that what might appear to be a crude measuring technique was perfectly adequate for the job. Once you get the idea about how these equations work, you should be able to think up still other applications from your own experience.

AN INDUSTRIAL EXAMPLE

In the radar examples that we have used so far, the analysis was fairly simple because we had as many errors for radar 1 and operator 1 as we had for radar 2 and operator 2. It is still possible to apply these techniques to problems in which the numbers of errors from different sources are not identical, as they were in the radar examples. These actually are the kinds of situations most frequently found in industrial applications. Let us illustrate how this technique works. As we explain this illustration, notice that we shall be computing the variance due to certain constant errors and certain variable errors.

Experimenting on a production process. Let us suppose that our industrial statistician was interested in analyzing in greater detail the sources of error in the bushing data given in Table 1. Let us suppose, further, that the bushings that he sampled in the production line were manufactured by five different machines. In order to perform his experiment without interfering with production, he assigned four different workers to turn out ten bushings each on each machine. He then tagged each bushing so that he could tell which bushing was made by

TABLE 7. SHOWS WHICH OF FIVE MACHINES AND WHICH OF FOUR WORKERS MADE THE FIRST 40 BUSHINGS LISTED IN TABLE 1

Bushing measurement	Machine	Operator	Bushing measurement	Machine	Operator
2.0039	1	B	2.0001	4	D
2.0014	4	B	2.0049	1	B
1.9980	3	A	1.9997	5	A
2.0000	1	C	1.9992	5	D
1.9973	2	A	2.0035	2	B
1.9996	1	D	1.9998	4	D
2.0010	5	B	1.9998	5	C
1.9999	1	D	2.0012	4	C
2.0003	2	D	2.0019	2	C
2.0037	2	B	1.9981	3	D
2.0021	3	B	2.0007	4	C
2.0006	5	B	2.0000	5	A
1.9976	2	A	2.0001	5	C
1.9978	3	D	1.9983	3	A
2.0006	2	D	2.0023	3	C
1.9943	1	A	2.0015	2	C
1.9993	4	A	1.9975	5	D
2.0016	4	B	2.0030	3	C
1.9970	1	A	1.9991	4	A
2.0005	1	C	2.0018	3	B

which worker and on what machine. This information for the first 40 bushings in Table 1 is shown in Table 7. Thus, the first bushing, which had an outside diameter of 2.0039 inches, was made on machine 1 when it was run by operator *B,* and so on. We have used only the first 40 bushings in order not to get involved with too many numbers.

Arranging the data. We can now rearrange the data in a more usable form as shown in Table 8. Here, the machines are listed across the

TABLE 8. THE SAME DATA AS IN TABLE 7 BUT REARRANGED SO THAT THEY ARE EASIER TO WORK WITH

Operator	Machine					Σ	M
	1	2	3	4	5		
A	1.9943 1.9970 $M = 1.99565$ $M_c = 1.99802$	1.9973 1.9976 $M = 1.99745$ $M_c = 1.99903$	1.9980 1.9983 $M = 1.99815$ $M_c = 2.00036$	1.9993 1.9991 $M = 1.99920$ $M_c = 2.00118$	1.9997 2.0000 $M = 1.99985$ $M_c = 2.00250$	19.9806	1.99806
B	2.0039 2.0049 $M = 2.00440$ $M_c = 2.00238$	2.0037 2.0035 $M = 2.00360$ $M_c = 2.00079$	2.0021 2.0018 $M = 2.00195$ $M_c = 1.99977$	2.0014 2.0016 $M = 2.00150$ $M_c = 1.99909$	2.0010 2.0006 $M = 2.00080$ $M_c = 1.99906$	20.0245	2.00245
C	2.0000 2.0005 $M = 2.00025$ $M_c = 1.99958$	2.0019 2.0015 $M = 2.00170$ $M_c = 2.00024$	2.0023 2.0030 $M = 2.00265$ $M_c = 2.00182$	2.0012 2.0007 $M = 2.00095$ $M_c = 1.99989$	1.9998 2.0001 $M = 1.99995$ $M_c = 1.99956$	20.0110	2.00110
D	1.9996 1.9999 $M = 1.99975$ $M_c = 2.00089$	2.0003 2.0006 $M = 2.00045$ $M_c = 2.00080$	1.9978 1.9981 $M = 1.99795$ $M_c = 1.99893$	2.0001 1.9998 $M = 1.99995$ $M_c = 2.00070$	1.9992 1.9975 $M = 1.99835$ $M_c = 1.99977$	19.9929	1.99929
Σ M	16.0001 2.00001	16.0064 2.00080	16.0014 2.00018	16.0032 2.00040	15.9979 1.99974	80.0090	2.00022

top of the table and the operators along the sides, and the bushings that were manufactured by each machine and each operator are shown in the table. Notice that, although we do not have the same number of operators as machines, this is a symmetrical set of data nonetheless. It is symmetrical in the sense that we have a sample of two bushings made by each worker on each machine.

Total variance. Let us see now what variances we can calculate for this set of data. First, we can calculate the total variance for the entire set of 40 bushings. This is the σ^2 for the 40 measurements in Table 7 or in Table 8. If you calculate this value you will find that it is equal to 0.000,004,45.

Machine variability. Next we can calculate the variance between machines. This is done by calculating the variance of the averages of the eight bushing measurements made on machines 1, 2, 3, 4, and 5; that is, by calculating σ^2 for the values 2.00001, 2.00080, 2.00018, 2.00040, and 1.99974. This variance turns out to be 0.000,000,13, and it is only a very small fraction of the total variance ($^{13}\!/_{445}$, or 3 percent). Now stop and think about what this means. This is the variance between the average bushing sizes we get when the bushings are made by different machines. Since it is small, we can be fairly sure that, on the average, different machines will produce bushings of very nearly the same size when the machines are operated by different people.

Operator differences. We can now calculate the variance between operators in exactly the same way. This is done by computing σ^2 for the averages 1.99806, 2.00245, 2.00110, and 1.99929. It is equal to 0.000,002,82 and is a little more than half the total variance in this set of data ($^{282}\!/_{445} = 63$ percent). This means that there are some large consistent differences between the sizes of bushings made by the four workers, even though they used the same machines. This is easy to check by looking at the sizes of the 10 bushings made by operators *A* and *B*, for example. Even though both men used the same machines, every bushing made by *B* was larger than the largest bushings made by *A*. Notice, incidentally, that these large differences between the results turned out by the men are indications of constant errors.

We can see now why this industrial statistician had each worker use every machine. If each man had used a different machine and only one machine, we could not be sure whether differences in the sizes of bushings were due to the machines or the men. If, for example, we had only the data for operator *A* on machine 1 and for operator *B* on machine 2, we would find a big difference between the average sizes of the bushings made—1.99565 as compared with 2.00360. But only when we have each man use each machine do we find that this discrepancy is due to large differences between the men and not to differences between the machines.

Interaction variances. The third kind of variance we can compute for the data in Table 8 is a little harder to understand. It is the variance between the average sizes of bushings made by each man on each machine when these averages are corrected for the differences between men and for the differences between machines. In order to correct for the differences between men, note that operator *A*, on the average, produced bushings 0.00216 inch smaller than the average size of all bushings made (2.00022 − 1.99806). This is another way of saying that *A* has a constant error of −0.00216 inch. Similarly, *B* made his bushings 0.00223 inch larger than the average (2.00245 − 2.00022); and so on. We can correct for these differences between the men by adding 0.00216 to all of *A*'s averages, subtracting 0.00223 from all of *B*'s averages, and so on. These corrections are corrections for the constant errors of the different men.

In a similar manner we can correct for the differences between machines by adding 0.00021 to all the averages for machine 1, subtracting 0.00058 from all the averages for machine 2, and so on. We add 0.00021 to all of the averages for machine 1 because this machine, on the average, tended to make bushings 0.00021 inch too small (2.00022 − 2.00001). This correction process means that we are correcting for the constant errors of the machines.

The results of this double correction are shown by the M_c values in Table 8. Thus, the value of 1.99802 for operator *A* on machine 1 is equal to 1.99565 + 0.00216 + 0.00021. The value of 1.99903 for operator *A* on machine 2 is equal to 1.99745 + 0.00216 − 0.00058, and so on.

If each operator behaved exactly the same on every machine, all the M_c values in the table would be almost exactly the same. If each operator behaved differently on every machine, then the variance of the M_c values would be large. In this example it turns out to be 0.000,001,33 and so accounts for nearly 30 percent ($^{133}\!/_{445}$) of the total variance. Let us look more closely into what is happening here. Note that the smallest bushings made by *A* were made on machine 1, the next larger ones were made when he used machine 2, the next larger on machine 3, the next on machine 4, and the largest on machine 5. Now look at *B*'s record. The sizes of the bushings he made on the different machines are exactly in the reverse order from *A*'s. *B* made his largest bushings on machine 1 and his smallest ones on machine 5. These inconsistencies in the way operators produce on different machines is known as an *interaction*.

What makes interactions? The results of a statistical analysis like this tell the statistician that there is an interaction in the data, but they do not tell him why the interaction is there. Finding out the reason for an interaction depends on how keen the experimenter is in understanding the work process. To show you the kinds of things that make interactions, we shall cite only one example. It does not necessarily explain the data in Table 8, but it will show what could make an interaction.

Let us suppose that the working areas on the five machines were at different heights from the floor, say 46 inches for 1, 44 inches for 2, 42 inches for 3, 40 inches for 4, and 38 inches for machine 5. Now let us further suppose that A is very short and B is very tall. You can easily imagine how a tall man operating the highest machine might get different results from those of a short man operating the same machine. When we come to the lowest machine, on the other hand, it is easy to see how we could find a reversal in the kinds of results the two men turn out. Factors like these which make it easier for some people to operate some machines and not others are what produce interactions.

Residual variance. The last kind of variance we can compute for the data in Table 8 is the average variance between bushings made by the same man on the same machine. The two bushings with diameters of 1.9943 and 1.9970 inches fall into this classification—they were both made by A on machine 1. The bushings with diameters of 1.9973 and 1.9976 were both made by A on machine 2. The bushings that are 2.0039 and 2.0049 inches in size were both made by B on machine 1, and so on. To get the residual variance compute the variance between each such pair of bushing sizes, and take the average of these 20 variances. It turns out to be 0.000,000,17 in this example. Since it is so small—it accounts for only 4 percent of the total variance—we can conclude that there are only very slight differences between bushings made by any one man on any one machine.

The residual variance gets its name because it is the variance left in our data when we have taken out all the meaningful variances we can think of. Notice that we could have gotten it by subtracting from the total variance, the variance between machines, between operators, and the interaction. Thus:

$$
\begin{aligned}
& 0.000,004,45 && \text{(total)} \\
- \; & 0.000,000,13 && \text{(between machines)} \\
- \; & 0.000,002,82 && \text{(between operators)} \\
- \; & 0.000,001,33 && \text{(interaction)} \\
\hline
= \; & 0.000,000,17 && \text{(residual)}
\end{aligned}
$$

Summary of analysis of variance. We have now accounted for all the variance in our data and are in a position to summarize what it all means. Most of the variation in the sizes of these 40 bushings can be traced to differences between the sizes of bushings made by different men. The next largest source of variation arises from the interaction, which means that different operators did not get the same results on different machines. The differences between the average sizes of bushings made by different machines are very small when these machines were operated by the four workers. And, finally, bushings differ very little in size if they were made by any one man on any one machine.

In actual practice, the statistician would also go on to apply tests of statistical significance to the variances he computed. This takes us beyond the scope of this chapter, however, and the interested reader is referred to the statistical texts mentioned in Chapter 2 for details of this procedure.

At any rate, the course open to the experimenter is now clear. If he wants to reduce the variability of the bushings made, he must find some way of eliminating differences between the kinds of work different men do. Adjusting each machine to each man's peculiar work habits, that is, correcting for his constant error, is probably the simplest way of doing this. Training the men to work to a more uniform standard might be another way. And, finally, instituting more adequate checks on the manufacturing process or making this stage of the process more automatic might also help reduce these differences.

Furthermore, the experimenter should try to track down and correct whatever it is about the machines that makes different men operate them differently.

SUMMARY

In this chapter we have tried to show how statistical techniques can be applied to the analysis of complex man–machine systems. We first developed some ideas about kinds of errors and their relative importance. We saw how errors combined and accumulated in complex man–machine systems. And, finally, we had a brief look at how this information about the accumulation of errors enables us to analyze sources of error and their relative contributions to man–machine systems. This has been only a very brief introduction to these interesting methods, but we must leave them now to inquire into some practical findings which these techniques have yielded.

SELECTED REFERENCES

1. ALGER, P. L. The importance of the statistical viewpoint in high production manufacturing. *J. Amer. Statist. Ass.*, 1941, **36**, 50–52.
2. BEHAR, M. F. The "accuracy" and other measuring properties of temperature instruments. *Instruments*, 1940, **13**, 240–242.

3. CHAPANIS, A.   Theory and methods for analyzing errors in man–machine systems.   *Ann. N. Y. Acad. Sci.,* 1949, **51,** Article 6.
4. COAKLEY, J. D.   Human influence on the product of automatic machines. Unpublished report of the Psychological Corporation, 522 Fifth Avenue, New York 18, N. Y., 1947.
5. GRUBBS, F. E.   Some methods for estimating precision of measuring instruments and product variability.   Ballistics Res. Lab., Aberdeen Proving Ground, Md.   Report No. 642, 2 January 1948.
6. LAWSHE, C. H., JR., and TIFFIN, J.   The accuracy of precision instrument measurement in industrial inspection.   *J. Appl. Psychol.,* 1945, **29,** 413–419.
7. SCHLINK, F. J.   Variance of measuring instruments and its relation to accuracy and sensitivity.   *Bull. Bur. Stand., Wash.,* 1919, **14,** 741–764.
8. SIMON, L. E.   On the relation of instrumentation to quality control.   *Instruments,* 1946, **19,** 654–656.
9. SMITH, E. S.   *Control charts: An introduction to statistical quality control.* New York: McGraw-Hill, 1947.

4. How We See

THAT COMPLICATED MECHANISM, MAN, NEEDS AND USES HIS EYES AS HIS major source of contact with his environment. The eye furnishes him with his primary means of knowing things, of finding his way about in life. And if man gets himself involved as a functioning part of a man–machine system, his effectiveness is very often determined entirely by the acuity and efficiency with which he can use his eyes. We can document that point very easily.

Take radar, for example. We are told that radar is the eyes of the fleet. But radar never sees. It is man who sees. If his eyes fail at a critical time, because they either are inherently poor or are placed at an undue disadvantage by poorly designed equipment, then radar fails, the ship fails, the mission fails. And, again, think of the demands imposed on the eyes of the pilot who is "flying blind." In spite of its name, this job is primarily a visual one.

Problems in vision. You can see without our belaboring the point further that visual problems are numerous and crucial in man–machine systems. How large should we make the markings on a dial? How should dials and indicators be illuminated? How can we employ the eye so as to get the most information from it at night? These are simple-sounding questions, but their answers have far-reaching practical implications. To deal adequately with these and a dozen similar questions we will need to examine systematically the eye and the way it works. That is our job in this chapter.

WHAT WE SEE

COLORS AND HOW WE MEASURE THEM

Radiant energy. It is now generally understood even by lay people that we see things either because they emit radiant energy or because radiant energy is reflected from them. The energy that our eyes are sensitive to is composed of electromagnetic radiations produced by electric charges moving through space at a very fast clip (roughly

186,000 miles per second). Although there is not complete agreement
among theoretical physicists about the exact nature of radiant energy,
it is conventional to talk about it as though it traveled in a wave form.
One fundamental way of measuring radiant energy is to measure the
distance from pulse to pulse of the vibration, that is, the wavelength
of the radiation. These wavelengths cover an enormous range, from
ten trillionths of an inch (the cosmic rays) to many miles in length
(Figure 15). As far as we can tell, all of them are the same kind of
radiation physically. They differ only in length.

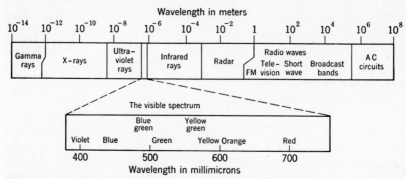

Fig. 15. The electromagnetic and visible spectra. Do not take the labels too
seriously. These energy waves are all the same—they differ only in length.
Actually, it is hard to say, for example, exactly where ultraviolet rays leave off
and visible light begins. People disagree also about the precise location of the
different colors in the visible spectrum.

Light waves. Somewhere in the middle of this spectrum, between
16 and 32 millionths of an inch in length (Figure 15), are the radiations we can see. These visible radiant energy waves are called light
waves. Isaac Newton discovered in 1666 that if you pass a beam of
sunlight through a triangular glass prism you get a wide band of different colors. He also surmised correctly that the reason this happened
was that the prism broke up the white light into its different wavelengths. In fact, it is from a spectrum such as this that the wavelengths of light can be measured. We never see wavelengths directly,
but they can be computed from physical measurements. If we look
at radiation that has only one wavelength in it, we will see a color—
one of roughly 150 different identifiable colors in the spectrum. We
do not have names for all these different colors, but some of the more
familiar colors we can see in the spectrum are shown in Figure 15.
Light waves are commonly measured in millimicrons (mμ), or Äng-

ström units (Å). Although we shall use only the former measure in this book, this equation shows how the two are related:

$$1\,m\mu = 10\,\text{Å} = 10^{-9}\,\text{meters}$$

Relative spectrum energy curves. We see things whenever light waves come from the objects we are looking at. The light waves may be generated in the objects, if they are self-luminous like the sun or lamps, or may be reflected from the objects, if they are not self-lumi-

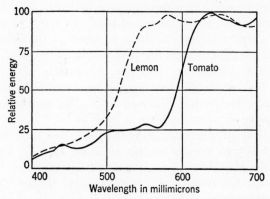

Fɪɢ. 16. Relative amounts of energy at various wavelengths in the light coming from a lemon and a tomato when they are seen in white light.

nous like grass or cloth. In coming from the object to our eyes, the light waves may also be modified if they pass through filters—like sunglasses, air with dust in it, or water. But regardless of where the light comes from in the beginning or how it is changed in the meantime, we can see something only if light comes from it and gets into our eyes.

Most of the light we see coming from objects has more than one single wavelength in it. And, of course, the intensity of the light may be different for different objects or for different wavelengths coming from the same object. One way of describing the light which comes from an object is to show the relative amount of energy at the various wavelengths in the bundle of light. When this type of information is presented graphically, we call it a relative energy spectrum. Figure 16 shows two such spectra, one for a lemon and the other for a tomato, when they are illuminated with white light (actually illuminant C which we shall discuss later).

There are several kinds of spectrum curves that we may encounter

in visual work. Spectral emission curves, for example, tell us the relative amount of energy at the various wavelengths in light rays coming
from a luminous object. Spectral transmission curves tell the relative
amounts of energy at various wavelengths that will pass through transparent objects. And spectral reflectance curves give the relative
amounts of energy at various wavelengths that will be reflected by
objects. These curves are very important in describing objects in
physical terms, and they may be combined in various ways. To compute the relative energy spectrum for the lemon in Figure 16, for example, we had to multiply a spectral emission curve for white light by
a spectral reflectance curve for lemon skin. In terms of what we see,
however, the really important thing to know is the relative energy
spectrum for the light that finally gets into our eye.

The eye is an integrator. The eye, fortunately or unfortunately,
however we look at the problem, cannot resolve different wavelengths
when they are combined in a ray of light. No matter how complex
the combination of wavelengths in a light beam, the eye always sees
one color. It is an integrating mechanism rather than an analyzing
one. If you look at a small section of lemon skin, for example, you
do not see the blue, blue–green, green, orange, and red wavelengths
which are being reflected—you only see yellow. Figure 17 shows five
different combinations of light waves that look exactly the same to
the eye. The uppermost figure, for example, shows a spectrum that
contains equal amounts of all the visible wavelengths—an equal-
energy spectrum. The second chart shows two single wavelengths,
which, when combined in the ratio of 1 to 0.78, produce exactly the
same visual sensation as the equal-energy spectrum. The same is true
for all of the other combinations shown in Figure 17. Even though
the combination of wavelengths differs markedly in all cases, the color
the eye sees for each of the five cases is exactly the same—very nearly
white.

Color mixtures. The fact that the eye is an integrating mechanism
actually makes the problem of specifying color a lot easier. It was
discovered a long time ago that every color we see around us can be
matched by a mixture of three colored lights—red, green, and blue.
This is very convenient because, if we want to specify the color of an
object, all we have to do is find out how much of a standard red, how
much of a standard green, and how much of a standard blue have to
be mixed together in order to match the unknown color. This information can then be put on a chart so that any one color can be compared with any other. Such a chart, shown in Figure 18, is called a

chromaticity diagram. This one was standardized by the International Commission on Illumination in 1931. The red, green, and blue lights that were standardized by the Commission are mathematically defined so that they are easy to work with. You will never see these standard colors, but that is no handicap since it is easy to convert from

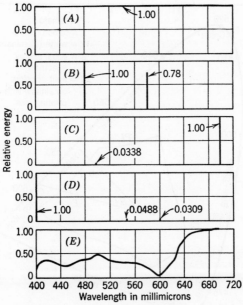

FIG. 17. All five combinations of wavelengths shown here look exactly alike to the eye—very nearly white. This is an illustration of the fact that the eye is an integrating mechanism rather than an analyzing one. (After Moon, 1936)

mixtures made with any set of colors to mixtures made with these standard ones.

It turns out, furthermore, that we need only two dimensions on this chart to portray all of the colors. The reason is this: The amount of green, red, and blue which are mixed to match any color add up to 1.00—or 100 percent. This means that if we know the amount of red and the amount of green in a mixture we can find the amount of blue by subtracting these amounts from 1. It would take us far beyond the scope of this chapter to explain precisely how visual scientists go about computing the position of a color on a chart like this from spectral emission, transmission, and reflectance data—either singly or in combination. These procedures, however, have all been worked out so that they are pretty mechanical and routine. If you ever have the job of figuring out the color specifications for a light or for a colored surface, read Hardy's *Handbook of Colorimetry;* [13] the techniques for working out the color specifications are all given there in simple clear language.

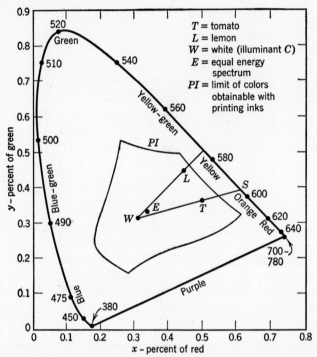

Fig. 18. This is a chromaticity diagram for plotting colors in terms of the amount of a standard red, green, and blue that will match them. The position of the spectrum colors is shown by the roughly triangular figure. The purest colors we can get with printing inks are also shown here.

The spectrum colors. Notice where the different colors are plotted in Figure 18. The location of all the spectrum colors is shown by the roughly triangular curve. The numbers along this curve are wavelengths. Since the spectrum colors are the purest we can ever find, all other colors we see fall somewhere inside this boundary. As a general rule, it is much easier to get pure colors with lights than with paints, inks, or dyes. The irregular-shaped line—labeled *PI*—near the center of Figure 18 shows about the purest colors we can get with commercial printing inks.

What "white" is. As we have already seen, white is a mixture of all of the colors. It can be matched by very nearly equal proportions of red, green, and blue and should be located somewhere near the center of this chart. But white turns out to be a fairly hard color to define. Most people will say that a Mazda lamp gives off white light, even though it is actually quite yellowish. Even daylight varies a lot in color: It tends to be a little reddish in the morning and evening, it varies a lot depending on how many clouds there are in the sky, and so on. The International Commission on Illumination has arbitrarily defined several "whites" and the one we have plotted in Figure 18 is illuminant C. This is about the kind of light we get from the summer sky when the air is clear, there are no clouds, and the sun is high. Incidentally, the point *E* shows the color of all those different wavelength combinations in Figure 17. It is just a shade more yellowish than illuminant C.

The use of the ICI diagram. A chromaticity diagram is very useful because it enables the scientist to tell a lot about how a color looks. He can tell right away that, if a color is far out to the right, it looks reddish. If the color is high on the chart, it looks greenish. If the color is near the lower left-hand corner, it does not have much red or green and so looks bluish. If a color is near the straight line running from 380 mμ to 780 mμ, it will look purple. We cannot find purple in the spectrum—it is actually a mixture of red and blue. That is why there are no numbers along that straight line.

Now let us look at something else this chart tells us. We have plotted in Figure 18 the colors of the tomato and the lemon which have the spectrum curves shown in Figure 16. First, let us draw a straight line from white through the point for the tomato color until it joins the spectrum line. The straight line intersects the spectrum line at point *S*—which corresponds roughly to 596 mμ. This means that if you look at this tomato under white light (illuminant C light) it will have the same color as a wavelength of 596 mμ—roughly orange.

Colorimetric purity. The distance of *T* along the line *WS* tells us how pure the color of the tomato is. The closer it is to *S*, the purer the color; the closer it is to *W*, the more washed out the color is. This is a measure of the colorimetric purity of the color; visual scientists refer to pure colors as saturated colors, to the washed-out ones as desaturated. Since *T* is about 0.64 of the way along the line *WS* (the length of the line *WT* divided by the length of the line *WS*), the color of our tomato is only moderately pure. Here is another interesting thing this computation tells us: We can also match the color of our tomato by mixing 64 parts of pure 596 mμ light with 36 parts of white.

We have also plotted the location of the color of our lemon in Figure 18. You can see that this lemon, viewed under white light, has about the same color as wavelength 577 mμ—almost pure sodium yellow— and that it is moderately saturated.

Another thing we might mention is that we can plot on this chart exactly how the tomato or lemon would look under any other kind of light—a Mazda lamp, for example. Finally, if we wish to find out what colors we can get by mixing any two colored lights at all—say 500 and 560 mμ—all we need to do is draw a straight line between those two points on the chart. That straight line will show all the possible color combinations we can get from mixtures of these two colors. So, all in all, this chart is a highly useful way of referring to the colors of lights or objects.

AMOUNT OF LIGHT

Photometry. When we have located the color of a light or object on a chromaticity diagram such as that shown in Figure 18, we have specified the color of it in terms of how it will look to the eye—as a color. But there is still another respect in which we must describe it. This is in terms of the total amount of light in it. We could have two reds, for example, which have exactly the same color, but one might be brighter than the other. It is possible to measure the amount of light by measuring either the amount of physical energy in the light or the effectiveness of that light in producing a visual sensation. The latter kind of measure is called a photometric measure and is the one most commonly used in visual work. It is more meaningful because it tells us how the physical energy is going to affect the eye—that is, how bright it will look. As we shall see later, we measure brightness or intensity in terms of its effect on the eye because energy at different wavelengths does not produce the same amount of brightness.

Intensity. There are three ways of looking at this problem of measuring the amount of light. You might want to know the total amount of light coming from a luminous object, the amount of light falling on an object, or the amount of light coming from an object which reflects light, that is, is not luminous. If we are talking about the intensity of a small point of light—a luminous object—it is usual to refer to it in terms of candles. A candle is an arbitrarily defined photometric unit which is standardized by the national laboratories of most major countries. A standard candle is maintained at the National Bureau of Standards in Washington, for example, and if you wanted to measure the intensity of an unknown light source you could compare it with that standard candle—or with other standards which had been calibrated at the National Bureau of Standards. If our unknown light source is twice as bright as the standard candle, it has an intensity of two candles. If it is half as intense as the standard candle, it has an intensity of one-half candle.

Illumination. The second kind of photometric measure is the foot-candle, which measures the amount of light falling onto a surface. A one-candle source delivers one foot-candle of illumination on a surface when the surface is at a distance of one foot. Since we shall use the term "mile-candle" later, we might explain that a mile-candle is the amount of illumination falling on a surface that is a mile away from a one-candle light. That is a very low order of illumination indeed.

An 8-candle source gives twice as much illumination as a 4-candle source and four times as much illumination as a 2-candle source. This information can be put into a generalization: The illumination falling on a surface is directly proportional to the intensity of the light source.

Another characteristic of illumination is that, if we move a surface twice as far away from a light, it will get one quarter as much illumination. If we move it three times as far away, it will get one ninth as much illumination. This forms the second part of the rule: The illumination on a surface is inversely proportional to the square of the distance between the surface and the light.

Brightness. The third kind of measure in photometry is the measure of brightness. Brightness is the amount of light coming back from a reflecting surface. You can readily see that this is a different kind of measure from illumination. Even though we may have an even amount of light falling onto the surface of a desk, the amount of light that comes back from different objects on the desk will vary greatly. The amount of light which will be reflected from a piece of black paper will be very small; the amount of light coming back from the white page of this book will be considerably greater. This is another way of saying that these two surfaces differ in brightness. A common unit of brightness is the apparent foot-candle. If we have a perfectly reflecting surface—a surface that reflects all the light that falls on it—and put one foot-candle of illumination on it, this surface would have a brightness of one apparent foot-candle. If we have a surface that reflects 90 per cent of all the light that falls on it—which is about as good as we can get with most white paper—then if we put one foot-candle of illumination on this surface, it would have a brightness of 0.9 apparent foot-candle. In short, if we want to measure the brightness of a surface in apparent foot-candles, we multiply the illumination on the surface (in foot-candles) by the overall reflectance of the surface. There are a great many different measures of brightness, but the apparent foot-candle (or foot-lambert, abbreviated ft-L) and the millilambert (mL) are the only two that we shall use in this book. A millilambert is almost exactly equal to an apparent foot-candle. The equation that shows how you can get from one to the other is

$$mL = 1.076 \text{ ft-L}$$

The specification of light stimuli. The complete specification of objects you see involves a few other things we have not mentioned. They are rather obvious, however, and do not need any special discussion. Here is the list: (1) We need to specify the total pattern of light beams coming into the eye. This means that we have to describe the size and shape of each homogeneous light beam. A homogeneous light beam is one that has the same distribution of energy in every part of it. (2) We must specify the wavelength composition for each homogeneous beam of light. We can do this by showing the relative amounts of energy at each wavelength in the light, or—what is more meaningful for our work—by specifying on a chromaticity diagram how this combination of wavelengths will look to us as a color. (3) We need to specify the amount or intensity of light in each homogeneous light beam. (4) We need to specify the length of time each light beam is on.

BASIC PROBLEMS OF VISIBILITY

Now that we know how to describe the things we see, we will discuss two important visual functions: visibility and visual acuity. Visibility means recognizing the presence of a light or object without having to recognize its shape or form. We might also call it detectability. Visual acuity means that we also have to recognize its form or shape. When we look up in the sky and can just barely see a blob which we think is an airplane way off in the distance, that is a case of visibility or detectability. When it gets close enough so that we can see that it has two engines, that is visual acuity. Visual acuity and visibility are not two entirely separate visual functions. We must have visibility before we can have visual acuity—visual acuity is just high order visibility. We shall see later that the factors affecting visibility also affect visual acuity. But there are some differences. We can see something long before we can recognize it. In general, therefore, we should expect curves for visibility to be somewhat lower than those for visual acuity. In addition, problems involving the recognition of lights are almost entirely visibility problems. Many visual experts will probably not agree with our use of the term visibility, but it seems to us that it best describes a number of the basic visual studies we want to talk about.

DAY AND NIGHT VISION

Now let us look at some interesting facts about the eye. From the standpoint of its function, the visual apparatus may be considered as two separate systems. One part operates most efficiently in ordinary illuminations, such as those that prevail throughout the day and in normally lighted rooms at night. When the illumination is decreased to about the level of full moonlight, around 0.01 foot-candle, the other part of the eye takes over.

Rods and cones. If we were to take off the front part of the eye and examine the inside with a microscope, we would find that there are two different kinds of nerve endings inside the eye. Anatomists and physiologists call these "rods" and "cones." The cones are found densely packed in the central part of the eye, the fovea. Toward the edges, in all directions from the center, the density of the cones decreases, and only a very few are found in the extreme edges. The rods, on the other hand, are entirely missing in the central part of the eye. Toward the edges in all directions, out to about 20 degrees from the center, the density of the rods gradually increases. A lot of experimental work points pretty conclusively to the cones as the nerve endings associated with daylight vision, and to the rods as those responsible for night vision. Individual rods and cones differ in sensitivity, so that most types of nerve endings operate over a fairly wide range of illumination. In general, however, the rods do almost all the work at starlight levels of illumination, whereas vision in daylight is largely a function of the cones.

Sensitivity to light. The sensitivity of different parts of the eye to light is pretty much the same at daylight levels of illumination. A light seen out of the corner of the eye will look just as bright as when we look right at it. This situation does not hold, however, in nighttime conditions. At night, the central part of the eye, the fovea, cannot see very dim lights because there are no rods there. But as we go out 5, 10, and 15 degrees from the center, the eye becomes more and more sensitive to light. Figure 19 shows the sensitivity of different parts of the eye at night. Zero degree represents vision in the direct line of sight—looking straight ahead. The other numbers represent lights which are at various angles from this straight-ahead direction. The nasal retina refers to that part of the eye that lies close to the nose. Since light rays cross over in entering the eye through the lens, light rays striking the nasal retina originate from objects on the temporal side of the body. To get down to actual cases, if a light ray strikes the nasal retina of the right eye, it must have come from the

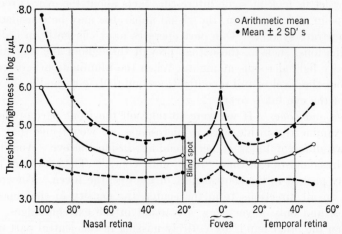

Fɪɢ. 19. The sensitivity of different parts of the eye at night. The solid line represents average values obtained on 101 subjects; the dotted lines give average values plus and minus two standard deviations. Note that the average eye is most sensitive to light about 20 degrees from the fovea. (After Sloan, 1947)

right side of the body; if a light ray strikes the temporal half of the retina of the right eye, it must have come from the left side of the body. One other thing about this chart: a microlambert, μL, is one one-thousandth of a millilambert. A micromicrolambert is one one-millionth of a microlambert. Hence, 1 $\mu\mu L = 10^{-9}$ mL.

The data in Figure 19 were obtained by Sloan [26] on 101 subjects, ranging in age from 14 to 70 years. These measurements were made with a 1 degree white test light. The solid line represents the average threshold values for the 101 subjects. The dotted lines are the average values plus and minus two standard deviations. Note that the eye is most sensitive—that is, it can see very dim lights—at about 20 degrees from the fovea.

Spectral sensitivity. Another important difference between the rods and cones concerns their relative sensitivity to light from different parts of the spectrum. If wavelengths containing equal amounts of radiant energy are viewed in daylight, they do not appear equally bright. Red and blue will appear dark, orange and green will appear intermediate in brightness, and yellow–green will look brightest. This state of affairs is shown in Figure 20 by the curve labeled "cone vision." If we decrease the overall intensity of the energy from the

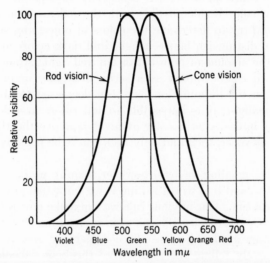

Fig. 20. These curves show the relative visibility or brightness of different wavelengths that have the same amount of energy. Notice that the eye is relatively more sensitive to longer wavelengths in daylight, that is, when the cones are working. At night, when the rods are working, the shorter wavelengths are relatively more visible. (After Troland, 1934)

different parts of the spectrum until only the rods are functioning, the visibility of the colors will be proportional to the values given by the left-hand curve in this illustration—the one labeled "rod vision."

The rod–cone shift. The practical importance of these data is that red and blue lights of equal size and intensity at cone levels of illumination and at night do not remain equally bright as we increase our distance from them. This happens because the amount of illumination at the eye decreases and proportionally more rods become active. Violet, blue, and blue–green lights outlive other colors in visibility as the distance between the light source and observer increases at night. This effect is known as the Purkinje phenomenon. The change in sensitivity of the eye to lights of different wavelengths is enormous and may amount to a factor of as much as 1,000. These facts were especially useful during the war, and they account for the fact that violet, blue, and green light could be much more readily detected at night by a distant enemy observer whose eyes were dark-adapted. Red, orange, and yellow lights, on the other hand, are not so easily detected at night by someone who is far away.

Color vision at night. Another important difference between the rods and the cones involves their sensitivity to color as color. True perception of color is not possible with the rods, as you can see for yourself if you try to determine the colors of objects by starlight. It is possible to distinguish between light and dark colors at night only in terms of the amount of reflected or emitted light. Under these circumstances all colors appear as a series of lighter or darker grays. In short, when the illumination has been decreased to about that of half full moonlight, it is impossible to tell colors as colors. If the brightness or intensity of a color at night is above the threshold for cone vision, however, then and only then can it be perceived as a true color.

Many light-signaling devices, however, require us to recognize the colors of lights, and it is worth asking if we can reach any conclusions about this problem. One obvious rule we can make now is this: Whenever it is necessary to identify colors in a signaling system correctly, the illumination at the eye must be considerably greater than is required for merely telling the presence of the light. Another general rule is that, the more complicated the color system is, the higher must be the illumination for each color. If we must recognize three different colors in a light-signaling system, we need more light than we would for recognizing two colors. The positive identification or recognition of four or five colors requires still more light than is necessary for the identification of three colors.

Recognition of colors. We shall cite here very briefly some interesting findings about the recognition of colored light signals which are near the limit of visibility. The experiment we want to tell you about was done with a point source of light, against a background about equal to a starlit sky, with exposures of 1½ seconds, and with two intensities of light—one which produced 1 mile-candle of illumination at the eye, and another which produced 2 mile-candles. The observers knew where the light was and looked in that direction. Over 30,000 observations were made with 73 colored lights which the observers had to identify as red, yellow, orange, white, green, or blue.

Two results turned up early in the experiment: With small point sources of light which are far away, it was impossible to tell the difference between blue and green. The same was true for yellow and orange. Red and green (or blue) were the easiest to recognize; then came white, and last yellow (or orange).

Because these findings are pretty important for many kinds of signaling systems in aviation, railroading, and shipping, we have summarized a part of the data in Figure 21. The two intensities of light

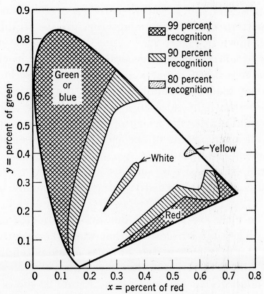

Fɪɢ. 21. This chromaticity diagram shows the best colors to use if we want to be able to recognize the colors of point sources of light used for signaling at night. (After Hill, 1947)

gave pretty much the same result, and we have shown here only the data for the 2 mile-candle light. The double-hatched areas on this chart show those colors that could be correctly recognized 99 percent of the time. The single-hatched areas show those colors that could be recognized correctly 90 percent of the time. Notice that there was no white light that could be recognized 99 percent of the time. Notice also that there was no yellow or orange that could even be recognized 90 percent of the time. In case you ever have to use yellow, though, we have drawn in the best yellows to use. These yellows could be recognized correctly 80 percent of the time.

Dark adaptation. If you go suddenly from bright illumination into darkness, the eye is not ready to go to work until it has had time to

become adapted to the new illumination. If you step into a movie at
night from a brilliantly lit lobby, at first you cannot see very much,
but after several minutes dim forms and large outlines become visible.
Then, as time goes by, more details of the environment become perceptible. This increase in sensitivity of the eye at low levels of illumination is called dark adaptation. Dark adaptation follows a fairly
definite pattern which can be charted by determining the minimum
amount of light you can see at various times after you go into the
dark. The pattern of this dark adaptation process to differently colored lights is shown in Figure 22.

The course of adaptation. In general, the decrease in visual threshold during the first 8 or 9 minutes is due to an increase in the sensitivity of the cones and, to a small degree, to the dilation of the pupil
which increases the light-gathering power of the eye. The additional
increase in visual sensitivity which occurs after 10 minutes is due to
the rods taking over. Most of the increase in the sensitivity of the
eye occurs during the first 30 minutes, although after that time there
is still a small but consistent increase in sensitivity. During these
first 30 minutes, the eye's sensitivity increases roughly ten thousand
times.

It should be clear by now that our eyes are really extraordinary
instruments. They are so sensitive that when they are fully adapted
they can see the flare of a match 10 miles away if the night is completely black and if there is no haze in the air.

Color and adaptation. One more thing Figure 22 shows very clearly
is that the eye is much more sensitive to violet light than it is to any
other colors. Green, white, and yellow lights are pretty good, but red
(R_I) and reddish orange (R_{II}) are not very visible. This fact is related to the Purkinje phenomenon we mentioned earlier. One thing
you should clearly understand, however, that, when the brightnesses
of these lights fall below about 5.5 log micromicrolamberts, you can
no longer recognize them as colors. Actually, you stop seeing the
colors in these lights right after the sharp break in the dark adaptation curve which occurs between 10 and 20 minutes. At those very
dim brightnesses, all colors—except R_I, deep red—look white.

Red goggles. The relative sensitivity of the rods and cones, as
shown in Figures 20 and 22, has provided us with a very important
aid to night vision. The rods are stimulated only a very little by red
light. By wearing goggles with red lenses in ordinary illuminations,
we can dark-adapt the rods with the lights on and still see well enough
with the cones to read or write. When we wear red goggles, the rods

in our eyes, for all practical purposes, are in complete darkness. The use of red lighting and red dark-adaptation goggles during the war must be familiar to all of you.

Instantaneous threshold following adaptation. The dark adaptation curves we have just been discussing show how the sensitivity of the eye increases if we give it enough time. For some practical problems,

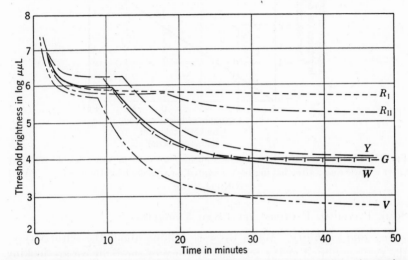

FIG. 22. These curves show the dimmest light we can see at various times after we go into the dark. It takes about 30 minutes for the eye to reach full sensitivity. Notice that we finally become most sensitive to violet (*V*) and that we are least sensitive to deep red (R_I) and reddish orange (R_{II}) light. (After Chapanis, 1947)

however, it is important to know how much light is necessary for vision immediately after the lights go out. If we step out of a brightly lit room into darkness, how much can we see immediately? Now that radar is being used for commercial vessels, a practical question is: How bright does a radar scope have to be so that a captain can see it after having looked at the brightly lit ocean? The brightness that is just visible immediately after we have been adapted to a certain brightness level is called the instantaneous threshold, and the curve of this function is shown in Figure 23. This chart tells us that if we have been adapted to a brightness level of 0.0001 millilambert (log = $\overline{4}.0$) we can see a light just about a fifth as bright (log = $\overline{5}.3$, or 0.00002 millilambert) immediately after we enter a dark room. But if we have been adapted to 1 millilambert—roughly equal to 1 apparent foot-candle (log = 0)—we can see a light about one hundredth as bright (log = $\overline{3}$.9) as soon as we enter the dark.

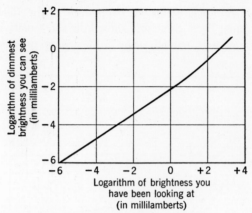

FIG. 23 This curve shows how bright a surface we can see immediately after we enter a dark room after having been adapted to various brightness levels. (After Nutting, 1916)

SOME PHYSICAL FACTORS AFFECTING VISIBILITY

Size and visibility. When we were talking about the sensitivity of the eye, we hinted at the fact that the size of the light we are looking at influences its visibility. Research studies show that point sources of light are much more efficient light signals than are large sources of light. The data supporting this claim are shown in Figure 24. This curve shows how much light circular areas must supply at the eye in order that they can just be seen. Notice that, when a circular light is 10 seconds or less in diameter, it needs to supply only 10^{-10} foot-candle of illumination at the eye in order to be seen. For practical purposes, a circular area 10 seconds or less in size may be considered a point source. When circular light areas become larger than this, however, they must deliver more light to the eye in order to be seen.

Another kind of data shows how visibility is related to the size and brightness of a light area. Figure 25 shows two sets of data on this problem. The two curves do not agree exactly but they show almost the same kind of function: you can see a large area at a much lower brightness than a small area. On the face of it, this might appear to contradict what we just said in the preceding paragraph. It does not, however. Let us explain the situation as follows:

Imagine a large light area, say a piece of white paper 3 feet square,

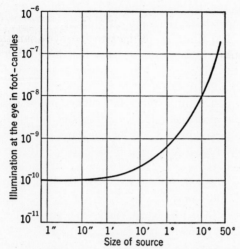

FIG. 24. A point source of light is the most efficient size of light. When the light is bigger than a point source, it has to supply more illumination on the eye before we can see it. (After Bouma, 1939)

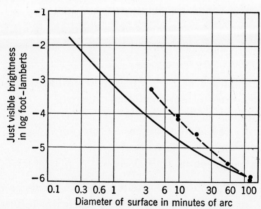

FIG. 25. These curves show how bright surfaces of various sizes must be so that we can just see them at a distance. These data are for completely black backgrounds. Although the two sets of data do not agree exactly, they both show that small areas must be brighter in order to be visible. (After Lash and Prideaux, 1943, and Blackwell, 1946)

and a small light area, say a piece of the same white paper 3 inches square. If you put the same amount of illumination on both pieces of paper, they will have the same brightness. But the big piece will deliver roughly 100 times more light to the eye than the small piece. Even though both pieces of paper have the same brightness, you will be able to see the bigger one further away because it sends a greater total amount of light to the eye.

Therefore, if you want a reflecting surface to be visible far away, make it as big as possible. The brightness of the surface, under any given illumination conditions, will be constant. With constant brightness you get better visibility with bigger areas. If you want to see a light as far away as possible, make it small. With a fixed amount of electric energy, you can crowd more visible light into a very small source than into a big one.

Time and visibility. In considering how time relationships affect visibility, we must consider two cases: (*a*) when we know where the light source is and are looking in that direction, (*b*) when we do not know where the light source is and have to hunt for it. In both cases a steady light source can be seen at much lower intensities than a flashing light source.

The equation which shows how intense a flashing light source must be when we know where the light source is and are looking at it, is

$$E = E_0 \left(\frac{t + a}{t} \right)$$

where E = illumination of a flashing source which can just be seen (measured in foot-candles at the eye)

E_0 = illumination of a steady source which can just be seen (measured in foot-candles at the eye)

t = duration of the flash (in seconds)

a = a constant equal to 0.21 second

We have also put the same information into Figure 26 so that you can see what this function looks like. Since intensity is directly proportional to illumination, we have plotted relative intensity of the just visible flash. Notice how much more intense we have to make a very short flash of light so that we can see it. Notice also, however, that the just visible intensity is very nearly constant for durations of 0.5 second or more.

For the second case—when we do not know where the flashing light is and have to hunt for it—the situation is much worse. Now we must consider how long we spend hunting for it, how large an area we search with our eyes, how much of the retina is sensitive enough to see that particular light, and so on. You can understand that it is hard to give a single function that will take all these things into account. One thing we can be sure of is that the data in Figure 26 are minimum values. They tell us how intensity is related to time under the best

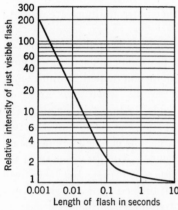

Fig. 26. This graph shows how intense a flash of light has to be in order that we can just see it. Notice that very short flashes must be much more intense than long flashes if we want to see them. (After Blondel and Rey, 1912)

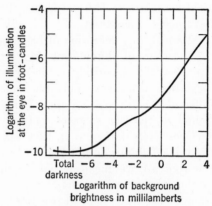

Fig. 27. This curve shows how intense point sources of light must be in order for us to see them against backgrounds of various brightnesses. (After Knoll, Tousey, and Hulburt, 1946)

seeing conditions. If we have to hunt for a light, we had better take a big safety factor into account.

Background brightness. The visibility of a point source is also a function of the brightness of its background. The relationship that shows this is Figure 27. This curve shows us that, when we are at starlight levels, a point source can be seen if it is very dim indeed, but, when we get up into the moonlight levels, then a point source must be roughly 10 to 15 times more intense in order to be seen. In daylight, a point source must be extremely intense in order to be seen.

Brightness contrast. In talking about the visibility of surfaces that are larger than a point source, visual scientists usually plot their data in terms of brightness contrasts. By brightness contrast, we mean how much lighter or darker an object is than its background. This difference is expressed as a ratio of the background brightness to give a measure called *percent brightness contrast.* The exact formula is

$$\% \, BC = \frac{\lfloor B_o - B_b \rfloor}{B_b}$$

Where $\% \, BC$ is the percent brightness contrast, B_o is the brightness of the object, and B_b is the brightness of the background. By definition, objects that are brighter than their surroundings are said to have *positive* contrast; objects darker than their surroundings are said to have *negative* contrast.

Although this definition of brightness contrast is well established in the literature of illuminating engineering, psychologists sometimes confuse it with an entirely subjective phenomenon called simultaneous brightness contrast. This phenomenon results when two areas of different brightnesses are placed side by side. Almost invariably, the lighter of the two surfaces looks lighter, and the darker of the two surfaces looks darker, than they really are. Psychologists can measure this effect but do not know why it occurs. A more exact term for the contrast we mean would be luminance contrast, but the term brightness contrast is already so well established that we shall continue to use it, as defined previously, throughout the book.

Our best source of information about the visibility of nonluminous areas comes from an extensive study conducted during the war by the Office of Scientific Research and Development. To conduct this study this agency took over the Lewis Comfort Tiffany Foundation, which is normally an art school in peacetime. Spots of light were projected on a screen some 60 feet away from a group of observers who reported whether or not they had seen the spot. A large number of such presentations were made with varying brightnesses, with spots of varying sizes, and with background brightnesses varying from full daylight to slightly less than the darkest night. In all, more than *two million* observations were recorded. Some 450,000 of these observations have now been analyzed, and they constitute what is probably the largest single study of human vision that has been reported to date.

Brightness contrast and visibility. Let us examine some of the data of this experiment. Shown in Figures 28 and 29 are a series of curves showing the least perceptible brightness contrast that can be seen by the normal eye with various background brightnesses. The different curves in Figure 28 represent the data for test objects of various sizes. A total of approximately 220,000 observations went into the plotting of this series of curves. Two relationships are shown very clearly by

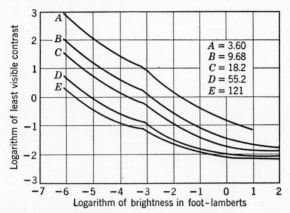

FIG. 28. These curves show how the least visible brightness contrast varies as a function of background brightness and size of target. We can see much smaller contrasts when the background brightness is high and the object is big. The target sizes *A, B, C, D,* and *E* are in minutes of visual angle. (After Blackwell, 1946)

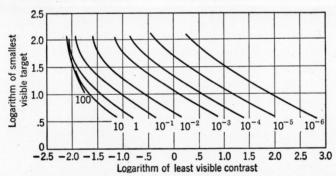

FIG. 29. These are the same data as in Figure 28. The different curves are for various brightness levels in foot-lamberts. These curves show the smallest objects we can see with various background brightnesses and with various contrasts between the objects and their backgrounds. (After Blackwell, 1946)

this series of curves: The first is that, as the brightness decreases, the brightness contrast of the just barely perceptible object must become greater. If we translate this into other words, it means that, when it gets darker, things must be a lot blacker or lighter than their backgrounds in order for us to see them. If there is more light, on the other hand, we can see objects that are just a little darker or lighter than their surroundings.

The other relationship clearly demonstrated in this graph is that, at any illumination, small objects must have more contrast in order to be seen than large objects. This latter relationship is more clearly demonstrated in Figure 29. There the size of the object is plotted against the brightness contrast of the just perceptible object. In this case, the different curves represent the data obtained at the various brightness levels.

Color contrast in daylight. Another kind of contrast is important in many visibility problems, namely, color contrast. Color contrast means how much difference there is between colors when they are equal in brightness. Under good daylight viewing conditions, equal color differences show up as a series of ellipses on a chromaticity diagram (Figure 30). The distances from the boundaries of any ellipse to the point in the center represent colors that have equal color contrast. Notice that we cannot get many greens that will look very different—the ellipses are big there. But we can get a lot of colors that look different in the blue, purple, and red regions. This diagram shows that, if you want to use colors of equal brightness to distinguish different objects, you should pick them out of different ellipses. You will get your best color differences, of course, if you pick colors from ellipses that are as far apart as possible. Be sure to note the similarity between these data and those shown in Figure 21.

Other factors in visibility. There are other factors which enter into the solution of visibility problems which we can only mention here. If visibility is necessary over great distances, the characteristics of the atmosphere will be very important. The data we have given are laboratory data; they represent the best possible seeing conditions. But if we are out-of-doors, rain, haze, dust, fog, and atmospheric boil will all decrease visibility. This means that we must take large safety factors into account in using this information. The general relationships will be about the same, but visibility will generally be poorer.

Application to radar displays. One useful application of these contrast data is in predicting the best operating conditions for cathode-ray tubes. This is a pretty important application because the cathode-ray tube is the display end of a modern radar. Targets, land masses, and sea return which the radar picks up eventually appear on the phosphorescent screen of this tube. Even under the best operating conditions, the screen is not very bright, the contrast is low, and the resolu-

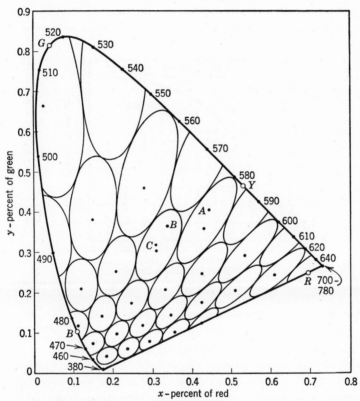

Fig. 30. The distances from the boundaries of any ellipse to the point in the center represent color differences that are equally noticeable. These data were obtained under good daylight conditions with colors that had the same brightness. (After Judd, 1936)

tion poor. Since distant targets may come in as very weak "pips" it is important to have the sweep line and screen brightness set at those values that are best for human vision. It is a big jump from laboratory data on brightness contrast to the brightness of phosphor screens controlled by electric voltages. Recent research [29] has shown that signal detectability in radar is comparable to and can be predicted from brightness contrast data such as are shown in Figures 28 and 29. The electrical units have to be translated into brightness units, but, once this is done, the application follows easily.

Other applications of contrast data. The whole art of camouflage depends on methods whereby low color and brightness contrast are used to conceal objects by decreasing their visibility. Standard camouflage for naval aircraft consists in painting the underside a light color, to present low contrast against the sky when seen from below,

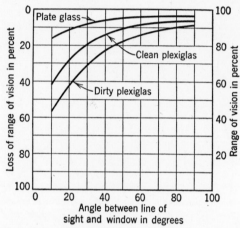

FIG. 31. These curves show how visibility is reduced when we look through plate glass, clean Plexiglas and dirty Plexiglas. Glass and Plexiglas reduce brightness contrasts and in this way reduce visibility. (After Olenski and Goodden, 1943)

and the top side blue, to match the sea when seen from above. When aircraft operate predominantly in one type of combat environment, as do naval aircraft, satisfactory camouflage can be achieved easily. If, on the other hand, the aircraft must operate under a wide variety of environmental conditions, a camouflage for all of these conditions is difficult if not impossible to achieve.

Another practical illustration of the importance of brightness contrasts is shown in Figure 31, which scarcely needs any interpretation. These data were obtained by subjects who looked through aircraft glass, clean Plexiglas and dirty Plexiglas. This figure shows that dust and grease on windshields act as an effective screen between the pilot and the outside world. Particles of dirt and grease scatter light haphazardly into the bundle of light rays which form an image of the object on the retina. This decreases the contrast and destroys the sharpness of the image. Diminished contrast also results from scratching or fogging of the transparent material, because each scratch or water droplet is a source of scattered light.

VISUAL ACUITY

How We Measure Visual Acuity

There are two different ways of measuring acuity. One is commonly used by physicians and the other by laboratory scientists. The two measures are obtained in much the same way, and one can generally be translated into the other. Our visual acuity is simply a statement about the smallest object whose shape we can recognize in a standard situation.

The eye chart. All of us, having suffered through at least a few physical examinations, are familiar with the physician's eye chart (see Figure 32). When it is used under carefully controlled conditions, this measuring device compares your visual acuity with what is supposed to be that of the average person. The letters of different sizes on the chart are supposed to represent what the average person can barely see at various distances. On many charts, the biggest letter can be just read at 200 feet, the next biggest letters are half as large and so can be read at 100 feet, and so on. If, at 20 feet from the chart, you can see what the average person can see at 20 feet, you have 20/20 vision. If, at 20 feet from the chart, you can only see those letters which the average person can see at 100 feet, you have 20/100 vision. That is not so good. But if you can see those letters which the average person can see only at 10 feet, you have 20/10 vision. That is excellent.

These measurements could be made, of course, by using letters of one size and having the subject move back and forth, but the principle is the same. When this procedure is used, however, a visual acuity of 20/40 becomes 10/20, one of 20/10 becomes 40/20. This system of measuring acuity has been used in the Navy. It might help you to remember what these various designations mean if you notice that the numerator of the fraction is the distance at which you were when you read the letters, the denominator is the distance at which the average person can read the same letters. In scientific work, these visual acuity measurements are frequently expressed in their decimal equivalents to make them easier to work with. Thus 20/20 vision equals 1.00; 20/40 or 10/20 vision equals 0.50; 20/10 or 40/20 vision equals 2.00; etc.

Visual angle. The other type of measure, commonly used in the laboratory for measuring visual acuity, expresses the size of the smallest object you can see in terms of the visual angle subtended by this

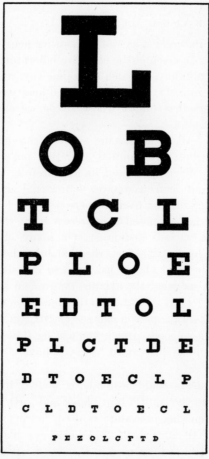

Fig. 32. This is a reduction of one kind of chart that can be used to test visual acuity. If you look at this chart from a distance of 20 to 30 feet, you will have illustrated a basic visibility function: visibility is a function of the size of the object you are looking at.

object at the eye. To measure visual angle, take the outside dimensions of the object you are looking at as the base of a triangle with the point of the triangle at the eye. The visual angle is the angle made by the "lines" that go from your eye to the outer edges of the object.

This kind of measure has its advantages because it gives us a single, simple number to work with. Furthermore, this type of measure involves no comparison with the visual acuity of a hypothetical average person seeing under average conditions. In general, and under normal indoor conditions, the average person can just barely see an object that subtends one minute of visual angle. This corresponds to 20/20 vision. A person with 20/40 vision can just barely see an object that is 2 minutes of visual angle in size. The limit of visual acuity under ideal conditions is about a half-second. This is roughly equivalent to seeing a wire, $\frac{1}{16}$ inch in diameter, a half-mile away!

Converting visual acuity into visual angles. The conversion from visual acuity to minutes of visual angle is simple. Here is the equation:

$$\text{vis } \angle = \frac{1}{VA} \quad \text{or} \quad VA = \frac{1}{\text{vis } \angle}$$

where vis $\angle$ = the minimum angular size, measured at the eye, of the smallest detail you can see, and VA = your visual acuity expressed in its decimal form. This simple equation is possible, of course, because of the convenient relation that 1 minute of visual angle equals a visual acuity of 1.00.

By the way, if you measure the size of the letter that is supposed to equal 20/20 vision ($VA = 1.00$) on a visual test chart, you will find that it is five minutes in size. That is all right, though, because the thickness of the strokes on the letter, and the white spaces between strokes—which are really the things you need to see if you are to read the letter—all equal one minute of visual angle when you are the correct distance away from the chart.

PHYSIOLOGICAL FACTORS AFFECTING ACUITY

Near and far acuity. If we are going to select men on the basis of their acuities, it is essential that we also specify the distance at which we measure them. We know now that a person may have excellent acuity at 20 feet and very poor acuity at 13 inches. Or vice versa. In general, acuity stays the same for distances greater than 20 feet. One reason why this happens is that the lens in the front of the eye has to change shape in order to focus near and far objects on the retina. This change in shape of the lens is called accommodation. Some people cannot focus on far objects. They are called nearsighted and have to wear glasses to correct the situation. Others cannot focus on near objects. They are called farsighted and have to wear glasses so that they can read. As a general rule, people tend to become more far-sighted as they grow older.

These facts have some practical implications. In some industries and in many military situations, men are selected for particular jobs on the basis of results obtained in physical examinations. Because visual acuity is related to accident proneness and efficiency in certain types of jobs, this is a critical item in the physical examination. It is now known that, if the job calls for good distance acuity, for example, truck driving, the men should be tested at 20 feet. But if the job calls for good near acuity, for example, toolmaking or operating a radar, then the men should be tested at a distance comparable to that used on the job. The factors that affect acuity seem to affect both near and far acuity alike. For this reason we shall not have to talk about distances in the following discussion.

Visual acuity and retinal angle in daylight. We all use our eyes so much that we commonly overlook certain peculiarities about seeing and would never notice them if they were not pointed out to us. Every once in a while, for example, somebody writes a popular article about the eye being just like a camera. In such a discussion the author usually compares the photographic film with the retina, that back part of the eye on which the images of outside objects are formed. However, this analogy is not correct in one very important respect. A photograph is usually sharp and in focus over its entire surface. The edges of the photograph are clear. But that is not the way the eye sees things. If, for example, you stare steadily at one letter on a printed page, it is impossible to read letters 2 inches away; or if you are looking at the road ahead while driving, you cannot read the road signs along the side. So the eye does not see everything so clearly as a camera all over its visual field.

This variation of visual acuity in different parts of the eye is plotted in Figure 33. In this illustration, zero degree represents the straight-ahead direction sometimes called the line of sight. Light rays from this direction strike the fovea—the center part of the eye. Visual acuity drops off very rapidly as we go toward the corners of the eye. As a matter of fact, when you are looking straight ahead, your visual acuity 5 degrees to the right or to the left of this central line of sight is just half as good as it is in the center of your eye. When we go out toward the edges of the eye, as far as 40, 45, and 50 degrees from the central line of sight, visual acuity is only about $\frac{1}{20}$ of what it is directly straight ahead.

The blind spot. Now one thing more before we leave this illustration. Notice that there is a blacked-off area in the figure. This is labeled the "blind spot." Even though most people do not realize it, everyone has a blind spot in each of his eyes. It is located about 15 degrees from the central part of the eye, on the side of the eye nearer to the nose and is about 7 degrees wide and about 5 degrees high. It is the place where the nerves and blood vessels come into the eye.

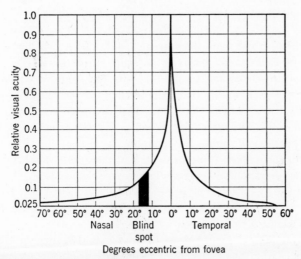

Fig. 33. This is a curve of daylight visual acuity for different parts of the eye. The center part of the eye, the fovea, has the best acuity in daylight. Notice how rapidly acuity drops off toward the corners of the eye. (After Wertheim, 1894)

This area of the eye is absolutely blind. We cannot see anything in it, and yet if we try to find a hole in our visual field, we do not see any such blind spot. Yet it would be a very simple matter to demonstrate it in the laboratory. There is an interesting story about this blind spot. It was discovered by Mariotte in 1668. When the Royal Society demonstrated this phenomenon to King Charles II, he used it to see how his friends would look with their heads cut off.

Seeing is deceiving. These two very simple facts, the variation in visual acuity in different parts of the eye and the presence of the physiological blind spot, may go unnoticed by very careful observers for years and years. Usually, when people have these things pointed out to them, their natural reaction is "How come I never noticed it before this?" There are two answers to this question. The first is that eye movements tend to obscure the blind spot from us. Our eyes are restless and their constant roving fills in the hole, as it were. We shall have something more to say about eye movements in a moment.

The second part of the answer is that seeing does not involve simply the eye; it involves both the eye and the brain. There is a very common saying that seeing is believing, but, before you finish this chapter, you will discover that in some cases seeing is deceiving. Sometimes our brain makes us see things that do not exist even when the brain is free from the allegedly evil effects of alcohol. We shall have more to say about this matter when we come to the section on optical illusions.

Visual acuity and retinal angle at night. In an earlier section we showed how nighttime sensitivity to light varies in different parts of the eye. But sensitivity to light is not the same as visual acuity. During the war, a lot of people confused the two and went around saying that if we want to see things best at night we should turn our eyes about 15 or 20 degrees to one side. That is true if we are trying to see a very weak light, for example, a distant lighthouse at sea. Very recent data show that the region of maximum *acuity* at night is about 4 degrees from the center of the eye (Figure 34). Other recent experiments by Gordon [11] at a single brightness level (-4 log milli-lamberts) agree with this since he finds the most acute region of the retina about 5 to 7 degrees from the fovea.

The physiological explanation of why visual acuity at night does not parallel light sensitivity is complex and need not concern us too greatly. We can say in very general terms, however, that these two visual functions depend on the density of the rod population and on the numbers of rods which connect to single nerve fibers in various parts of the eye.

Figure 34 also contains some other useful information. You can see there that acuity depends very much on the amount of light. At very dim brightnesses acuity is best at about 4 degrees from the fovea, but the acuity there is considerably poorer at night than it is in daylight. A general function relating acuity to brightness is given later. The important point here is that Figure 34 gives us more evidence about basic differences between rods and cones and between seeing in daylight and at night.

We can now summarize what we know about day and night vision in this way: In daylight, the eye is equally sensitive to light all over. At night, we see lights best when they are about 20 degrees from the line of sight. In daylight, visual acuity is very poor, relatively speaking, just a few degrees from the central line of sight, but at night the eye is most acute about 4 or 5 degrees from the central line of sight. Strange as it may seem, in order to see best at night, we must *not* look directly at an object but use off-center vision—look away from it in order to see it most clearly.

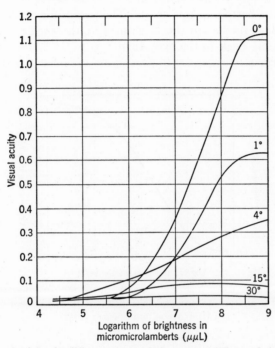

Fɪɢ. 34. Visual acuity in different parts of the eye at different brightness levels. At high brightnesses the center of the eye (0 degrees) is most acute. At very low brightnesses, between log 5 and log 6 micromicrolamberts, the eye is most acute about 4 degrees from the center. (After Mandelbaum and Rowland, 1944)

Physical Factors Affecting Visual Acuity

We should like now to shift our emphasis to some other basic factors affecting visual acuity. In contrast to the previous section, our concern here is how visual acuity is influenced by physical factors in the environment. We will find that the same sorts of factors that affect visibility also affect visual acuity. One or two new factors can be taken into account, however. There are so many research studies on these factors that it would be impossible to review them all here. What we shall try to do, therefore, is pick out representative data to illustrate each of the points we want to make.

Brightness and visual acuity. We have already had occasion to mention the importance of the first factor—illumination or brightness. The data in Figure 35 are an average of six recent studies on visual acuity as a function of the amount of light present. Notice, however, that we have plotted brightness in millilamberts instead of illumination along the bottom of this chart. The reason for this is that visual acuity is more related to the brightness of the surface—the amount of light coming back to the eye—than it is to the illumination falling onto the surface.

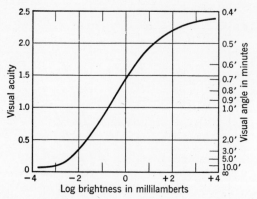

Fɪɢ. 35. This curve shows how visual acuity varies as a function of background brightness. It is an average curve taken from the results of several recent studies. (After Moon and Spencer, 1944)

There are several interesting things to notice about this curve. First, notice how rapidly visual acuity increases as the brightness increases in the middle range of values—from 0.01 to 100 millilamberts. Then, notice too that visual acuity does not increase so much after that. There is only a slight additional increase in acuity when the brightness of the surface increases beyond 100 millilamberts. It is also important to note, though, that visual acuity appears to increase indefinitely—even if slowly—as we increase the brightness of the surface. This is a rather important finding, because it means that there is no such thing as the "best amount" of light. If we increase the amount of light falling onto a surface we will always get better and better acuity. The important practical problem is to get enough brightness so that we can do the kind of visual task we need to do.

The practical importance of data like these is that they enable us to make useful predictions about how much light is necessary to see objects of various sizes. But remember that these are minimum figures—the visual acuity represents the smallest detail that we can just barely see at these various brightnesses. If we want to see something without difficulty, then we need more light than this graph shows.

Visual acuity at night. These data are important for telling us about seeing not only at high brightnesses, but at low brightnesses as well. The decrease in acuity at low brightnesses and at night means that identification must depend on the perception of generalized contours and outlines and not on small distinguishing features. Wires, picket fences, and telephone poles may be invisible a few hundred feet away at night. Aircraft and ships are least visible when viewed from dead astern because their areas are smallest in that direction. For this reason, night interception tactics during the war required that enemy aircraft be followed from rear above or rear below, rather than from rear level. Similarly, small terrain features, a small building, smokestack, or a bridge may not be visible from the air at night, and recognition must depend on rather large ground features—surf and sand, large clumps of trees, rivers, lakes, and large concrete installations.

Time and visual acuity. The second factor affecting visual acuity is time: An object becomes more visible the longer you can look at it. This law is so reasonable that it hardly needs illustration. Magicians make use of this principle all the time, and it accounts for the saying, "The hand is quicker than the eye."

You can get some idea about the importance of time in visual acuity from Figure 36. The experimenters who did this study had a number of different visual acuity targets of different sizes, illuminated them to different brightnesses, and then flashed them on for very short periods of time. The observer's task was to try to identify the visual acuity targets correctly during that short exposure. The results in Figure 36 are plotted in terms of speed, that is, the reciprocal of time in seconds. The higher points on these curves mean that the subjects had less time to see. It is evident here that, when the subjects had more time to look at the target, that is, when the speed values were low, they could see much smaller objects. When, on the other hand, they had only a very brief look at the targets, the test objects had to be much bigger before they could be seen. You can see again from this chart the influence of the first factor, brightness. For any particular exposure time, the subjects were able to see smaller targets the more light they had on the target. Of course, the range of brightnesses covered in this experiment is only a very small fraction of the total range of brightnesses covered in the experiments summarized in Figure 35.

Visual acuity and brightness contrast. Basic data showing the relationship between visual acuity and the brightness contrast of objects are contained in Figure 37. The two parts of this figure were obtained from two different studies. In general, they agree fairly well for the lower contrast values but not very well for the high contrast values.

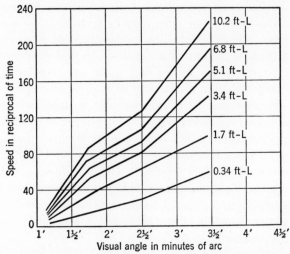

FIG. 36. At any brightness level, we do not need so long a time to see when we look at bigger objects. We also need less time to see when we increase brightness even though we look at objects that are the same size. (After Ferree and Rand, 1922)

These differences are due to differences in the experimental conditions used in the two studies. The data on the left-hand side of this figure were obtained with very long exposure times: The subjects were allowed to look at the target for three seconds or more. The data on the right-hand side of this figure were obtained with fairly brief exposure times: The subjects were allowed to see the target for only 0.17 second. Since we already know that visual acuity is related to the length of time that we look at an object, it is not surprising to find that these two sets of data do not agree completely. For our purposes, however, it is easy to see that visual acuity at any particular brightness increases as the contrast of the object against its background increases.

Interrelationships among factors. Each of these factors in visual acuity is easily understood when we consider them one at a time. A difficulty arises, however, because they are all interrelated, so that predicting visual acuity under a given set of circumstances may become fairly involved. In discussing many visual acuity and visibility functions (see Figures 28, 29, 34, 36, and 37, for example) we discussed a couple of factors at the same time. We know now, for example, that a reduction in any one of these factors—illumination, size, contrast, or time—may be compensated for by an increase in one or more of the

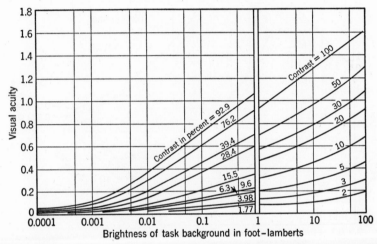

Fig. 37. Visual acuity as a function of brightness contrast and background brightness. Visual acuity increases both when we have more light and when the contrast between the object and its background increases. (After Connor and Ganoung, 1935, and Cobb and Moss, 1928)

others. For example, an object that is so small that you cannot see it may be made visible by increasing the illumination on it or by increasing the contrast between it and its background, or both. This is true within certain limits because it is easily possible, of course, to get an object so small that it can never be seen by the unaided eye.

Fortunately for us, these basic factors have been investigated in their various interrelationships, and Figure 38 shows how visual acuity varies with different contrasts and brightnesses and two different exposure times. We are trying to show so many interrelationships here that it is necessary to use a three-dimensional diagram, and even then we do not quite include all the information we would like. The area above this three-dimensional curve is the region of clear seeing; the area below the curve represents the region of the invisible. By means of this curve we can tell from the size of an object, its contrast, and

the amount of illumination on it whether or not that object will be
clearly seen or not seen. This plot of the boundaries of normal vision
was derived from over 100,000 separate measurements, and it forms
the basis for many of our predictions about visual acuity under many
practical conditions. Notice, however, that this set of data does not

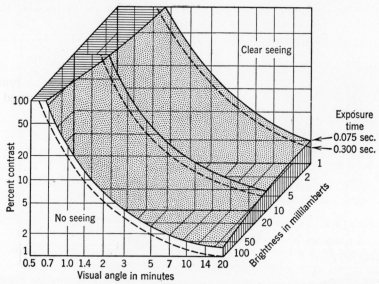

Fig. 38. The curved three-dimensional surface shows the relationship among visual
acuity, contrast, and background brightness for two exposure times. This is a
combination of the data shown in Figures 36 and 37. We can see things clearly
if the combination of seeing conditions is above the curved surface; we cannot
see if the seeing conditions fall below the surface. (From M. Luckiesh, Light,
vision and seeing, in O. Glasser, ed., *Medical physics*, Chicago, Year Book Publishers, 1944, p. 673)

cover the complete range of brightness values. But this is the best
we have on this problem, and the complete investigation of the inter-
relationship of these factors must wait upon further research.

Brightness of surround. In our discussion so far we have been concerned with visual acuity as a function of brightness, contrast, and
time of exposure for an object along or very close to the central line
of sight. Most practical problems in illumination engineering require
that one other factor be taken into account, namely, the brightness of
a large area surrounding the visual task. For all practical purposes
the visual field of the eye represents the amount of space that we can
see. This visual field is limited by the contours of the face. Above,

it is limited by the eyebrows, to one side by the nose, and below by the cheek bones. For the average observer, the visual field is about

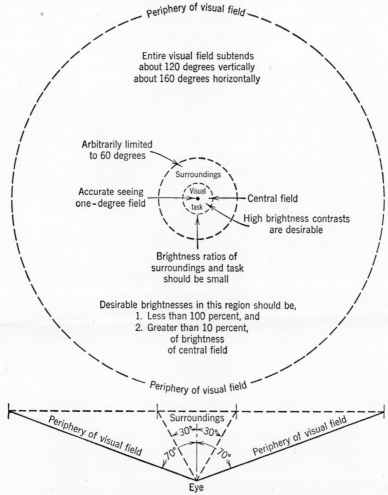

FIG. 39. The illuminating engineer has to consider the entire visual field in the design of interior lighting. (From M. Luckiesh, *Light, vision and seeing*, Van Nostrand, copyright 1944)

160 degrees in size horizontally and about 120 degrees in size vertically. For most problems we can divide this visual field into three areas as shown in Figure 39. The central field is fairly small in size

and is the place where we have our most accurate vision. That portion of the visual field which surrounds the central field up to 60 degrees constitutes the surroundings. Finally, around the surrounding 60-degree portion is the periphery of the visual field.

Visual acuity a function of surround brightness. We can change the visual acuity of the eye by merely increasing or decreasing the

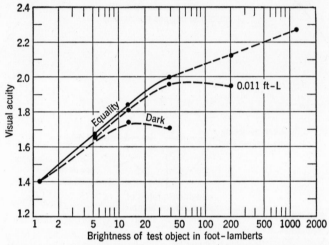

FIG. 40. Visual acuity as a function of the brightness of the central area for three brightnesses of surround. Notice that visual acuity is best when the surround is equal to the central area in brightness. (After Lythgoe, 1932)

brightness of the surroundings. The results of one investigation undertaken to explore this function are shown in Figure 40. This figure shows that visual acuity is greatest when the surrounding area is about the same brightness as the central field. This means, for example, that, if we are looking at a dial, our eyes are most sensitive when a large area around the dial is about the same brightness as the dial face. We say "about the same brightness" because a number of other studies seem to indicate that acuity is best when the surrounding area is just a little bit dimmer than the object at which we are looking. If the surrounding area is very much different in brightness, visual acuity is not so good, and we get our greatest loss when the surrounding area is brighter than the visual task. For best acuity, the surrounds should not be less than one tenth as bright as the central field.

As a practical illustration of this principle, two investigators, Hanes and Williams,[12] have shown that detectability of targets on radar scopes actually improves if the illumination in the room is kept a little higher than is usually the case. Detectability is best when the eyes are adapted to about the same brightness level as the radar scope. This appears to be true in the laboratory, but other factors must be considered in the design of brightnesses and illuminations for interior work spaces.

Glare. Dazzle, or glare, produced by light sources of relatively high intensity in the visual field also affects acuity. In general, it reduces the sensitivity of the eye and the visibility of an object or task. Usually when we try to increase the illumination in the radar room to get better detectability of radar scopes, we find that we have increased the glare so much that we are worse off than when we started. There are too many shiny surfaces around. In the following discussion we shall distinguish two kinds of glare: successive and simultaneous.

Successive glare. This is the kind of glare you experience when your eyes are suddenly flooded with light more intense than you are adapted to. When you step out of a theater into a brightly lit street you experience successive glare. Or when someone suddenly snaps his headlights on directly in your face on a dark night you are exposed to successive glare. Under such conditions how much light is a glaring light? We have very good data on this problem as a result of some extensive research by Nutting.[24] He adapted the eye to a wide range of brightness levels and then suddenly exposed a much brighter field. The observers were required to state whether the increased light was uncomfortable. In spite of what might appear to be a highly subjective kind of report, the results were remarkably consistent. He found that the amount of light that appeared to be uncomfortable depended on the level of brightness to which the eye is adapted. If this brightness level B is expressed in millilamberts, then a light will glare if it is brighter than the value G computed from the following equation:

$$G = 1700B^{0.32}$$

This relationship is also illustrated in Figure 41.

Simultaneous glare. Simultaneous glare is the kind we experience when there is a bright localized source of light in the visual field at the same time as a more general illumination. This kind of glare, we know, is distracting and annoying and may even cause extreme discomfort and pain. Glare sources that are particularly annoying are bright light sources in the direct visual field or reflected images of light sources from polished surfaces. As a result of many years of research on this problem certain fundamental relationships concerning glare have been well established.

Glare and visual acuity. The first of these is that glare reduces visual acuity directly as the brightness of the glare source. The impairment of visual acuity, therefore, is directly dependent on the candlepower of the glare source toward the eye and inversely proportional to the square of the distance of the glare source from the eye. A second relationship is that the effect of any glare source becomes less as

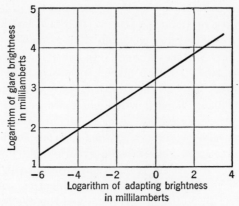

Fig. 41. This chart shows how much light is a glaring light when our eyes are suddenly flooded with more light than we are adapted to. (After Nutting, 1916)

the angular distance from the direct line of vision increases. This relationship is shown in Figure 42. This illustration shows the eye looking at an object with the direct line of vision represented as a horizontal line at the bottom of the figure. In the upper left-hand corner is a lamp furnishing 10 foot-candles of illumination on a test object. If we introduce a glare source 40 degrees above the direct line of vision, the effect is merely one of slightly decreased acuity. If we bring this same glare source down to within 20 degrees of the direct line of sight, the effect of the glare is definitely annoying. As we bring it down to 10 degrees, there is a distinct effect of strain, and within 5 degrees the effect is downright painful. The percentages on the right tell us how much effect the glare source has on the eye.

Glare and brightness level. Another relationship we know is that the effect of any glare source decreases as the general brightness level increases. If we increase the illumination on the object from 10 to 100 foot-candles, the effect of this same glare source is considerably less. Then, finally, we know that we can evaluate the effect of several glare sources if we weight each one for its distance from the primary line of sight. All of these factors are important for the engineer who designs illumination for the interiors of work spaces.

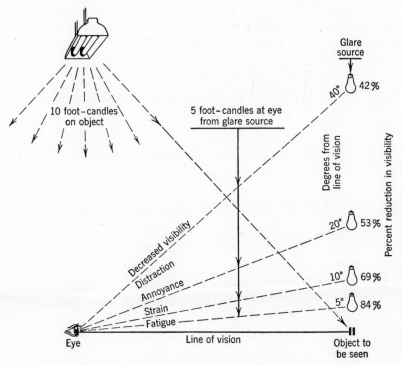

Fɪɢ. 42. Glare becomes worse as it comes closer to the direct line of vision. (After Luckiesh, 1944)

EYE MOVEMENTS

When we were discussing visual acuity we commented that most people do not notice how their visual acuity drops off toward the edges of their eyes. One reason we do not notice this and a lot of other very obvious things about our seeing process is that the eyes are never still. When we photograph somebody's eyes in the laboratory, we find that they are restless. They are always moving and looking from one place to another. This constant restless motion of the eye presents the brain with a whole lot of overlapping pictures which give us the impression of a complete clear visual field.

Eye movements. Scientists have spent a lot of time studying eye movements and have classified them into certain basic types. It is not necessary for us to go into all the types of movements that the eyes make, but it is important to know a little about the way the eyes move. The average person has an idea that when he is reading a book or newspaper his eyes make nice even smooth movements in following the lines of print. Actually that is not the case. If you do not believe it, watch the way your wife's eyes move when she reads the newspaper

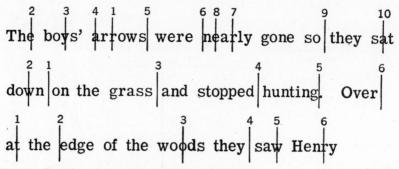

FIG. 43. Location of successive fixation points of the eyes of a subject in reading three lines of text. The vertical lines show where the eyes stopped; the numbers above the vertical lines show the order in which the points were fixated. (After Buswell, 1920)

tomorrow morning. You will find that what actually happens is that her eyes move in a series of jerks. They literally hop over the words in the sentence. From actual measurements in the laboratory, we know now that in reading, the eye is moving about 10 percent of the time; the other 90 percent of the time it is stationary. We know, too, that the eye does not look at every word, but that it tends to stop at every second, third, or fourth word, depending on how difficult the reading material is.

Saccadic movements. In Figure 43 are shown three lines of print which were read by a subject in an experimental laboratory. The vertical lines on these three lines of print indicate where his eyes stopped in reading and the numbers above these vertical lines indicate the number of the stop. In the first line, for example, the eyes of this subject stopped first at the second "r" in "arrows." Then his eyes went back to the "e" in "The," then to the "y" in "boy" and so on. These small jerky movements of the eye in reading are called saccadic movements. During actual movements, the eyes receive only blurs and streaks. The eye sees only while it is still.

APPLICATIONS

All this might be very interesting to the scientific psychologist, but what has it got to do with engineering psychology? It has a lot to do with seeing in certain kinds of situations.

Radar detectability. For example, take the detection of targets on radar scopes. Certain wartime studies have shown that radar operators may sit and look at a scope for many minutes and not see a new target which has appeared on the scope. This may seem a little hard to believe, but actual experiments show it to be true.

One of the reasons why we suspect this situation happens is: There is a very bright sweep line, so called, on the scopes of most radar sets. This sweep line is continually rotating around the radius or moving back and forth across the radar scope. We think that the radar operator's eyes follow this radar sweep around in this typical series of jerky rapid movements—trying to keep pace with the radar sweep line. Since we know that the eye does not see when it is actually in motion, the probability of detecting a new target pip on the face of the scope depends a great deal on the way in which the eyes move and where they happen to be pointed at any particular time. We think that further study of the basic movement patterns of the eye will clarify our understanding of why targets are or are not picked up on the radar scopes under certain conditions.

Visual search. This knowledge about eye movements also was very useful in certain scanning problems during the war. The RAF, for example, worked out a series of search–scan patterns for aircraft observers so that they could increase their probability of detecting life rafts on the open sea. The ocean is a very large place, and, if we search in a random haphazard manner, our chances of picking up a small object are very slim. You can also see now why we could not give a good formula for the brightness of a flashing light when we have to hunt for it. The careful systematic observer might be able to spot it very easily. But the man who rolls his eyes around wildly would probably have a hard time finding the light.

OPTICAL ILLUSIONS

We said earlier that seeing really involves both the eyes and the brain. In many cases the brain * takes the picture that is formed by

---

* Our use of the word "brain" in this way is a very loose one which will offend many academic psychologists. Even though psychologists have a lot of fancy names for these phenomena, the truth of the matter is that they really do not

the eye, distorts it, and makes us see things that really are not so. Some of these discrepancies between perception as registered in the brain and the actual picture that is formed in the eye are called optical illusions. You have all undoubtedly seen a number of these illusions, but it might be instructive to look at a few of them again.

Mueller–Lyer illusions. Shown in Figure 44 are a number of illusions which go by the name of the Mueller–Lyer illusion. In this figure all the horizontal and vertical lines are exactly equal in length,

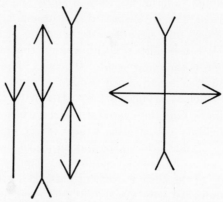

Fig. 44. Sometimes seeing is deceiving. All the horizontal and vertical lines are divided exactly in the middle. Do they look it? These are examples of the Mueller–Lyer illusion. (From O. Glasser, Optical illusions, in O. Glasser, ed., *Medical physics,* Chicago, Year Book Publishers, 1944, p. 825)

and all are divided exactly in the middle. However, those lines that seem to be enclosed by the arrowheads look shorter than the others. Practical applications and illustrations of this illusion are found very frequently in architecture, particularly in Gothic and Roman columns which hold up heavy buildings, and in fences. This illusion also explains why some people look out of proportion in some kinds of clothes.

Vertical illusion. Another common illusion is the illusion of the vertical, as shown in Figure 45. In this illustration the height of the top hat is exactly identical with the width of its brim, but most of you will agree that it looks a lot taller than it does broad. This figure illustrates a very common illusion—the universal tendency to overestimate figures in the vertical dimension and underestimate them in

know in most cases why our perceptions do not correspond with the pictures formed on the retina. Learning, attitudes, set, and many other factors play an important role, but precisely how they interact to influence what we see is still incompletely understood.

the horizontal dimension. That is why the carrier Midway, for example, does not look anywhere near as long as the Chrysler Building is tall; yet they are practically identical in length. If you want to look taller than you are, wear clothes with long vertical stripes.

Perspective illusion. Another very common illusion is the illusion of perspective as shown in Figure 46. In this case, the three men are all equally tall, but the one on the right appears to be considerably taller than the one on the far left. This illusion occurs because the human eye has been trained to associate perspective with distance. It is largely a matter of experience, therefore; and young children, who have not yet been trained to associate perspective with distance, almost always say that the three men are the same size.

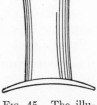

Fig. 45. The illusion of the vertical. Is the hat as tall as it is broad? (From O. Glasser, Optical illusions, in O. Glasser, ed., *Medical physics*, Chicago, Year Book Publishers, 1944, p. 825)

Autokinetic illusion. The illusions we have just discussed are all static illusions—they consist of stationary arrangements of lines. Many others are associated with movement in one way or another. If, for example, you stare at a point of light in a completely dark room, pretty soon the light will appear to move. This is known as the autokinetic illusion. Flight experiments have shown that this illusion can be seen very easily in formation flights at night. There is even some evidence to show that a few night accidents may have been caused by a pilot trying to follow what he thought was a wavering light on the plane ahead of him. This illusion, fortunately, can be overcome if we use flashing lights instead of steady ones, if we continually check the position of the light against some fixed reference line like a window frame, and if we move our eyes frequently and do not stare at the light.

Fig. 46. The illusion of perspective. Which man is tallest? (From O. Glasser, Optical illusions, in O. Glasser, ed., *Medical physics*, Chicago, Year Book Publishers, 1944, p. 826)

Other illusions of movement. There are some other compelling movement illusions that we see occasionally. Have you ever sat in a train in a railroad station with another train on the next track? If so, you have probably caught yourself thinking that your train was starting up when actually the other one was moving. Other illusions of movement and position are so compelling that pilots have to remind themselves that they cannot trust how they feel but have to trust their instruments in blind flying.

Applications. All these illusions are very interesting, but are they really important? We have already given a few illustrations of their importance and wish we could go into this problem more thoroughly. But we shall have to be content with just a few more examples. Information about illusions would come in very handy, of course, if we ever had to design a crazy house for an amusement park. And without illusions we could not have motion pictures or moving signs. Basic information about time relations—and this information is now available—is especially important if we want to get the most realism out of moving signs. Then, too, the effects of static illusions show up in many types of visual display—maps, charts, plotting boards, or even paintings—in which we have to make estimates about distances or lengths of lines.

Illusions in radar displays. Our final illustration, to show that illusions may appear in some intricate machines, comes from a study being conducted by a group of psychologists at Lehigh University. These investigators studied three sector-type radar presentations as shown in Figure 47, which are being used in a new radar system called GCA (ground control approach) for guiding planes into airports when visibility is poor, for example, in fog, rain, or at night. In the first presentation, the gently sloping line in the center of the scope represents the normal glide path pattern for an aircraft coming in on a blind landing. The vertical spacings on the right-hand margin of the first scope represent deviations in feet from this normal glide path. The bright blob above the glide path and about in the center of the scope is an aircraft making an approach on the landing strip.

Because of the triangular structure of this type of radar presentation we have a situation that resembles very closely the conditions for the perspective illusion we saw in Figure 46. The investigators had a number of radar operators estimate the distance of the aircraft above and below the glide path, and they discovered that, as the aircraft came in closer to the point of the triangle, the operators tended to exaggerate greatly their estimates. There was a very strong tendency for the operators to overestimate the amount of deviation of the aircraft from the glide path. This continued to be so even when the investigators put in two extra reference lines, as shown in the second radar presentation. The errors were smaller, but the illusion was so strong that it overcame the effect of the two additional reference lines. They finally had to use a radar presentation as shown in the third sector before they could completely eliminate the tendencies to overestimation.

SUMMARY

In summary, we have discussed in this chapter a number of fundamental facts about how we see. We started with a discussion of how we can describe the physical stimuli we see. We defined visibility and visual acuity and looked at a number of factors that affect these functions. We discovered that our day eyes see differently from our night eyes. We found that we see differently with different parts of our eyes. We realized that size, brightness, contrast, time, and glare were very important in determining how well we can see. And we finished with some optical illusions to prove that sometimes seeing may be deceiving.

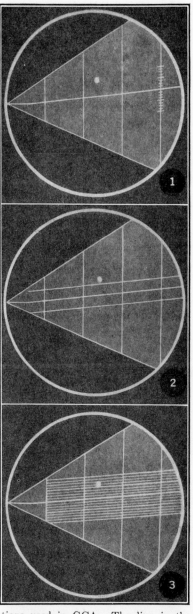

FIG. 47. Three sector-type radar presentations used in GCA. The line in the center of number 1 shows the glide path for an aircraft coming in on a blind landing. The little spot is the aircraft. The displays labeled 1 and 2 are subject to the perspective illusion shown in Figure 46; number 3 is not. (After Ford and Getz, 1948)

In writing this chapter we had to pick only a few studies out of literally thousands. We had to leave out a lot of other interesting things about how we see—we did not discuss color blindness, for example. And we have had to leave out a lot of applications of this information to man–machine systems. But if you understand the principles we have tried to set down here, you will be in a much better position to design machines so that men can see and use them more effectively.

SELECTED REFERENCES

1. BLACKWELL, H. R. Contrast thresholds of the human eye. *J. Opt. Soc. Amer.*, 1946, **36**, 624–643.
2. BLONDEL, A., and REY, J. Sur la perception des lumières brèves a la limite de leur portée. *J. Phys., Paris,* 1911, **1**, 530–550.
3. BOUMA, P. J. Illumination and blackouts. *Philips Tech. Rev.*, 1939, **4**, 15–19.
4. BUSWELL, G. T. An experimental study of the eye–voice span in reading. *Suppl. Educ. Monogr.*, 1920, **17**, 105.
5. CHAPANIS, A. The dark adaptation of the color anomalous measured with lights of different hues. *J. Gen. Physiol.*, 1947, **30**, 423–437.
6. COBB, P. W., and MOSS, F. K. The four variables of the visual threshold. *J. Franklin Inst.*, 1928, **205**, 831–847.
7. CONNOR, J. P., and GANOUNG, R. E. An experimental determination of the visual thresholds at low values of illumination. *J. Opt. Soc. Amer.*, 1935, **25**, 287–294.
8. FERREE, C. E., and RAND, G. The effect of variation of visual angle, intensity, and composition of light on important ocular functions. *Trans. Ill. Engng. Soc.*, 1922, **17**, 69–102.
9. FORD, A., and GETZ, M. H. The perspective illusion in radar sector scopes. Institute of Research, Lehigh University, Bethlehem, Pa., Technical Report No. 1, 10 June 1948.
10. GLASSER, O. Optical illusions. In O. GLASSER (Ed.). *Medical physics.* Chicago: Year Book Publishers, 1944, 824–827.
11. GORDON, D. A. The relation between the thresholds of form, motion, and displacement in parafoveal and peripheral vision at a scotopic level of illumination. *Amer. J. Psychol.*, 1947, **60**, 202–225.
12. HANES, R. M., and WILLIAMS, S. B. Visibility on cathode-ray tube screens: The effects of light adaptation. *J. Opt. Soc. Amer.*, 1948, **38**, 363–377.
13. HARDY, A. C. *Handbook of colorimetry.* Cambridge, Mass.: The Technology Press, 1936.
14. HILL, N. E. G. The recognition of coloured light signals which are near the limit of visibility. *Proc. Phys. Soc., London,* 1947, **59**, 560–574.
15. JUDD, D. B. Estimation of chromaticity differences and nearest color temperature on the standard 1931 ICI Colorimetric Coordinate System. *J. Opt. Soc. Amer.*, 1936, **26**, 421–426.
16. KNOLL, H. A., TOUSEY, R., and HULBURT, E. O. Visual thresholds of steady point sources of light in fields of brightness from dark to daylight. *J. Opt. Soc. Amer.*, 1946, **36**, 480–482.

17. Lash, J. D., and Prideaux, G. F. Visibility of signal lights. *Illum. Engng.*, 1943, **38**, 481–492.

18. Luckiesh, M. *Light, vision and seeing.* New York: Van Nostrand, 1944.

19. Luckiesh, M., and Moss, F. K. Light, vision and seeing. In O. Glasser (Ed.). *Medical physics.* Chicago: Year Book Publishers, 1944, 672–684.

20. Lythgoe, R. J. The measurement of visual acuity. *Spec. Rep. Series, Med. Res. Coun., Lond.*, 1932, No. 173.

21. Mandelbaum, J., and Rowland, L. S. Central and paracentral visual acuity at different levels of illumination. AAF School of Aviat. Med., Randolph Field, Texas, Res. Rep. No. 1, Project No. 220, 23 June 1944.

22. Moon, P. *The scientific basis of illuminating engineering.* New York: McGraw-Hill, 1936.

23. Moon, P., and Spencer, D. E. Visual data applied to lighting design. *J. Opt. Soc. Amer.*, 1944, **34**, 605–617.

24. Nutting, P. G. Effects of brightness and contrast in vision. *Trans. Illum. Eng. Soc.*, 1916, **11**, 939–946.

25. Olenski, Z., and Goodden, N. W. Clearness of view from day-fighter aircraft. Farnborough Royal Aircraft Establishment, Report No. Aero 1862, October 1943.

26. Sloan, L. L. Rate of dark adaptation and regional threshold gradient of the dark-adapted eye: physiologic and clinical studies. *Amer. J. Ophthal.*, 1947, **30**, 705–720.

27. Troland, L. T. Vision: I. Visual phenomena and their stimulus correlations. In Murchison, C. (Ed.). *A handbook of general experimental psychology.* Worcester: Clark University Press, 1934, 653–703.

28. Wertheim, T. Ueber die indirekte Sehschaerfe. *Ztschr. f. Psychol.*, 1894, **7**, 172–187.

29. Williams, S. B., Bartlett, N. R., and King, E. Visibility on cathode-ray tube screens: Screen brightness. *J. Psychol.*, 1948, **25**, 455–466.

30. *IES lighting handbook: The standard lighting guide.* Illuminating Engineering Society, 51 Madison Avenue, New York, New York, 1947.

5. Instrument Dials and Legibility

IN THE LAST CHAPTER WE HAD A LONG LOOK AT SOME OF THE BASIC LAWS of vision. In this chapter and the next, we are going to move on to some problems of visual displays as we see them in man–machine systems. Everything we said in the last chapter about illumination, contrast, glare, and so on is important whenever we think of any kind of visual display, whether it be a dial, an aircraft status board, or a billboard. We shall not mention all these factors again for each visual-display problem we talk about, but we should keep them in mind.

WHAT VISUAL DISPLAYS ARE

In almost every man–machine system there has to be some kind of display somewhere or some time—if the operator is to know what is going on. The word display, applied to man–machine systems, means some way of providing information which an operator cannot or does not get directly through his senses. A fuel gage is a display because it gives us information about the status of the gas tank. If we have a curved pipe leading into the tank on our car, we cannot see how much gas is in it, even if we want to. We must depend on the information provided by our gage display. A speedometer is also a display. Although we can get some idea about how fast we are driving by how fast the landscape whizzes by, our judgment about speed from such cues is very inaccurate. If we get stopped by a traffic policeman, the only kind of evidence that will stand up in court is what we swear the speedometer read.

The importance of visual displays. Visual displays are important because we depend so much on our eyes to tell us what is going on or what to do next. This is so obvious that there are not very many data on the relative importance of the eyes, ears, and sense of "feel" and touch in operating complex machinery. A recent study [1] however, illustrates the point very well. An extensive time-and-motion analysis was made of pilot performance in flying a 4-engine aircraft, the Navy R5D (Army C-54 or commercial DC-4). Here, briefly, is what the study tells us about the importance of different kinds of displays in the pilot's task:

There were 60 controls which the pilot normally used in taking off, cruising, and landing. Of these 60 controls, 53 (88 percent) were operated in response to some sort of visual cue—a dial, indicator, or some cue outside the plane. For 12 (20 percent) of the controls, the operator used some sort of auditory cue—the sound of the motors, a radio signal, or verbal command. Finally, in operating 8 (13 percent) of the controls, operators relied on a kinesthetic or tactile cue—the "feel" of the controls or the pilot's bodily orientation. These percentages add up to more than 100 percent because some controls were operated in response to one or another type of cue on different occasions. But the conclusion is clear: The pilot relies much more on his eyes than he does on his other senses in flying an aircraft. We have good evidence to convince us that this is generally true of operators using most kinds of machinery, industrial and commercial, as well as military.

Do not take it for granted that we approve of this state of affairs. As scientists we have to consider the possibility that we are overloading the eyes. Perhaps we would be better off if we tried to get more information by auditory or tactual displays and less by means of visual displays. As you will see in Chapter 9, it is possible to fly a plane by making use of information supplied by auditory displays. This whole general area of the best kind of display, or combinations of displays, has not been investigated scientifically, and there is much useful work that could be done. In this chapter, however, it is our business to worry about visual displays, and we had better get on with that story.

Displays are perceptual problems. In technical lingo, psychologists call problems of visual displays "perceptual problems" because they demand more than just seeing. The eye and the brain are involved. In perception, the observer must not only see things but also interpret what he sees. He must relate what he sees to what he already knows and make judgments and decisions on the basis of what he sees. When a target pip shows up on a radar scope, not only does the operator see that there is a bright spot there, but he also tries to estimate the position of the target in terms of its location and distance from the radar. He performs a complex mental judgment about the range of the target, for example, by knowing what distances the range rings on his radar scope represent. All these words—perceive, interpret, judge, estimate —indicate some higher mental function being carried on at the time the eyes are seeing. We have already discovered that the brain is a mighty fallible piece of machinery. It should not surprise us very much, therefore, to discover that our study of visual display systems might just as well be labeled "studies in human error."

Dials and other visual displays. There is so much material to cover in talking about visual displays that we must take two chapters to do it. This chapter takes up a very special class of visual displays— dials. These rate a chapter all to themselves because dials are used almost everywhere in all kinds of man–machine systems. There is now enough information about dials to make a fairly complete story about them. The next chapter deals with other broader aspects of visual displays.

WHAT ARE DIALS FOR?

During the last 20 years our engineers have done a marvelous and ingenious job of developing indicators and display instruments. If we look around the control stations on ships, submarines, locomotives, buses, and planes, and in industrial plants, we see an impressive array of beautiful and accurate instruments. No matter how well they have been engineered, however, there is always the important problem: Do these instruments tell an operator what he needs to know?

Check reading. The dials on instruments serve three functions. In the simplest case, the dial may be there just to tell an operator that something is working or not working. Or, if it is a warning device, it may be there to tell him to do something quickly. This is either–or information. Let us look at some illustrations. If you have an automobile with a turn-signaling indicator on it, you know that when you want to make a left-hand turn you push a little lever so that a light blinks on the rear end of the car. At the same time, a light will start blinking on the dashboard, or on the steering wheel, and will continue to blink until you have made the turn—or until you turn the indicator off. The only reason the blinker is on the dashboard is to show that the direction indicator is working. Instruments that exist merely to show that something is working have a check-reading function. Most of the time these instruments do not need any dials at all.

Qualitative indications. Sometimes an instrument is there so that we can tell if things are all right, and, if they are not all right, in what direction they are off. The temperature gage on the automobile is such an instrument. You do not really care whether the engine temperature on your car is exactly 130, 140, or 150 degrees. All you really need to know is that the temperature is about right. But if the radiator springs a leak, you also want to be able to see the temperature needle start going up. When it gets too high, you know that you had better stop and check the water. Instruments for this purpose do not need any numbers on the scales. All the driver needs to know is that a certain range is normal for his car. When the needle starts climbing, he had better stop. As a matter of fact, several new cars now supply temperature gages without any numbers on them at all, and drivers say that they work very well. Instruments of this sort are used for qualitative reading.

Many engineers are surprised to find that a lot of the fancy gadgets and instruments they put in man–machine systems are of this type. A pilot, for example, is not really interested in the precise cylinder head temperature or manifold pressure of his engine.[8] He only wants to know whether the readings are reasonable, and he also wants to be able to see when the readings start going off.

Precise quantitative readings. Frequently, however, dials are used for reading precise numerical values. A navigator, for example, wants to be able to read a compass exactly so that he can plot the direction his ship is going and find out whether it will land where he wants it to land. The altimeter on an aircraft may serve two different functions. Most of the time the pilot wants to know in a general way that he is, say, around 20,000 feet. Occasionally, however, he does want to get an exact quantitative indication of how high he is. When he comes in for a landing, for example, he wants to know that he is exactly 1,050 feet above the ground so that he can make a proper approach to the airport.

Analyzing the function of a dial. For our purposes, the whole point of this discussion is that the engineering psychologist needs to examine closely the purposes of the instruments that are installed in man–machine systems. He needs to ask himself: What kind of information does the operator need about the machine that he is running? Does he need to have a check reading or a warning signal, that is, does he merely want to know when to do something? Or does he need to have a qualitative reading: must he know only when something deviates from a normal position and in what direction it goes off? Or, finally, does he really need to have a precise quantitative reading so that he can find out something exact about the machine he is operating?

These are important questions because they get right at the heart of visual displays on man–machine systems.

And, in using such a classification of instruments, there is a general principle we should keep in mind: A dial should not supply more information than the operator needs or can use. If the pilot only needs to know his altitude to the nearest 50 feet, there is no reason to give him an altimeter that reads to the nearest 20 feet. If an engineer needs to know roughly how much water there is in a boiler, maybe a simple qualitative dial will do the trick. And remember that for many purposes a dial might not be necessary at all; a light or buzzer might do just as well.

Throughout the rest of this chapter we are going to look at dials that are supposed to do the third kind of job, namely, provide us with exact quantitative information.

DO DIALS DO WHAT THEY ARE SUPPOSED TO DO?

Errors in Dial Readings

A good way to approach the problem of dials is to examine the kinds of mistakes people make in reading them. These records provide us with some valuable information about how to design good dials.

AAF survey. Just recently, two U. S. Army Air Force psychologists, Fitts and Jones,[3] systematically interviewed a large number of experienced pilots. They asked each man if he had ever made or had seen anyone else make "an error in reading or interpreting an aircraft instrument, detecting a signal, or understanding instructions." They checked very carefully to be sure that the men were actually present when the events they reported occurred. We can get some idea about the kinds of stories they got from these verbatim accounts:

1. It was an extremely dark night. My copilot was at the controls. I gave him instructions to take the ship, a B-25, into the traffic pattern and land. He began letting down from an altitude of 4,000 feet. At 1,000 feet above the ground, I expected him to level off. Instead, he kept right on letting down until I finally had to take over. His trouble was that he had misread the altimeter by 1,000 feet. This incident might seem extremely stupid, but it was not the first time that I have seen it happen. Pilots are pushing up plenty of daisies today because they read their altimeter wrong while letting down on dark nights.

2. I was an instructor in a P-38 combat training group. One of my students had a generator go out. The procedure for this emergency was as follows: set props to 2,600 rpm while control of same can still be maintained, turn off all electrical equipment and try to save some reserve battery strength

for using radio in contacting the tower for landing instructions. The setting 2,600 rpm was considered sufficient if the ship were forced to go around after making the final approach. The tachometer on this particular ship was of the type where the indicator needle makes one complete revolution for each 1,000 rpm, and the number of revolutions of this needle is indicated by numbers 1, 2, or 3 coming up behind a square cutout on the instrument. The pilot proceeded as instructed after loss of the generator and upon return approached the runway but was forced to go around with full throttle on both engines. He could not get sufficient power to regain air speed and pick up his flaps and landing gear. The result was that he ditched in the water several hundred yards off the end of the runway. Later investigations of the pitch of the props indicated that they had been set for about 1,600 rpm instead of 2,600.

3. We had an alert one morning about eleven o'clock, because about 35 Japanese planes had been picked up on the radar screen. In the mad scramble for planes, the one I happened to pick out was a brand new ship which had arrived about two days previously. I climbed in, and it seemed the whole cockpit was rearranged. Finally, I got it started, but the Japs hit just about that time. The rest of the gang had gotten off and were climbing up to altitude. I took a look at that instrument panel and viewed the gages around me, sweat falling off my brow. The first bomb dropped just about 100 yards from operations. I figured then and there I wasn't going to take it off, but I sure could run it on the ground. That's exactly what I did—ran it all around the field, up and down the runway, during the attack.

Number of errors reported. In all, 624 pilots were questioned— either by direct interview (100 men) or by questionnaires (524 men) —and they replied with 270 "pilot-error" experiences like those just described. The data do not show how many men reported more than one incident, but it is clear that at least 187 different men (30 percent of the total) reported incidents. This may seem like a lot, or not many, depending on one's point of view. However, the things that were reported were the really serious and dramatic errors. These are minimum figures. There were undoubtedly far more which were less serious and so were forgotten. Many errors may never have been noticed. And there were undoubtedly other errors which never got reported because the pilots never lived to tell about them.

Results. Of the 270 errors reported, several have to do with errors involving auditory signals, hand signals, and other things that do not concern us here. The data in Table 9 are selected and greatly condensed from the report by Fitts and Jones. They speak for themselves.

Errors in reading three-pointer altimeters. One of the most striking findings of this study was the number of errors made on the altimeter.

TABLE 9. CLASSIFICATION OF 227 "PILOT-ERROR" EXPERIENCES COLLECTED BY
FITTS AND JONES

	Number of errors
Type of error	

I. Errors in interpreting multirevolution instruments:

    A. Errors involving an instrument which has more than one pointer, e.g., misreading the altimeter by 1,000 feet, the clock by 1 hour, etc.   **40**

    B. Errors involving an instrument which has a pointer and a rotating dial viewed through a "window," e.g., misreading the tachometer by 1,000 rpm, the air-speed meter by 100 mph................   **8**

II. Reversal errors, e.g., reversals in interpreting the direction of bank shown by a flight indicator, reversals in interpreting direction from compasses, etc..   **47**

III. Legibility errors:

    A. Instrument markings difficult or impossible to read because of improper lighting, dirt, grease, worn markings, vibration, or obstructions..   **32**

    B. Parallax: Difficulty in reading an instrument because of the angle at which it is viewed..   **5**

IV. Substitution errors:

    A. Mistaking one instrument for another, e.g., confusing manifold-pressure gage with tachometer, clock with air-speed meter, etc...   **24**

    B. Confusing which engine is referred to by an instrument.........   **6**

    C. Difficulty in locating an instrument because of unfamiliar arrangement of instruments..   **6**

V. Using an instrument that is inoperative, i.e., reading an instrument which is not working or is working incorrectly..................   **25**

VI. Scale interpretation errors, i.e., errors in interpolating between scale markers or in interpreting a numbered graduation correctly.........   **15**

VII. Errors due to illusions: Faulty interpretation of the position of an aircraft because body sensations do not agree with what the instruments show..   **14**

VIII. Signal interpretation errors: Failure to notice a warning light in the aircraft, or confusing one warning light with another..............   **5**

In fact, the three-pointer altimeter was about the most difficult aircraft instrument to read correctly. For this reason, another U. S. Army Air Force psychologist [5] made a special study of errors in reading this instrument. He devised a series of test booklets showing the altimeter in various settings. Then he had 97 pilots and 79 male college students each read 12 instrument settings, thereby getting a total of 1,164 readings for the pilots and 948 readings for the college students. Of all these readings, 11.7 percent of those made by the experienced pilots and 17.4 percent of the readings made by the college students were in error by 1,000 feet or more.

We do not need to go into the full details of the kinds of errors that were made in reading this instrument, but we can illustrate briefly two sorts of things that were done. Figure 48 shows two altimeter settings. The altimeter on the left reads 13,960 feet. Eleven mistakes were made by pilots who read this as 14,960. Fifty-one mistakes of

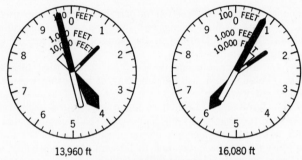

13,960 ft   16,080 ft

FIG. 48. These are two altimeter settings that were frequently misread by pilots. The one on the left reads 13,960 feet. Pilots frequently read it as 14,960. The one on the right reads 16,080 feet. Pilots frequently read it as 10,680 feet. (After Grether, 1948)

this same type were made by pilots and 35 by college students on similar kinds of settings. The altimeter on the right side of Figure 48 reads 16,080 feet. Seven mistakes were made by pilots who read this as 10,680. Forty-two mistakes of this same type were made by pilots and 52 by college students. We are sure you will agree that these are serious mistakes and that this altimeter must be a very difficult instrument to read.

Conclusions and interpretations. Now let us get back to the general picture, shown in Table 9, of the kinds of errors made in reading aircraft instrument dials. The Army psychologists have made some interpretations of their data which apply to general problems of dial design. Some of their recommendations may be little more than hunches, but they come from people who know most about the problem. They certainly tell us what to look out for when men use dials.

1. Serious errors in using and interpreting instruments and dials are frequently made by experienced men. Note, for example, that of the 270 "stories" of pilot errors, 125 were by men who were first pilots at the time the incident occurred. Only 48 incidents were reported by men who were

cadets. In the other study of the altimeter errors, pilots made nearly as many mistakes as college students.

2. Errors in using and interpreting instruments can occur either in daylight or at night, and under all sorts of weather conditions. They are also found in all kinds of aircraft.

3. The most frequent single type of error involved the altimeter, a multi-revolution indicator. This type of dial design is used because a very long scale is needed to present the information. However true that may be, the survey shows that we need a more satisfactory method of displaying information of this kind.

4. A principle of uniform direction of motion ought to be used in dial instruments, if we are to hope for correct interpretation of instruments. In other words, all dials should rotate in the same direction for indicating increasing magnitudes—and vice versa.

5. We need to improve warning devices and other visual means of conveying signals. There should also be some way of indicating when particular instruments are not working.

6. We need to have more information about instrument legibility and the kind of precision possible with different styles and sizes of dials, scales, pointers, and numerals. Scales should be designed so that there will be minimum confusion in going from one dial to another, especially when the graduations mean different things on different dials.

7. There need to be better ways of identifying particular instruments under day and night conditions.

8. Studies need to be made on the best arrangement of instruments on a panel.

9. Instruments should be standardized from one piece of equipment to another, from one aircraft to another, from one ship to another.

INTERPRETATION OF GROUPS OF DIALS

We have been talking mainly about frank *errors* in reading dials. But *time* as well as errors is important in using dials. Again the best research on this point comes from the U. S. Army Air Force psychologists.[16] They wanted to find out how much time pilots required to comprehend the position of the aircraft in which they were flying and to initiate control movements that would return the aircraft to straight and level flight. They studied these recoveries under both contact and instrument conditions. Under contact conditions, the pilots could see out of the aircraft and see the ground, the clouds, and the surrounding terrain. Under instrument conditions, all the outside world was blacked out so that they had to rely only on their instruments to tell them the position of the aircraft.

Comprehension time versus recovery time. The pilot wore goggles, and at a given signal the goggles were removed from the pilot's eyes so that he could assume control of the aircraft. These psychologists measured two things: average comprehension time and average recovery time. Average comprehension time is the time between the opening of the goggles and the beginning of the first correct control movements. It includes the time for accommodating and focusing the eyes, for comprehending what is seen, and for initiating a control movement. In actual flying, comprehension time corresponds to the time required by a pilot to focus on his panel and "Go on instruments, after he flew into a cloud, or to change to contact flight after breaking out of a cloud." Recovery time is the amount of time that elapses between the start of the first correct control movement and the completed return to straight and level flight.

Results. This experiment showed that the average comprehension time for these 20 pilots was 1.35 seconds for contact flying and 1.55 seconds for instrument flying. The average recovery time was 9.5 seconds for contact flying and 11.0 seconds for instrument flying. So we can see that when the pilots were flying under contact conditions their complete recovery—comprehension time and recovery time together—was about 1.7 seconds faster than when these recoveries were made on instruments.

These time differentials are very important in modern aircraft which may travel at speeds close to 1,000 feet a second. At 600 miles per hour, for example, the pilot travels 1,190 feet before he makes his first reaction and 8,360 more feet before he recovers on contact flying. When he is flying on instruments, the figures are 1,360 and 9,680 feet, respectively. If we add both comprehension time and recovery time together, the difference between contact and instrument flying is the difference between 9,550 feet and 11,040 feet. In all, this difference amounts to more than a quarter of a mile.

Another important finding was this. In 7 out of a total of 160 experimental recoveries, the pilot first moved the aileron control in a direction that would increase, rather than decrease, the bank movement of the aircraft. Six of these mistakes were made during instrument recoveries and only one during a contact recovery.

Conclusions. This study shows us that there is room for considerable improvement in flight instruments. The present flight panel is far too difficult to understand. Not only can pilots react faster to normal outdoor visual stimuli but also even experienced pilots very often misinterpret the information that the present flight panel gives them. We must be wary in making sweeping conclusions, but we would probably find the same trouble in other displays, if we studied them.

The problem. You can get some idea why there is trouble here if you look at Figure 49, a pilot's-eye view of the interior of a DC-6

Fɪɢ. 49. This is a pilot's-eye view of the interior of a DC-6 aircraft cockpit. Do you wonder that the engineering psychologist is faced with some tough display problems? (Courtesy of American Airlines Inc.)

aircraft cockpit. This is a bewildering complex of instruments and controls. Although we have picked as our illustration the interior of an aircraft, very much the same kind of picture is seen when we look in the control center of a ship or submarine. In industrial applications large display systems of this sort are found, for example, in the control centers of modern refining plants, in the nerve centers of systems of dams (such as the TVA system), and in electric generating plants.

This is the problem: How can the scientist make complex visual displays like this foolproof and easy to understand? A big order!

THE SHAPES OF DIALS

Until very recently, engineers had very little scientific information to use in designing the most readable kind of dial. They usually made their dials meet other require-
ments—engineering convenience, for one thing. Round dials, for example, are probably very popular because, as one engineer puts it, "You can wrap ten inches of scale around a three-inch dial." Customer preferences have also had a lot to do with the kinds of dials we see around us. Automobile speedometers are designed primarily to "look nice." But in this section, we are going to ignore these other factors and look at dials only from the standpoint of maximum readability. In some cases, as we shall see, the most readable dial may turn out to be more complicated than the usual kinds of dials.

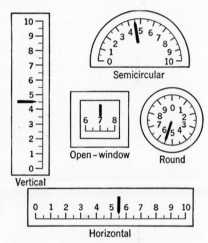

Fig. 50. Here are five different dial shapes studied by Sleight. (After Sleight, 1948)

SINGLE-REVOLUTION DIALS

A recent study [17] by a psychologist at Purdue University gives us some valuable leads on the most readable kind of single-revolution dial. He compared the five dials shown in Figure 50. Notice that he used the same sizes of numbers, the same sizes of pointers, and the same distances between numbers on all of the dials. He also put these dials in a special viewing box so that they could be exposed for 0.12 second—just long enough for one quick glance. In all the trials, the pointer was set exactly on one of the numbers, or on one of the small marks between two numbers. The subjects knew this and were required to read the dial to the nearest half unit.

Results. In Figure 51, you can see the percentage of incorrect readings made by 60 subjects in reading these dials. Since there was a total of 1,020 readings for each dial, the differences between dials are all highly significant from a statistical point of view. Notice that the open-window dial gave the fewest errors; there were only 5 out of the whole batch of 1,020 trials (0.5 percent). The round dial was next

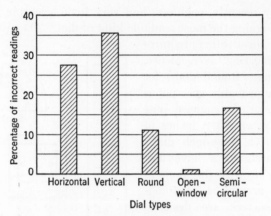

Fig. 51. This chart shows the percentage of incorrect readings made by 60 observers in reading the dials shown in Figure 50. Notice that the open-window dial was best; the round dial next best. (After Sleight, 1948)

best with 10.9 percent, and the horizontal and vertical dials were poorest—27.5 and 35.5 percent errors, respectively.

Looking to see when and where errors occurred also turned up some interesting points: (1) There are many more errors when the pointer is halfway between two numbers—for example, at 2.5, 3.5, 4.5, and so on—than when the pointer is exactly on a number—for example, on 2, 3, or 4. (2) On the horizontal, vertical, and semicircular dials, more errors occur at the ends of the dials—around the numbers 1, 1.5, 2, 2.5, and 3 and 7, 7.5, 8, 8.5, and 9—than in the middle of the dial—at positions 4, 4.5, 5, 5.5, and 6. Round and open-window dials did not suffer from larger errors at the ends of the dial probably because these dials do not have clearly defined ends.

In addition, this investigator did a preliminary experiment with five exposure speeds (0.28, 0.20, 0.17, 0.14, and 0.12 second). He arranged the conditions in this preliminary experiment so that he could do an analysis of variance on the data. The results showed that the variance due to the dial types was very significant and that the variance contributed by the different exposure speeds was less than 1 percent of the total variance. This means, of course, that exposure speed—within the range studied—is not an important variable. Nonetheless, a word of caution is in order about the interpretation of this experiment. The subjects had only brief glances at these dials since the longest exposure was just about a quarter of a second. It may be that if they had some other kind of job to do, for example, read a number of these dials rapidly, the results might have come out differently. But for the time being, this is the best information we have.

THE DESIGN OF MULTIREVOLUTION DIALS

As we have already seen, multirevolution dials are among the most difficult to read. As best we can tell, the trouble seems to be that people must combine the readings of two or more separate pointers in order to get the information they want. On the other hand, multi-revolution dials are used because one revolution of a pointer on a circular dial does not give enough scale length to provide as much accuracy as is needed. The altitude range in which conventional aircraft operate (roughly 0–40,000 feet) cannot possibly be covered accurately in one revolution of a pointer on a dial of ordinary size. Altimeters are not the only sensitive instruments with long scales. The clock is another such instrument, as are also the aircraft tachometer and airspeed indicator.

An experiment on multirevolution dials. Because of the difficulties involved in reading such instruments, another U. S. Army Air Force psychologist did an experiment [4] on nine different dial designs to see if he could find one that would be easy to interpret. For each dial design he prepared a test booklet. The cover of each booklet showed the operator the kind of dial design in that booklet and provided a sample on which he could obtain practice. Inside the booklet the dial design was reproduced with 12 different settings. Under each picture was a space for writing in the reading.

Results. This reading test was then taken by 97 Army Air Force pilots and 79 college men without any Army Air Force air-crew experience. Their tests were scored for the time taken to read the dials as well as for dial-reading errors. In Figure 52, we see the results. This figure shows the conventional three-pointer altimeter and the five dial designs which proved best in the experiment.

Remember that the experimental designs were simulated on paper. Engineers may have some trouble actually constructing some of these.

Even so, it is the business of the engineering psychologist to find out scientifically what is best for the operator and to let others worry about how close the "ideal" can be approached in engineering practice.   In this case, the engineers have chosen the design shown in the upper right corner of Figure 52 and are now busy building it.   From

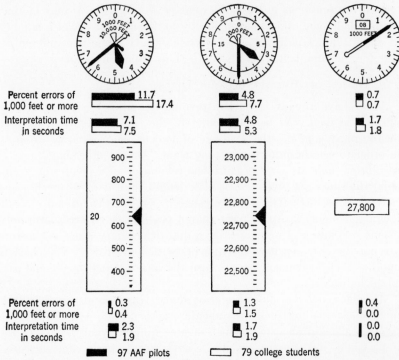

Percent errors of
1,000 feet or more
Interpretation time
in seconds

FIG. 52.   This shows the conventional three-pointer altimeter (upper left) and the five best altimeters found in the study by Grether.   The number of errors and average reading time for pilots and college students are shown beneath each dial.
(After Grether, 1947)

the laboratory experiments we expect it to be a considerable improvement over the conventional altimeter.

An experiment on 24-hour clock dials.   There is even room for improvement in the design of clock faces.   A clock is something you learn to read very early in life and is the one kind of dial you probably read more often than any other.   And yet research on the most readable kind of clock has been ignored until very recently.   The problem arose because military time is reckoned on a 24-hour basis.   Telegraph offices and business concerns—especially those that have international connections—are also beginning to compute time in this way. On a 24-hour system, time from noon until midnight runs from 12 to 24 hours. Thus 3:45 P.M. becomes 1545 hours. If only an ordinary 12-hour clock is available, you have to remember to add 12 to all the afternoon hours.

A U. S. Army Air Force investigator did an experiment [6] on 11 different types of clock dials in an attempt to discover the most readable

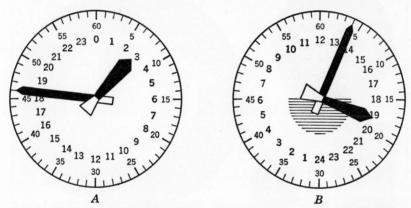

A **B**

Fig. 53. These are the two best 24-hour clock dials found in a study by Grether. The one on the right is probably a little better than the one on the left. (After Grether, 1948)

one. Some were 12-hour clocks; others were 24-hour clocks. Some had numbers on the minute scale; others did not. Some had numbers on all the hour marks; others did not. In all, seven different variables of this sort were explored.

Results. If time has to be reckoned on a 24-hour system, a 24-hour clock is better than a 12-hour clock. The two best 24-hour clock dials are shown in Figure 53. Although there was very little difference between these two in terms of the speed and accuracy with which they could be read, the one on the right is recommended over the other one. In this clock, the shaded portion indicates the hours of darkness, that is, from 6 P.M. (1800 hours) to 6 A.M. (0600 hours); and noon (1200 hours) comes at the top of the dial, as in ordinary 12-hour clocks.

DIALS OR COUNTERS?

In the experiment on multirevolution dials, Grether inferred that a direct-reading instrument—like a counter—was a lot easier to read than any kind of dial he used. Since he used only a paper-and-pencil test, however, we need to know whether counters are more efficient than dials in actual operational use. Fortunately there are some studies [2] to answer this question for us. These happen to have been done on radar equipment, but they provide us with some useful information about the relative efficiency of dials and counters.

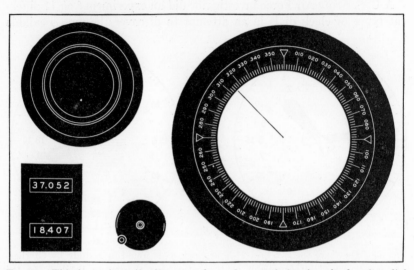

Fig. 54. This is a schematic diagram of a radar panel showing the bearing dial around the radar scope (right) and the range dials (lower left).

A laboratory study. In one of these studies, four different pieces of standard radar equipment were used. In these radar equipments, there is a large bearing dial—reading from 000 to 359 degrees—around the radar tube. A bearing cursor, something like a pointer, moves around this dial so that an operator can tell the position of a target he has located on the radar scope. A schematic diagram of one of these radars is shown in Figure 54. The other radars were something like this, but they differed in the size of the dials, in the markings of the dials, and in their position with regard to the range counter. In addition to these four standard radars, this investigator also used a breadboard model of a direct-reading bearing indicator and range indicator, as shown in Figure 55.

Results—time. Figure 56 shows the average times required by the 5 operators to read bearing and range information from the 4 standard radar units and from the experimental bearing and range counters. Notice that it took these operators on the average about 3.5 seconds to read a bearing and range from the standard radar units, and notice also that it only took them about 1.8 seconds to read a bearing and range from the experimental counters—a saving of about 47 percent in time. The analysis of variance applied to these data shows beyond any doubt that this result is statistically significant.

FIG. 55. This is a breadboard model of a direct reading bearing and range indicator used in tests against radar displays like those in Figure 54.

Results—errors. Now let us look at the errors made by these operators in reporting targets from the various pieces of equipment. Figure 57 shows the total numbers of bearing errors made by the 5 operators in reading 250 target settings from each piece of equipment. The results are so clear-cut that little comment is called for. There were

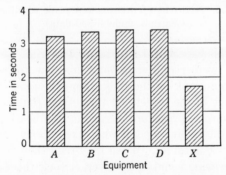

FIG. 56. This shows the average time required by operators to read a bearing and range from four standard radars, *A, B, C, D,* something like the one in Figure 54. *X* is the direct-reading counter shown in Figure 55. Operators can read the counters in about half the time they need to read radar dials. (After Chapanis, unpublished data)

a lot fewer errors when operators read their bearings from the direct-reading counter than when they read their target bearings from the conventional circular scales.

Operational tests. This first experiment, however, was a kind of laboratory approach to the problem, because the men were not actually operating the equipment at the time they made their readings. It was a test merely of the efficiency with which they could read these various scales. Then, too, only a breadboard model of a direct-reading counter was used. In order to be sure that this difference in favor of the direct-reading counter would still hold up under actual operational conditions, the experimenter had a direct-reading bearing counter constructed and hooked up to the bearing crank on a remote radar indicator.

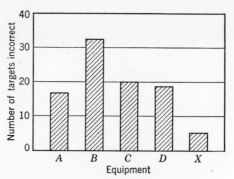

Fig. 57. These are the numbers of bearing errors made in reading the same dials as those in Figure 56. Notice how few errors were made with the counters. (After Chapanis, unpublished data)

Results. In this experiment a series of 160 trials were run in which radar operators were required to hunt for new targets, operate the bearing and range crank on the radar, read the scales, and report the bearing and range of the target. It turned out that, when these operators used the normal procedure of reading the bearings on the circular dial around the radar scope, it took them about 12.8 seconds to do the entire job for one target. When they read their bearings from the direct-reading bearing counter, however, it took them about 11.1 seconds, a saving of 1.7 seconds per target in favor of the bearing counter. In this case, it turned out very nicely, because this was exactly the amount of saving that was found in the laboratory experiment.

In the operational experiment there were not enough trials run to get a large number of errors, but it is interesting to note that 4 percent of the readings made from the bearing dial were seriously in error. With the bearing counter, however, only slightly more than 1 percent of the targets were in error, and so the results in this case look rather clear-cut. If we want to get accurate readings from dials, a direct-reading counter can increase both speed and accuracy.

Disadvantages of counters. But this does not mean that we should run out and change all our dials to the direct-reading type, for they do have certain disadvantages. These same experiments show that it is a lot harder to use a direct-reading counter for setting information into the equipment. It is also a lot harder to use a bearing counter when the readings are changing very rapidly. The reason is obvious. When a counter is used for setting information into a piece of equipment, the numbers rotate so rapidly that the operator has to stop every once in a while to find out where he is. A dial, however, is stationary, and the pointer moving within it furnishes the operator with a very helpful cue.

All in all, then, these experiments tell us that a direct-reading counter is better than a circular scale when we want to read information from the instrument. The circular scale, however, is better if settings must be reproduced or set into the equipment.

THE DESIGN OF DIAL SCALES

But there is more to the dial problem than just the shape of the dial. The scale itself is probably the most important part of it. How many marks should there be on it? How far apart should they be? How many of the marks should be numbered? The specific factors that make the dials most legible are still incompletely understood. We made a start on these problems during the war, however, and we have some fairly definite conclusions on some of these questions.

For convenience in talking about the researches that have been done on dial scales, we have grouped them under certain headings. These are arbitrary groupings, and we must understand that the scale factors are all interrelated. The number of marks we can put around a dial is related to the size of dial we use. The spacing between markings is also a function of the size of the dial and the number of marks we put around it. Most of the studies we can find have been done with fairly small dials (4 inches or less in diameter) which were read at fairly short distances (30 inches or less). To ascertain how much we can depend on these studies, we will describe the kinds of dials that were used.

The Number and Spacing of Dial Markings

As a first guess, we might say that, the more dial marks we have, the more accurately we will be able to read a dial. Actually, that may or may not be true. A few years ago a U. S. Army Air Force psychologist studied a number of different dial designs.[12, 13, 14]   He was trying to discover some of the factors that increase their legibility. In Figure 58, for example, are three of the dials used in the experiment. These are aircraft tachometer dials. With very short exposures —0.75 second—or quick glances at these dials, pilots were able to read the dial on the extreme left the most accurately. The percentages of error in reading these dials were 34 for the dial on the extreme left, 41 for the dial in the middle, and 44 percent for the one on the right. The general conclusion of his studies was this: The cleanest dial from

Fɪɢ. 58. These are three tachometer dials studied by Loucks. Taking short glances at each dial, observers made fewest errors with the one on the left.
(After Loucks, 1944)

the standpoint of design—the one with the *fewest* dial markings— gives the best results.

Another study. Although the study just mentioned gives us a valuable lead, it does not give any real quantitative data to work with. To get down to practical cases: Should there be a marker at every unit, every 5 units, or every 10 units?

Information on this point comes from another study [10] which made use of dials covering a range of 0 to 100. One kind of dial had 100 marks, one at every unit, and is designated the 100 × 1 dial; another had 20 marks, one at every 5 units, the 100 × 5 dial; the last had marks only at every 10 units, the 100 × 10 dial. Each kind of dial was made in three sizes: 0.7, 1.4, and 2.8 inches in diameter. Three samples of these dials are shown in Figure 59.

The men who read these dials were given unlimited time but worked under two different kinds of instructions: (*a*) Speed and accuracy instructions—"Read these dials as fast and as accurately as you can;" (*b*) Accuracy instructions—"Read the dials as accurately as you can." All the dials had to be read to the nearest unit, regardless of the scale markings.

Results. Figures 60 and 61 show what happened in the experiment. For one thing, accuracy is consistently better when the subjects are told to be as accurate as possible (Figure 60). Of course, they took

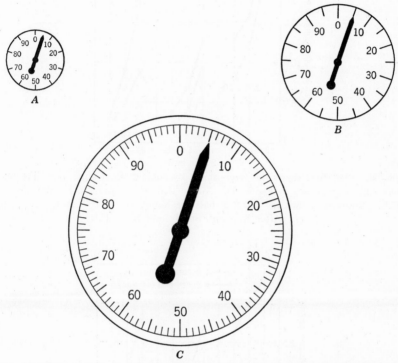

Fig. 59. These are three samples of the kinds of dials studied by Kappauf *et al.* The smallest dial shown here is a 100 × 10 dial; the medium-sized one is a 100 × 5 dial; the largest a 100 × 1 dial. Each of the sizes shown was made up with 10, 20, or 100 marks, so that there were nine different dials in all. (After Kappauf, Smith, and Bray, 1947)

more time (Figure 61) when they were working under accuracy instructions. That is to be expected.

The second obvious point about these data is that speed and accuracy, for both kinds of instructions, are highest for the biggest dials. Since these experimenters did not try any dials bigger than 2.8 inches, however, we cannot be sure from this study that this is the best size of dial to use.

The third thing these data show—and this point is not so obvious until you study the curves—is that the dials graduated by 10's are

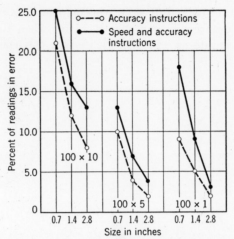

FIG. 60. This chart shows the errors made by subjects in reading nine different dials like those shown in Figure 59. Notice that errors decrease for the bigger dials. Notice also that the 100×5 dials are about as effective as the 100×1 dials. (After Kappauf, Smith, and Bray, 1947)

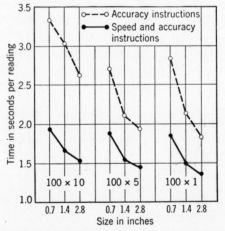

FIG. 61. This chart shows the average times required to read nine different dials like those shown in Figure 59. These data match those shown in Figure 60. We need less time to read a bigger dial. Notice, however, that there is not much difference between the 100×5 and 100×1 dials. (After Kappauf, Smith and Bray, 1947)

consistently worse than the dials graduated by 5's and 1's. But notice this: There are no clear-cut consistent differences between the dials graduated by 5's and those graduated by 1's. If we put the results of this study together with the results obtained in Loucks' short-exposure experiment, it appears that we should get best results if we use a 100 × 5 dial.

The analysis of variance of the error data brought out one or two points that cannot be illustrated graphically. First, as we might expect from Figure 60, the differences between the errors made with the two kinds of instructions, with the different sizes of dials, and with the different scales, were all highly significant from a statistical standpoint. Also significant in a retest experiment were the differences between subjects and two of the interactions involving the subjects: subjects × sizes, and subjects × scales. This is disturbing because it means that all people do not give the fewest errors with the same size of dial or the same kind of scale. We cannot tell why this is at the present time, but it means

FIG. 62. This is a sample of one of the kinds of dials used by Grether and Williams. (After Grether and Williams, 1947)

that we may have a little trouble trying to work up some generalizations about the best kind of dial for all people.

Another study on the best size of dial. We might mention one other study which has some data on this point. Grether and Williams did an experiment [7] with four sizes of dials: 1, 1⅞, 2¾, and 4 inches. Each size of dial was made with four different angular separations between the dial markers: 5, 10, 20, and 40 degrees. Each dial covered a range of 0 to 50 units, and each had five graduation marks corresponding to 0, 10, 20, 30, 40, and 50. Finally each of the 16 dials was tested under daylight and nighttime conditions, using fluorescent illumination. You can see an illustration of one of their dials in Figure 62.

Eighty subjects were used, and each subject had 20 trials on each dial. The dials were 30 inches from the subjects' eyes. The subjects were given unlimited time but were told to read each dial as accurately and as fast as possible. They had to estimate the position of the pointer to the nearest tenth of the distance between graduations.

The error results are in the average number of tenths the subjects were off under each condition—this means that the errors are relative.

Accuracy and size of dial. For the 1-, 1⅞-, and 2¾-inch dials, accuracy increased as the dial size increased. This was true for all marker spacings. With the 4-inch dial, accuracy improved from the 5- and 10- to the 20-degree spacing but was worse for the 40-degree spacing. The important point is that there does not appear to be any such thing as a "best" size of dial. It looks as though the spacing is really the critical factor.

Accuracy and spacing of markers. To follow up the point we just made, note that accuracy increases for all sizes of dials as the spacing is increased from 5 to 20 degrees. For the 40-degree spacing, however, accuracy increased for the 1- and 1⅞-inch dials but decreased for the 2¾- and 4-inch dials. These facts indicate that (a) accuracy depends on both the size of the dial and the distance between markings; and (b) a dial and the spacing between marks can be too big as well as too small.

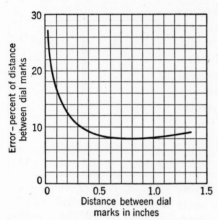

FIG. 63. The data for different sizes of dials and different spacings between markers are all fit by this one curve. This means that, if we want accuracy, we should allow about a half-inch between numbered markers. (After Grether and Williams, 1947)

Fortunately, this complicated set of results can be reduced to very simple terms. If the distances between the dial markings are measured in inches instead of degrees, a single smooth curve fits all the data for all dial sizes with remarkable consistency. This function is shown in Figure 63. It reveals that, no matter what the size of the dial, we get the best relative accuracy when the distance between dial markers is about 0.6 or 0.7 inch. Errors increase rapidly when the markers are closer together than this. They also increase—but not so rapidly—when the separation between markers is greater.

Another study on dial-marker spacing. This conclusion on the spacing of markers sounds so pat that it might seem a little hard to believe. The same sort of result, however, came out of another recent study.[9] In this, the dial designs were very similar to those designated by the letters *A* and *B* in Figure 59. There were 100's dials, that is, dials reading from 0 to 100; 200's dials, reading from 0 to 200; 400's and 600's dials. For each of these four different scale lengths, there was one set of dials graduated by 5's; that is, there were marks corresponding to 0, 5, 10, 15, and so on; and another set graduated by tens; that

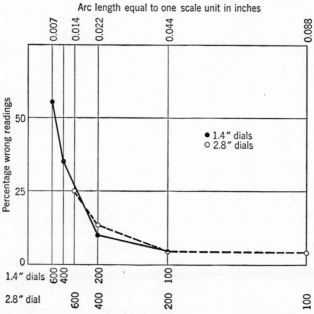

Fig. 64. This shows the errors made in reading dials graduated by fives. Notice that we get fewest errors when the space between markers is about a quarter of an inch—0.044 × 5. (After Kappauf and Smith, 1948)

is, there were marks corresponding to 0, 10, 20, 30, and so on. Finally, each of these dials came in two sizes: 2.8 inches in diameter and 1.4 inches in diameter. Sixteen different kinds of dials were studied in all.

Plan of the experiment. Each subject read 30 dials of each type and size. His instructions were to make each reading to the nearest unit. Since readings had to be made in units, and not simply to the nearest scale division, the subjects had to interpolate to fifths or tenths of divisions. The subjects were instructed to be as accurate as possible in their readings—to read as carefully as they would when making slide-rule calculations.

Results—accuracy. Figures 64 to 66 give the results. Figure 64 shows the percentage of reading errors for the dials that were gradu-

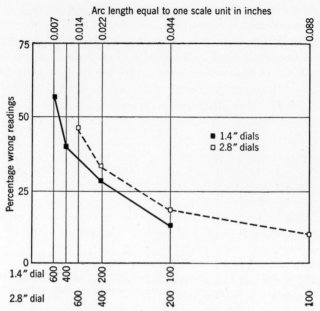

FIG. 65. This shows the errors made in reading dials graduated by tens. In this case we get fewest errors when the space between markers is about a half-inch. (After Kappauf and Smith, 1948)

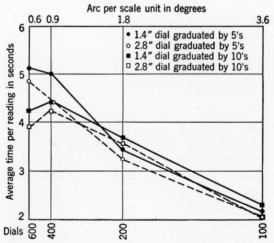

FIG. 66. We read dials fastest when they are least cluttered with markers. (After Kappauf and Smith, 1948)

ated by 5's. Any reading that was not read exactly to the nearest unit was scored incorrect. Arc length was measured in inches of circumference devoted to each scale unit. Thus, as shown at the bottom of the figure, a 600's dial, 1.4 inches in diameter, has each unit on the scale represented by 0.007 inch. A 200's dial of the 1.4-inch size and a 400's dial of the 2.8-inch size have the same arc length for one unit of the scale distance. The same is true for the small 100's dial and the large 200's dial. The solid points in this figure are for the small dials; the open points for the large dials. Since these points overlap pretty well, we can see that the number of errors made in reading these dials was a function of the linear distance for each scale unit and was independent of the dial size.

Figure 65 shows the data for the series of dials that were graduated by 10's. Notice that there were more errors for these dials than for the dials graduated by 5's. For the 400's and 600's dials of the smaller size, however, the number of errors seemed to be about the same whether the scales were graduated by 5's or 10's.

But here is the crucial point: in both Figures 64 and 65 we get fewest errors when the arc length per scale unit is 0.04 inch or longer. In order to make these results comparable to those obtained by Williams and Grether we must multiply the values in Figure 64 by 5; those in Figure 65 by 10. The reason for this is that Williams and Grether recorded their data in terms of the length of the scale between scale markers. The data of Kappauf and Smith are recorded in terms of the length of the circumference between the scale unit that the subjects were required to read to. When we make this correction, the two sets of data agree very well for the dials graduated by 10's. For the dials graduated by 5's, we get minimum errors when the spacing between markers is about a quarter of an inch.

Results—speed. Figure 66 presents data on the speed of reading these dials. In this figure, average reading time in seconds is plotted as a function of arc per scale unit, where the arc is measured in degrees. The most significant finding here is that speed appears to increase as we increase the number of degrees subtended by each scale unit. As we increase the number of degrees between each marker, of course, the dial looks less cluttered. All this brings us back to the conclusions of the first study we mentioned: If we want to design a dial for speed of reading, the cleanest one gives us the best results.

Spacing between markers on polar coordinate displays. Another study [11] on the spacing between markers was done on an entirely different kind of display. The results came out so close to those of the dial studies that it seems appropriate to mention them here. This study was done on a polar coordinate plot, like those shown in Figure 74 of Chapter 6. The display has a series of concentric rings to indicate various distances from the center. These are called range rings. Little spots of light appeared at various places in this display, and the operators were required to estimate the positions of the spots between any two range rings. The spacings between markers on different displays were ⅛, ¼, ½, 1, 2, 4, 5, 6, 8, and 10 inches.

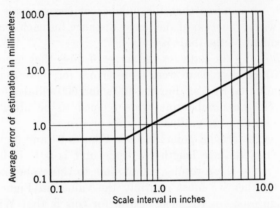

Fɪɢ. 67. Ability to estimate the position of a point between two markers on a polar coordinate display decreases when the distance between markers is more than ½ inch. The average error of estimation shown on the ordinate is the absolute error in estimating position on the display. (After Leyzorek, 1949)

The results of this experiment can be expressed in two ways. First, we can show the discrepancy, or error, between the subject's estimate and the actual location of the spot in terms of distance on the display in millimeters, as has been done in Figure 67. Here the average error of estimation was constant for the ⅛-, ¼-, and ½-inch scales but began to increase greatly for scales with more space between them. The second way we can plot these data is to show the average error as a percentage of the separation between markers, as has been done in Figure 68. Now we see that percentagewise the errors of estimation for scales of ⅛ and ¼ inch are high, and the errors reach a minimum for scales of ½ inch or greater. Although the actual error in terms of distance increases for these scales, the increase in error is a constant fraction of the separation between markers.

Here again the ½-inch spacing emerges as the best. If we want to have a lot of markers on a display, we wish to have them as close together as possible, but there is no reason for getting them any closer than we can use them efficiently. The best compromise between a large number of markers—to represent a large total range of values—and accuracy of interpolation between markers seems to be a half-inch.

Consistency of spacing. There is still another point we should stress while we are on the subject of spacing between dial markers: consistency. Wherever possible, we should have the same spacing be-

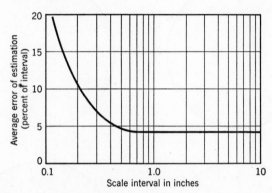

Fɪɢ. 68. Ability to estimate the relative position of a point between two markers decreases when the distance between markers is less than ½ inch. The average error of estimation shown on the ordinate in this figure is expressed as a percentage of the interval between markers. (After Leyzorek, 1949)

tween markers throughout the whole length of the scale. Also, if we have to read a number of dials that are near each other, the spacing on each dial should be the same. There are two series of studies, by Loucks [12, 13, 14] and by Vernon,[18] to support this conclusion: Markers that change in value from one part of the scale to another or from one dial to another are very confusing and increase the number of errors considerably. Most slide rules, since they have logarithmic scales on them, violate this important psychological principle of legibility. In the case of the slide rule, however, it is not quite so important; we usually have enough time to study the scale and get our settings accurately.

Wʜᴇʀᴇ Sʜᴏᴜʟᴅ ᴛʜᴇ Sᴄᴀʟᴇ Sᴛᴀʀᴛ?

A different kind of problem that concerns the scale on a dial is: Where should it start? Should the zero be at the top, bottom, or to one side? In Loucks' studies he varied the zero position of the scale and came to the conclusion that it did not make any difference in reading accuracy so far as he could tell. Grether found, in his study of clock dials, that there was not very much difference in results between using clocks that had 0 hours (midnight) at the top and using those that had it at the bottom. But when he tried to shift the minute scale around, he was not so successful. He got definitely better re-

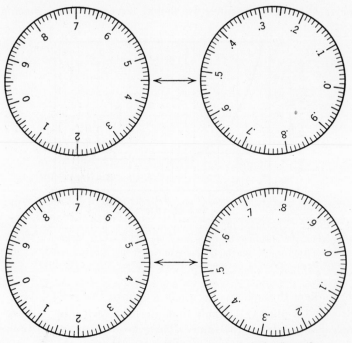

Fig. 69. Which pair of dials can you read the faster?

sults when the 0–60-minute position was at the top. The reason may be that we have so many habits built up about reading minutes from clocks but none about reading hours from 24-hour dials.

Conclusion. It is probably safe to say that we can shift the starting point on a scale quite a bit without affecting accuracy. This fact is of considerable importance. It means that instruments can be rotated so that the pointers will lie in a given position under normal operating conditions—a matter we will take up later when we talk about patterns of dials.

Separating the beginning and end. An experiment by Vernon brings up a point related to the problem where to start and end scales: Whenever possible, there should be a clean break between the beginning and end of the scale. The dials used by Loucks (Figure 58) followed this principle. The dials used in the experiments by Kappauf and his associates (Figure 59) did not.

Direction of change. A final recommendation related to the beginning and end of the scale is this: The scale should increase from zero in a clockwise direction. In Figure 69 there are two pairs of dials, one above the other. The upper pair are to be read together. One of them is a coarse-reading dial and the other a fine-reading dial. Try to read the exact number that the pointer indicates on both upper dials. Try to read these dials accurately and fast. Then look down to the next pair below, and see which pair of dials you consider easier to read. Although we know of no actual experimental work on this problem, we think you will agree that the numbers ought to increase in the same direction. At least there should be consistency on any piece of equipment.

DIAL POINTERS

A dial pointer is not a scale problem in a strict sense, but it is important because it tells us where to look on a scale. Our conclusions about pointers are brief because there are not many studies on them.

Pointer width. We do not need to have a wide pointer for best legibility. Loucks found that under incandescent light a pointer $1\frac{1}{8}$ inches long and $\frac{1}{32}$ inch wide was as good as one $1\frac{1}{8}$ inches long and $\frac{3}{32}$ inch wide. Under strong ultraviolet light, the narrow pointer was actually better.

Pointer length. The length of the pointer is very important, however. When only the end of the pointer ($\frac{7}{16}$ or $\frac{9}{16}$ inch) shows, Loucks found that errors increase markedly under both incandescent and ultraviolet light. Vernon studied the lengths of pointers from the other direction. Instead of cutting off the inner part of the pointer, she moved the tip in closer to the center. As we might expect, her results show that errors increase considerably when there is a large gap between the tip of the pointer and the scale.

GENERAL CONCLUSIONS

Experiments on dial scales are still being conducted very actively. We may be a little rash in drawing conclusions at this stage of the game, but here are some general conclusions about dials which seem fairly safe:

1. A dial about 2.75 or 3 inches in diameter is probably the best all-around size if we are going to read it at a distance of 30 inches or less.

2. Marks should be located at the 0, 5, 10, 15, 20, etc. (or 0, 50, 100, 150, 200, etc.), positions. The marks at the 0, 10, 20, etc. (or 0, 100, 200, etc.), positions should be longer than those at the 5, 15, 25, etc. (or 50, 150, 250, etc.), positions. Only the marks at 0, 10, 20, etc., should be numbered.

3. The distance between the numbered markers should be about a half-inch as measured around the circumference of the dial.

4. The separation between scale markers should be the same all around the dial.

5. There should be a gap between the beginning and end of the scale.

6. Values on the scale should increase in a clockwise direction.

THE ARRANGEMENT OF DIAL DISPLAYS

PATTERNING

As we have already seen, in many types of dial display systems, the operator is not interested in knowing *exactly* the dial reading at any one time. In aircraft, for example, the pilot does not care particularly whether the manifold pressure is 37.5 or 38 pounds per square inch. All he really wants to know is whether or not the manifold pressure is within a normal safe-operating range. For this reason many aircraft instruments have a small narrow green band painted along the outside edge of the dial to indicate the normal operating or safe range.

"Unpatterned" dials. Even with this additional help, however, there is another factor that tends to add to the confusion of the operator. In Figure 70, the nine dials in the upper half of the figure represent a hypothetical group of dials such as we might find in an aircraft instrument panel. The safe ranges for each dial is indicated by a small black band around the edge of the dial. If you examine the figure carefully, you will discover that two of the dials show something is amiss, since they are not pointing at the normal safe-operating range.

Alignment patterns. Suppose now that we had patterned this system of dials. One possible type of pattern is shown by the group of nine dials in the lower half of the figure. In this case, the normal safe-operating ranges are indicated at the top of the dial. We had to shift the number scales around to do this, of course. Now so long as everything in the aircraft is perking along smoothly, all the needles on the dials will be pointing straight up, and you will probably agree that it is much easier to spot the two dials that show something is wrong.

Unpatterned Dial Display

Patterned Dial Display

FIG. 70. The dials in the upper diagram are unpatterned; those below are patterned. Patterning helps us see at a glance which ones are not indicating "normal" readings.

Actual experiments [19] with instruments mounted in a Link Trainer show beyond any doubt that the patterned dial display is easier to use than a mixed dial display. These same experiments also attempted to find out what the best pointer position is for the patterned display. Only three different arrangements were tried: (1) 9-o'clock positions, that is, with all the needles pointing to the left, (2) 12-o'clock positions, as shown in Figure 70, and (3) 3-o'clock positions, that is, with all the needles pointing to the right. Because of the limited scope of

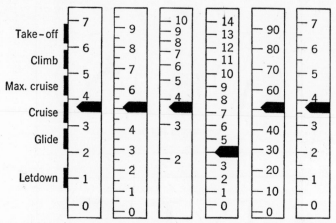

Fig. 71. This is a hypothetical patterned dial display for aircraft. Under any set of flight conditions, the pointers will be lined up in a row. This lets us pick out rapidly the dial which shows that something is wrong.

these experiments we should not conclude that the "best" position has been located scientifically. The results show, however, that the 3-o'clock alignment position is worse than the other two. The 9- and 12-o'clock positions are about equally good, although there is some indication that the 9-o'clock positions may be slightly better than the 12-o'clock.

Another patterned dial display. Another type of patterned dial display is shown in Figure 71. Notice that in this case we have transformed the circular dials into rather long narrow ones. The various scales have not been identified because this is a hypothetical dial display. The important thing to notice is that, when the aircraft is flying along normally for one type of condition, for example, at cruising speed, all of the pointers should be aligned in a row. If one of the engines or components is not functioning properly and the needle deviates from the normal operating condition, it is very easy to spot one out of alignment. Notice also that it is possible with this type of dial display to set up a number of different conditions. It is not necessary for all of the dials to be graduated in the same units, nor is it necessary for them all to start at the same zero position. We have shown here several different kinds of possible scales which would work in a patterned dial display of this sort. The first two, for example, are linear scales; the third is a logarithmic scale. Two have numbers running from 0 to 7, one from 0 to 14, and still another from 0 to 90. The particular spacings or numbers on the scales are not important so long as all of them can be aligned to indicate normal settings for any type of operating condition.

STANDARDIZATION

Another very important problem is standardization. When our basic research has progressed far enough so that we know what makes dials effective and when and where to use what kind of dials, we will have to standardize.

The important principle here is that groups of dials that are used for the same function should be standardized in location, from one situation to the next, from one airplane to the next, or from one ship to the next. The problem is an especially pressing one in the case of aircraft, but it holds equally well in all kinds of man–machine systems.

McFarland [15] tells about an investigator from Northwest Airlines who recently conducted a large survey of pilot opinion among a representative group of the Airlines Pilots Association. Most of the pilots agreed that standardization of instrument locations is a very necessary and vital step in the design of instrument panels. Most pilots believed that it really did not make very much difference what the final arrangement was so long as the dials were clearly visible and their location was consistent from one plane to the next. In spite of this unanimous opinion on the part of the pilots, however, another recent survey showed an almost complete lack of uniformity in the arrangement of dials on commercial two-engined aircraft now being built. The problem is one that needs prompt and careful attention.

As an example of how bad these things can get, there are three radio receivers on the panel of the B-314. On two of them, the controls and dials are rotated clockwise to increase the frequency; in the third receiver, they rotate counterclockwise. In the same aircraft, the co-pilot's air-speed indicator is rotated clockwise by a corresponding motion of the setting knob, but the pilot's meter has a reverse action. The situation is further complicated by the fact that these adjustments vary from one aircraft to another. The pilot, therefore, has to determine the action of his instruments by trial and error each time he flies a different plane.

Recently our laboratories have been doing a lot of research on radar indicators. In most of this equipment the bearing control is on the left, the range control on the right. This is a sensible arrangement since operators normally read target locations in that order—bearing first, range next—left to right. Recently we received a brand new piece of equipment from the factory, and where do you suppose the bearing and range controls were? They were backwards—range control on the left, bearing on the right. Our subjects who are trained on the old equipment are always a little confused when they turn to the new equipment.

One thing the experimenter can always expect when any kind of standardization of dials is agreed on and used is a large number of complaints from people who are not used to the particular arrangement of the visual display system. But it is really not a serious disadvantage, because the eventual benefits of standardization far outweigh any minor inconveniences that result from another training period.

SUMMARY

In this chapter we have come to grips with some practical problems of seeing. We talked mostly about a limited class of visual displays —dials. We saw that dials are not so effective as they can be. People persist in misreading dials. Like it or not, that is the fact. Fortunately, there are a number of design factors which can be used to reduce these errors greatly. Some of these have been verified by actual experiments; others are no better than expert opinions. We have tried to summarize the best information we can get at the present time. Ten years from now we will be able to do a much better job.

SELECTED REFERENCES

1. CHANNEL, R. C. An analysis of pilots' performances in multi-engine aircraft (R5D). Office of Naval Research, Special Devices Center, 15 April 1947.
2. CHAPANIS, A. Unpublished data, 1946.
3. FITTS, P. M., and JONES, R. E. Psychological aspects of instrument display. I: Analysis of 270 "pilot-error" experiences in reading and interpreting aircraft instruments. Aero Medical Laboratory, Air Materiel Command, Dayton, Ohio, Report No. TSEAA–694–12A, 1 October 1947.

4. GRETHER, W. F.   The effect of variations in indicator design upon speed and accuracy of altitude readings.   Aero Medical Laboratory, Air Materiel Command, Dayton, Ohio, Report No. TSEAA–694–14, 2 September 1947.

5. GRETHER, W. F.   Analysis of types of errors in reading of the conventional three-pointer altimeter.   Aero Medical Laboratory, Air Materiel Command, Dayton, Ohio, Report No. MCREXD–694–14A, 16 March 1948.

6. GRETHER, W. F.   Factors in the design of clock dials which affect speed and accuracy of reading in the 2400-hour time system.   *J. Appl. Psychol.*, 1948, **32**, 159–169.

7. GRETHER, W. F., and WILLIAMS, A. C., JR.   Speed and accuracy of dial reading as a function of dial diameter and angular separation of scale divisions. In FITTS, P. M. (Ed.).   *Psychological research on equipment design.*   U. S. Government Printing Office, 1947, 101–109.

8. HIBBARD, D. L.   Human engineering and instruments.   *Instruments*, 1945, **18**, 760–763.

9. KAPPAUF, W. E., and SMITH, W. M.   A preliminary experiment on the effect of dial graduation and dial size on the speed and accuracy of dial reading. *Ann. N. Y. Acad. Sci.*, 1948 (In press).

10. KAPPAUF, W. E., SMITH, W. M., and BRAY, C. W.   A methodological study of dial reading.   Department of Psychology, Princeton University, Report No. 3, August 1947.

11. LEYZOREK, M.   Accuracy of visual interpolation between scale markers as a function of the separation between markers.   *J. Exp. Psychol.*, 1949, 39, 270–279.

12. LOUCKS, R. B.   Legibility of aircraft instrument dials: A further investigation of the relative legibility of tachometer dials.   AAF School of Aviation Medicine, Randolph Field, Texas, Report No. 1, Project No. 265, 27 October 1944.

13. LOUCKS, R. B.   Legibility of aircraft instrument dials: The relative legibility of various climb indicator dials and pointers.   AAF School of Aviation Medicine, Randolph Field, Texas, Report No. 1, Project No. 286, 25 November 1944.

14. LOUCKS, R. B.   Legibility of aircraft instrument dials: The relative legibility of manifold pressure indicator dials.   AAF School of Aviation Medicine, Randolph Field, Texas, Report No. 1, Project No. 325, 7 December 1944.

15. McFARLAND, R. A.   *Human factors in air transport design.*   New York: McGraw-Hill, 1946.

16. MILTON, J. L., JONES, R. E., MORRIS, J. B., and FITTS, P. M.   Pilot reaction time: the time required to comprehend and react to contact and instrument recovery problems.   Aero Medical Laboratory, Air Materiel Command, Dayton, Ohio, Report No. TSEAA–694–13A, 26 May 1947.

17. SLEIGHT, R. B.   The effect of instrument dial shape on legibility.   *J. Appl. Psychol.*, 1948, **32**, 170–188.

18. VERNON, M. D.   Scale and dial reading.   Medical Research Council, Unit in Applied Psychology, University of Cambridge, England, Report No. A.P.U. 49, June 1946.

19. WARRICK, M. J. and GRETHER, W. F.   The effect of pointer alignment on check reading of engine instrument panels.   Aero Medical Laboratory, Air Materiel Command, Dayton, Ohio, Report No. MCREXD–694–17, 4 June 1948.

6. *Visual Displays*

IN THE LAST CHAPTER WE INTRODUCED ONE PARTICULAR KIND OF VISUAL display—dials. We treated dials in a separate chapter because we know more about them than we do about most other kinds of display. In this chapter we shall look at some of the broader problems of visual displays.

There are many variations and combinations of displays, and we cannot hope to do full justice to them all here. As a matter of fact, we do not have many good sound generalizations in this field. Because of this diversity and lack of good generalizations, we shall have to discuss a number of things that may not seem to go together very well. We shall talk about symbolic and pictorial displays, numbers and scales, legibility of symbols, tables, graphs, charts, and so on. This means that we cannot present a neat logical outline. But we hope that this chapter will introduce some of the major problems and research findings in this field.

SYMBOLIC AND PICTORIAL DISPLAYS

In Chapter 5 we pointed out that it takes a pilot longer to straighten his aircraft when he must rely on instruments than it does when he can see outside. Pilots just naturally seem to fly better when they can see what is going on outside. This state of affairs, both in aircraft and in other places, is serious enough that instrument designers and engineering psychologists have been studying the best kind of a display to use. We would like, of course, to have displays that allow us to get information as fast and as accurately as possible.

USES OF SYMBOLIC AND PICTORIAL DISPLAYS

One of the problems of designing displays is concerned with the use of pictorial instead of symbolic displays. Before we go any further, perhaps we should explain the difference between them.

Symbolic displays. Most instruments and dials are symbolic displays. By means of pointers, scales, or lights, these instruments present an *indirect* story of what is going on. We do not get a natural visual picture from them. Most of them use numbers, and to make any sense of these numbers we have to know some rules about what they mean. A speedometer is a good example of a symbolic display. When a speedometer reads 50, we have to know what 50 means. We also need to have some idea about what miles means, what hours means, and what miles *per* hour means.

We learn all this, of course, but the learning goes on so gradually throughout life, that we probably do not pay much attention to it. With some instruments, the learning process is much more evident. The first time most aviation cadets have to deal with an aircraft instrument panel, they discover that they must do a lot of learning fast in order to make sense of readings on manifold-pressure gages, tachometers, and a dozen other gages.

Pictorial displays. A pictorial display is one that presents a realistic picture of what is going on. If we wanted to show speed by means of a pictorial display, for example, we would have to reproduce all those visual stimuli that whiz by when we drive. Actually, this example is a little far-fetched; a more realistic example is the artificial horizon indicator in aircraft. This tells a pilot whether he is flying straight and level. Information of this sort could be presented symbolically, of course, by having a pointer on one dial indicate how many degrees the wings are tilted and another one show how many degrees the nose is pointing up or down. A pictorial display for doing the same job is shown in Figure 72. Here, notice that a line represents the horizon of the earth, and a miniature plane represents the aircraft in which the pilot is flying. This is a kind of small picture of what is going on—of what the horizon looks like with respect to the position of the plane. This is what we mean by a pictorial display.

Inside-out versus outside-in displays. There are actually two ways of making pictorial displays—inside-out and outside-in. The inside-out display resembles what we see when we are actually inside a moving vehicle looking out at the world. If we wanted a display of that sort for an automobile, then, when the automobile turns right, poles, buildings, and so forth would have to swing around us from right to left. In other words, the environment moves around us in an inside-out display. Also, we do not see much of the vehicle itself, since we are inside the vehicle.

The outside-in display, on the other hand, resembles what we see when we are sitting on a hilltop looking down at the world below. We are fixed, the earth is fixed, and we see cars moving around in this fixed environment. A lot of little toy cars moving around on a map would provide an outside-in display.

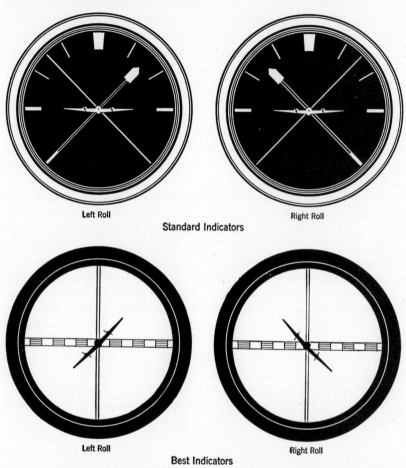

FIG. 72. Two kinds of artificial horizon showing a left roll and a right roll. The two top indicators have been standard on aircraft and are examples of inside-out displays. The lower indicators are outside-in displays, and research has shown that they are better. (After Loucks, 1947)

Examples of pictorial displays. We will not describe the uses of symbolic displays because many of them are already familiar to you. But what are some practical uses for pictorial displays? One place where inside-out displays have been of great value is in training devices.

During the war, it was absolutely impossible to have each new sailor or soldier start his training immediately with complicated machines of war. There were not enough to go around and, even if there had been, it would have been too dangerous and too costly to run them for recruits. For these reasons, the services made wide use of synthetic training devices—gadgets which simulated the real thing in as realistic a manner as possible. Link trainers, gunnery trainers, submarine trainers, and hundreds of other trainers saved us millions of dollars a year. But training devices also have their uses in peacetime and in industry. Realistic automobile trainers have been used, for example, to let novices get the knack of driving before they actually get onto the road. That saves money both for the novice and for other people who do not get their cars banged up.

Outside-in pictorial displays are also coming into use more and more to make it possible for key persons to "size up" a complicated situation. They were used during the war, for example, to show fighter directors where enemy raids were coming in, how many planes were in each raid, and where friendly fighter planes were. Little blocks were moved around on a huge map to represent the altitude, composition, and direction of all raids. There was so much information to absorb rapidly that this was about the only way in which it could be done. Teleran is another important outside-in display. This is a radar picture which shows a pilot where he is, where the airport is, where the runways are, where other planes are, and where obstructions are around the airport. It is, in short, a miniature complete map. Although it is still in the experimental stage, it promises to be immensely valuable in helping pilots get around in bad weather. Similar kinds of displays should be useful for the men who control airway traffic from the ground. The problem here is complex, of course, because we have to present three-dimensional information. But, looking into the future, it seems clear that air traffic is going to increase heavily during the next twenty years. When it does, the problem of getting aircraft into and out of airports under poor weather conditions is going to be difficult. Someone will have to know where all the planes are so that he can get the nearest ones down first and give flight directions to the others until it is their turn to come in.

ADVANTAGES AND DISADVANTAGES OF PICTORIAL AND SYMBOLIC DISPLAYS

Now that we have shown what symbolic and pictorial displays are, it might be worth while to size up the advantages and disadvantages of each.

Versatility, simplicity, and compactness. The most obvious advantage of the symbolic display is its versatility and compactness. We can represent almost any situation in a very small space with a symbolic display. One little dial can represent a great distance, if there are enough numbers on it. But it is almost impossible to get some kinds of information into a pictorial display. How could we picture manifold pressure, or cylinder head temperature, for example? We can show the altitudes of 50 aircraft with 50 altimeters, but it would take a lot of equipment to show this same information pictorially.

Accuracy of information. A second advantage of the symbolic display is that information can be presented much more precisely. The use of dials, with numbers and markers, gives much more accurate information than a small picture of the situation does. We can tell our height above the ground very easily from an altimeter, much better than we can by looking at the ground or a pictorial representation of the ground and ourselves. The symbolic display presents the information as a precise quantity.

Training required. On the other hand, pictorial displays require much less training to read than do symbolic displays. Symbols are substitutes for the real thing, and that means we need training in interpreting them. Actually, of course, psychologists will tell you that we need a lot of training to recognize the meaning of pictorial representations. In Chapter 4, when we were talking about optical illusions, we mentioned that children do not see the illusion of perspective. That is something we learn from experience. But the learning we need for pictorial displays goes on all our lives and is so gradual that we do not notice it. Certainly most adults need little training to interpret a pictorial display. They have long ago learned about upness, downness, farness, the meaning of lights and shadows, and so on.

Interpretability. The pictorial display can usually be interpreted much faster than the symbolic display, because the pictorial display is a miniature of the real thing. For example, if you see a little car marked on a map, you do not need a handbook of mathematical tables to tell you where that car is, at least not if you are familiar with the general area. But suppose you were told where the car is by its latitude and longitude on two dials; or suppose you were told that it is 1,500 miles due west of the Empire State Building. How long would it take you to figure out just where that car is?

The more complex a situation gets, the harder it is to interpret symbolic displays, and the more useful are pictorial displays. If a man in a control tower at LaGuardia Field had to keep track of just one plane, he would probably manage all right with a few meters and dials. But suppose he has to keep track of 50 planes with the same few meters and dials. We expect that he would retain his sanity only a short while.

Realism. Pictorial displays are without question more realistic than symbolic displays. And the inside-out display is more realistic than the outside-in display. Yet there is some question whether the more realistic display is easier to interpret. Most of us seem to do all right when we stand on the curb and tell our wives how to park the family car. Likewise, operators controlling robot planes by radio have no trouble so long as they can see the plane. These situations, however, correspond to outside-in displays, which are less realistic in many cases than inside-out displays.

The standard artificial horizon used in Army aircraft is an inside-out display—the horizon moves while the plane is stationary in space. On purely logical grounds, that is the reasonable display to use, since it shows exactly the same thing the pilot would see if he could look out to the horizon. Loucks, however, was not satisfied with reasoning alone. He did an experiment,[12] comparing an outside-in with an inside-out horizon indicator. To his and everyone else's amazement, he found that the best indicator has the horizon fixed and the plane moving. This is the outside-in display. It shows how a plane would look if we were watching it from behind. This probably means that we think of the outside as fixed space, even though the outside actually changes when the plane noses down or banks over. It is easier to interpret what the plane is doing in this fixed space than it is to think of the plane as fixed and then have to interpret an unrealistic movement of the outside environment (see Figure 72).

RESEARCH NEEDED

We have presented here a few viewpoints and some problems. We have given some arguments for and against symbolic and pictorial displays. But you will probably agree that there is room for a lot of research here. We need to have a lot of basic research in order that we can design the best kind of visual display for particular purposes. Let us list briefly some of the questions that need answering:

1. What are the situations in which pictorial displays can be used more profitably than symbolic displays?
2. What are the situations in which inside-out displays are better than outside-in displays?
3. How much realism do we need in a pictorial display? We cannot,

obviously, get complete realism in a pictorial display. How much of that realism can we forego without losing in interpretability?

4. What types of distortion can we permit in a pictorial display?

5. What kinds of symbolic information can be blended into a pictorial display to make up for the lack of precise quantitative information that we cannot get into most pictorial displays? What are the best ways of doing this blending?

NUMBERS AND SCALES

As we saw in Chapters 2 and 3, numbers are very handy things to have around. They let us count things, measure things, balance our checking accounts, and so on. They are also used widely on visual displays. Sometimes the numbers on visual displays are merely labels. The number "1" on a highway sign is a label for a particular road. But many types of visual displays have numbers on them so that we can measure and compute things. Numbers on dials, scales, slide rules, and meters exist for that purpose. Since it is impossible to have a number for every possible marker on a scale, we have to do some perceiving, judging, or estimating when the things we want to measure do not fall exactly opposite a marker with a number on it. Strange as it may seem, the way we do our perceiving in such a case depends on the kinds of numbers we have on the scale. That is the subject of this section: how different numbers affect the speed and accuracy with which we can use scales.

Number Preferences

One of the first things we notice in this matter of numbers is that people have peculiar number habits and number preferences. On many dials and scales we must estimate the last digit of a reading by interpolating between scale markers. If the pointer on a dial comes to rest somewhere between two marks labeled 50 and 60, we must determine whether that position corresponds to 51, 52, 53, or any of the other numbers between 50 and 60. If we recorded a large number of readings of random settings with a scale of this sort, we should expect that the final interpolated digits would be randomly distributed among the digits 1 to 9. Actually, the data would not come out that way. Most people seem to prefer some digits and to avoid others.

Kinds of observations. The results of one study of these number preferences are shown in Figure 73. One set of data in this figure is based on 1,000 readings of a millivoltmeter scale. In this case, the observer read a scale to the nearest millivolt and estimated tenths of millivolts by interpolation. Another series of measurements is based on 1,000 thermometer readings from a weather station in England. In this instance, the observers read thermometers to the nearest degree and estimated tenths of a degree by interpolation. Still another series of measurements is based on 1,258 measurements with a ruler graduated in millimeters, tenths of millimeters being estimated. And finally, from an agricultural experiment station, there are 854 weight measure-

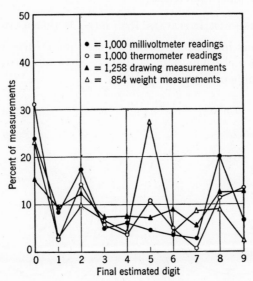

FIG. 73. When interpolations have to be made between scale markings, some numbers are used much more often than others. (After Yule, 1927)

ments on grain which was weighed to the nearest gram, with estimations made to the nearest tenth of a gram.

Results. We can see from these data that observers tend to prefer 0, 2, and 8 as a final digit. The digits 1, 3, 4, 6, and 7 were almost universally avoided. Sometimes the digit 5 was used frequently; in other cases it was not. The same is true of the digit 9. Various types of body measurements—head lengths, head circumferences, and heights —and even ages taken from census returns show the same tendency.

Conclusions about number preferences. We can make certain general conclusions about number preferences among people on the basis of such studies. (1) Most people have number preferences even if they think they are highly trained in the use of scales. (2) Number preferences tend to be highly personal. Different people have different preferences. (3) Any one individual is very consistent in his number preferences over a long period of time. (4) Overshadowing individual differences, the general tendency is for most people to prefer the digits 0, 2, and 8, and to avoid the digits 1, 3, 6, and 7. (5) Errors due to number preferences can be reduced if the observer knows about this human error, if he trains himself to make unbiased scale readings, and if he keeps reminding himself that even the best observers occasionally show strong number preferences.

NUMBERS FOR SCALE INTERVALS REQUIRING INTERPOLATION

Although this information about number preferences is interesting, what is much more important is that we have more trouble working with some numbers than with others.

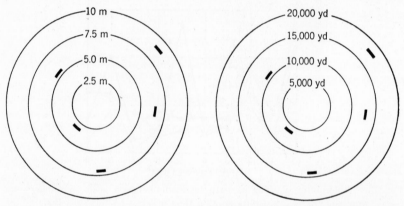

FIG. 74. The numbers used for the scales in these two series of range rings represent exactly the same distances. And yet research has shown that we can estimate distance much more accurately with the scale on the right. (After Chapanis, 1947)

Scale intervals for radar scopes. Most radar scopes have fixed range rings on them to represent different distances for targets appearing on the face of the scope. Two samples are shown in Figure 74. The little black lines represent different targets. The center of the scope is where the radar is, and the black circles represent different distances from the radar. The radar scope on the left has the range rings labeled 2.5, 5.0, 7.5, and 10 miles. The one on the right has range rings labeled 5,000, 10,000, 15,000, and 20,000 yards. Both scales actually represent the same distance, because 2.5 nautical miles equals 5,000 yards. So the scales are really the same. But the problem is this: Can you estimate the positions of the targets just as accurately with one scope as with the other?

Data. One study [7] was aimed at just this question, although a lot of other scale intervals were also used. The whole list was 1,000, 2,000, 3,000, 4,000, 5,000, 6,000, 7,000, 8,000, 9,000, and 10,000 yards and 2.5 miles. The radar operators in this experiment had all the time they wanted and were told to estimate the positions of targets as accurately as they could. The results were quite consistent. The 1,000- and 10,000-yard scales had the best percentage accuracy. Actually we should not be too surprised at this finding because we are used to dealing with a decimal number system all the time. And the 10,000-yard scale, of course, is the same as the 1,000 with another 0 added to it. It is interesting, however, that the next best scale interval was 2,000 yards; then came 5,000 and 4,000. After that, the errors began to increase considerably. Nine thousand, 8,000, 6,000, 7,000 and 3,000 were bad, and 2.5 miles was the worst. The 2.5-mile scale, in fact, gave errors that were nearly twice as great as those with the 5,000-yard scale, although both measured the same distance.

We do not know why some of these numbers are harder to work with than others. It may be that some numbers are harder to sub-divide, or some numbers are just plain awkward. But you will agree that the numbers on a visual display affect the precision of your judgments.

Another study. A related study [2] compared scale intervals of 5, 10, and 20 miles and used only two range rings. Targets appeared at 19 positions between markers—$\frac{1}{20}$, $\frac{2}{20}$, $\frac{3}{20}$, $\cdots$, $\frac{19}{20}$ of the distance between two range rings. In this study, the 20-mile scale came out slightly better than the 10-mile scale, and the 5-mile interval was the poorest. The reversal between the 10- and 20-mile scales may have been due to the fact that somewhat larger displays were used. We saw in the last chapter that accuracy of interpolation depends on the distance between scale markers. At any rate, this reversal of the two best scales is not too serious. These scales are still better than any of the others.

NUMBERS FOR SCALES NOT REQUIRING INTERPOLATION

In the experiments we just reviewed, the observer had to interpolate between two markers. A target or point could appear anywhere be-tween these markers. There is another very large study on the effec-tiveness of various scales when no interpolation is required. Here a pointer comes to rest exactly at a scale marker, and the observer has to figure out what that marker is.

A study by Vernon.   Vernon did not try out all possible permuta-
tions of scales and markers, but she did try out a lot of different ones
—80 in all.   In her experiments 24 RAF pilots had a 2-second glance
at each of the different scales.   The pointers always fell exactly on
one of the markers so that their only job was to figure out what the
reading was on that particular scale.

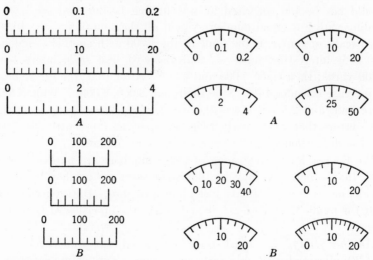

FIG. 75. Some examples of the   FIG. 76. Some examples of the types
types of straight scales used in   of circular scales used in Vernon's
Vernon's experiment.   experiment.

Vernon's experiment was pretty complicated.   But let us see if we
can describe the kinds of scales she used.   First, she used both straight
and circular scales.   Figures 75 and 76 show us only small parts of
both kinds.   In one part of the experiment, she kept the number of
scale divisions constant (10 for the straight scales, 5 for the circular
scales) but varied the scale numbers.   In Figures 75 and 76, the scales
labeled *A* are examples of this.   Notice that the number of scale divisions between numbers is the same.   The thing that is different is the
numbers on the scales.

In another part of her experiment, she kept the scale numbers constant (100 for the straight scales and 10 for the circular scales) but
varied the number of scale divisions.   Some samples of these scales are
shown in the sections labeled *B* in Figures 75 and 76.   In all, she tried
2, 4, 5, 8, or 16 scale divisions between each pair of numbers.

Decimals versus whole numbers. The first major conclusion that was reached from her data was that scale numbers that are decimals are much harder to work with than those numbers that are not. This was true for all numbers and for both the straight and circular scales. Scale intervals like .01, .1, .02, and so on were much harder to read correctly than scale intervals like 1, 10, 2, 20, and so on. One other thing: If we have to use decimals on scales, we should not put a 0 in front of the decimal point. We should use .01 or .1 instead of 0.01 or 0.1. Although many mathematicians like to have that 0 there, it is very confusing to the people who have to read scales fast.

Numbers for scale intervals. The next important finding concerns the number assigned to the scale intervals. Since many of the numbers are very much alike, Vernon grouped her data as shown in Figure 77. She figured, and probably rightly so, that changing a number by 10 does not make the mental processes any different. The first impression you get from looking at Figure 77 is that some scale numbers produced a terrific number of errors, whereas others were fairly satisfactory. The best scale numbers are the decimal ones: 1,000, 100, 10, and so on. Scale intervals in 4's are about the most difficult.

If you look at Figure 77 more closely you will also notice some surprising differences between the straight and circular scales. Scale intervals in 5's are good for the circular scales and bad for the straight ones. How does this happen? Look back now to Figures 75 and 76. There you see that Vernon used 10 scale divisions between numbers on the straight scales and only 5 scale divisions between numbers on the circular scales. Thus, in terms of scale divisions, the "5's" circular scale and the "10's" straight scale, are the same—all of which may make you suspect that the value of the smallest scale division, as well as the size of the scale interval, is also important.

Number of smallest division. To look a little deeper into this matter of scale divisions, we have regrouped Vernon's data according to the numerical value of the smallest scale division. You see these regrouped data in Figure 78. A straight scale with a scale interval of 20, 2, .2, .02, or .002, for example, would have the smallest scale division equal to 2, .2, .02, .002, or .0002. A circular scale with a scale interval of 1,000, 100, 10, 1, .1, .01, or .001, on the other hand, would have the smallest scale divisions equal to 200, 20, 2, .2, .02, .002, or .0002. Now you can see that fewest errors occur when the smallest scale division is in the decimal system. Scale divisions in 2's are not much worse. Scale divisions in 5's are bad; and scale divisions in 4's, 25's, and 8's are very difficult.

Number of scale divisions between numbers. A general conclusion that seems justified on the basis of the second part of Vernon's work is that 8 and 16 scale units between numbered markers are hard to read. Two scale units between numbered markers are easy if enough room

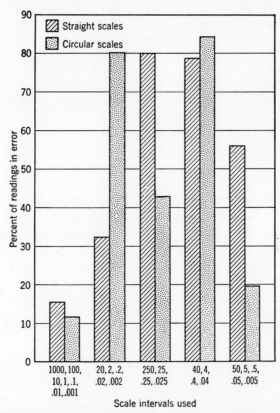

Fɪɢ. 77. This figure shows that the number of errors made in reading a scale depends on the scale interval used. The scale interval refers to the numbers marked on the scale, as in Figures 75 and 76. (After Vernon, 1946)

is left between the numbered markers. Four scale units are satisfactory also. This is one instance where a scale with the smallest division equal to 2.5 is all right. The second scale from the top in the right-hand column in Figure 79 has its smallest division equal to 2.5, but it was easy to read. The fifth scale down from the top in the left-hand column of Figure 79 also has the smallest division equal to 2.5, but it was hard to read. This, incidentally, is a good illustration of one of those interactions we discussed in Chapter 3.

Five scale divisions are difficult if the scale numbers run 0, 40, 80, 120, or 0, 2, 4, 6. They are easy to read if the scale numbers run 0, 10, 20, 30. Ten scale divisions between numbered markers are hard to

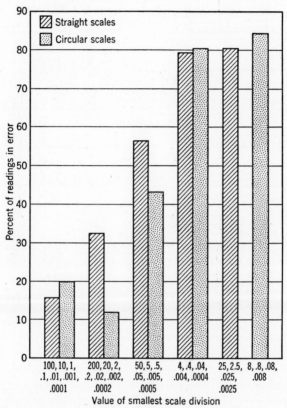

Fɪɢ. 78. This figure shows that the number of errors made in reading a scale depends on the numerical value of the smallest scale division. (After Vernon, 1946)

read for scales like 0, 25, 50, 75, or 0, 5, 10, 15, but are easy for scales like 0, 10, 20, 30, or 0, 20, 40, 60.

Examples of good and bad scales. Perhaps the best way of summarizing the results of this study is to show some examples of good and bad scales. We have shown a number of both kinds in Figure 79. In general, the relative difficulty of these scales is about the same if we multiply or divide the scale numbers by 10. This means that the top right scale would be easy to read even if the numbers went 0, 1, 2,

3, or 0, 100, 200, 300. The same is true for the other scales. Of course, the best designs shown here for straight scales are also the best for circular scales.

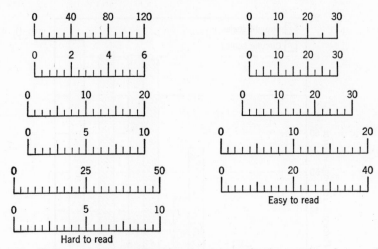

FIG. 79. Here are some examples of scales that are hard to read, and some that are easy to read. In general, we get the same relative difficulty if we multiply or divide all the numbers by 10. (After Vernon, 1946)

LEGIBILITY OF NUMBERS, LETTERS, AND SYMBOLS

A very important factor in most visual displays is the legibility of the numbers, letters, and symbols used. In Chapter 4 we talked a lot about visibility and visual acuity. This discussion, however, was largely oriented toward the purely physical and physiological aspects of these problems. It turns out that there are some important perceptual problems involved in legibility too. Even if we take a group of letters, all the same size on the same background, with the same degree of contrast and the same illumination, we can read some letters better than others. Capital O's and Q's, for example, are very frequently confused when they are seen at a distance. A's and V's, on the other hand, are practically never confused. We do not need a complicated analysis to understand right away why this is so.

LEGIBILITY OF TYPE

Most of the work on legibility has been done with different kinds of printer's type. Reading is a visual task which most people in the United States indulge in from the time they are 5 years old. The problem of finding which kind of type is easiest on young eyes as well as old ones has interested psychologists, ophthalmologists, printers, and teachers for many years. Out of a lot of research, we can make some tentative recommendations. Our summary of these recommendations, as a matter of fact, is taken from the books by Paterson and Tinker and Luckiesh and Moss.

Styles of type face. It seems that we can read type styles that go by the names of Garamond, Antique, Scotch Roman, Bodoni, Old Style, Modern, Caslon, Cheltenham, and Kabel Light all about equally well. This book is printed in Linotype 21, which is a Modern face. American Typewriter type—just like we have on typewriters—definitely slows us down. Of the types that Paterson and Tinker studied, the only other style that is difficult to read is Old English. This kind of type has so many angles and curlycues that it slows readers down by about 14 percent.

Type form. We read material in capital letters much more slowly than material in lower-case printing. Results of objective tests on this point agree with how readers feel about it. Most readers definitely do not like to read material printed entirely in capitals. The reason is probably that we destroy word form when we use capitals. If we take another look at the word *destroy*, we will notice that the "d," "t," and "y" stand out because they are either above or below the body of the word. When we print DESTROY in capital letters, however, those cues are lost. All in all, therefore, a safe rule is that we should AVOID PRINTING IN CAPITALS. Bold-face type is read about as well as ordinary type. Most people, however, do not like to read type in this form, and it is probably wiser to *restrict the use of italics* **and bold-face printing to short sections which require emphasis.**

Type size, line width, and leading. Conclusions about type size, the width of the printed line, and leading (the amount of space between lines) are very complex because all these factors are interrelated. The best type size for one width of line is not necessarily the best size for another width. Also the best spacing between lines with one size of type is not necessarily the best spacing to use with another size of type. When the best line widths and leading are used in each case, however, it appears that 9-, 10-, 11-, and 12-point type sizes are about equally legible. Speed of reading is slowed with 8-point type and markedly slowed with 6-point type. The conclusions on these points are all so complicated that you had better look up the book if you are really interested in getting the best possible arrangement for printed materials. The text type in this book, by the way, is 10 point.

Color of print and background. The last series of conclusions we shall discuss here concerns the legibility of print as a function of color. Paterson and Tinker definitely find that black print on white is more legible than white on black. They find white on black to be so illegible, in fact, that they recommend that this combination should never be used where *readability* is important. They also tried a number of different colored inks on different colored papers. The interesting thing here is that the colors by themselves are not very important. The really important thing is the amount of brightness contrast between the letters and their backgrounds. Many colored inks are not very readable simply because we cannot get much contrast between them and the paper. So here again we see that our basic information about seeing applies to a practical problem of legibility.

Summary. You can see by now that the scientist can contribute a lot of very useful information about the legibility of type for practical reading problems. Actually, our summary here has touched only the high lights of this interesting work. There are whole books on this subject alone. But we must leave these studies and turn to some other problems of legibility more directly concerned with visual displays in man–machine systems.

LEGIBILITY OF ISOLATED SYMBOLS

For all their value in telling us how to make books more readable, the work we have just reviewed does not give us final answers to many practical problems. For that there are four reasons.

The kind of material. The first reason why studies on the readability of type do not solve all our problems is that the seeing problems we encounter in reading are not the same as in most visual display problems. In ordinory reading you do not really see indiwidual letters. You read by words, and somelimes grouqs of words, which we take in at a single glence. If you read this paragraph very rapidly, you perhaps did not catch the five mistakes in the last two sentences. In one psychological experiment, for example, words like "Woodson Wilrow" and "psychment departology" were exposed for very short times. The subjects in this experiment had no difficulty at all in reporting that they saw "Woodrow Wilson" and "psychology department." The point is that the total context of all the letters and words helps us to read rapidly. But many visual displays do not have whole words on them. Dials, for example, have single numbers with no context to help us fill in the meaning. Whenever single letters or numbers are used on displays, the legibility problem becomes more difficult.

Kinds of seeing conditions. The second difficulty with reading experiments is that the seeing conditions are good. The experiments by Paterson and Tinker, for example, were done with the reading material in good light and at a normal reading distance. These conditions, unfortunately, are not always met with most visual displays. Instruments and dials sometimes have to be read when the light is very poor. Aircraft status boards, plotting boards, and highway signs have to be read from great distances. For many types of visual display, then, we want to get the maximum legibility of single letters or symbols under unfavorable conditions.

Kinds of performance measured. The third difficulty with many of the experiments on reading is that we cannot be sure that they used measures of performance that are relevant to our purposes. Paterson and Tinker, for example, used very short reading periods—about 2 minutes—in their experiments. It is quite possible that their conclusions might have been altered if they had their subjects read for an hour or more. Further, their tests were primarily concerned with the speed of reading and did not measure other important factors, for example, comprehension. The experiments by Luckiesh and Moss rely heavily on the rate of eye blinking as a measure of the relative readability of various kinds of type. But it is difficult to see what the blink rate has to do with legibility, and, as a matter of fact, recent experiments by other investigators throw serious doubt on the validity of the blink rate for studies of this sort. These few criticisms are enough to show you that the experiments to date did not measure as many things as we should like to have measured.

Basic studies versus comparative tests. The fourth objection to experiments on reading brings up the distinction between basic research and comparative tests. Most of the research on the legibility of type compares existing type styles. These studies take the kinds of type already in use and compare them in terms of readability. At that, these studies have compared only a dozen or so out of a hundred or more in existence. But these are not basic studies. They do not get at the real factors that make symbols legible. It is possible, for example, that we might design a kind of type that is a lot more legible than any now in existence. But we need the basic studies to tell us how to do it. All we can tell from the studies of Paterson and Tinker is that certain kinds of type are more readable than others. We still do not know whether they are the *best possible* kind of type.

These objections are very important ones. Under the circumstances, we had better take another look at the legibility problem.

Factors affecting symbol legibility. When we start investigating this problem, we find that the simplicity of a number or letter markedly affects its legibility. Different amounts of shading, and different numbers of hair lines in numbers also make them harder or easier to read. So does the amount of white space included within the outline of numbers and symbols. And finally, emphasizing certain parts of numerals and symbols will make them much more readable. The B, for example, is a lot more legible if we put a little overhang on the top and bottom. The same is true of the letter D. We can make it easier to distinguish C and G if we have well-marked gaps in the letters and put a well-marked cross-piece in the letter G. The Q needs a definite strong oblique stroke so we will not confuse it with the letters O or C, and the W needs a high center prong so it will not look like an M. S is a difficult letter no matter what we do. It is always being confused with other letters.

A comparison of letter designs. As an illustration of the importance of these factors, we can cite an experiment by Mackworth,[14] a British psychologist working at Cambridge. He was interested in improving the legibility of letters and numbers on sector maps used for air raids. The letters and numbers on the upper half of Figure 80 were the kind in use when he made his investigation; those in the bottom half were the ones he designed. Since these sector displays were often viewed across a large room, he ran tests at 25, 30, 35, and 40 feet. The average misreading errors at every distance are much lower for the new design (see Table 10). But for our purposes here it is important

TABLE 10. AVERAGE PERCENTAGE OF ERRORS MADE IN READING THE LETTERS
AND NUMBERS IN FIGURE 80 AT VARIOUS DISTANCES

After Mackworth, 1944

| | Viewing distance in feet | | | |
	25	30	35	40
Old design	5.2%	12.5%	20.6%	38.7%
New design	1.9%	5.3%	12.5%	22.5%

to notice the design changes that brought about the improvement. Have someone hold Figure 80 far enough away so that you can just barely see the letters. Then see how much easier it is to tell the difference between the "O" and "Q," the "C" and "G," the "G" and "6." Then notice how this increased legibility was produced—by a strong oblique stroke on the Q, a heavy bar on the G, a large gap in the C, and so on. A combination of little things like these can improve legibility a great deal.

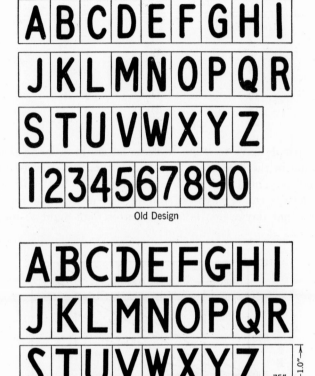

Old Design

New Design

FIG. 80. These are the old and new designs of letters used by Mackworth in his experiment. (After Mackworth, 1944)

The best stroke width. Another factor in the design of letters and numbers is the stroke width—the width of the lines used in the letter or number. Table 11 shows the heights and stroke widths of some letters used in one study. The stroke width of the series *B* letters is one eighth of the height of the letter, and in the series *D* letters, the stroke width is one sixth of the height of the letter. Figure 81 shows

TABLE 11. HEIGHT AND STROKE WIDTH OF TWO SETS OF SYMBOLS USED IN A STUDY OF THE LEGIBILITY OF HIGHWAY SIGNS

From Forbes and Holmes, 1939

Height of number or letter, inches	Stroke width, inches	
	Series B	Series D
4	½	1 1⁄16
6	¾	1
8	1	1⅜
10	1¼	1 11⁄16
12	1½	2
18	2¼	3
24	3	4

how close people have to stand to these letters in order to read them at night and in the daytime. When the letters were viewed at night, they were floodlighted with artificial illumination. Notice that thicker series *D* letters can always be seen farther away than the thinner letters and that day vision is always better than night vision, as we might expect.

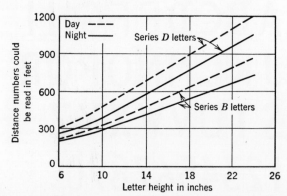

FIG. 81. These curves show how easily two different letter designs can be recognized at night and in the daytime. Artificial illumination was used at night. The series *D* letters had thicker lines than series *B*. (After Forbes and Holmes, 1939)

In another study,[18] various stroke widths were compared when all letters had the same height. The best stroke width was 18 percent of the height of the letter, which corresponds very closely to the one-sixth height of the series *D* letters in Figure 81.

The most legible numbers. Another series of experiments done by a psychologist at Cornell [4] was concerned with the legibility of numbers on automobile license plates. All of the numbers he used had outside dimensions of 42 x 80 millimeters, and he compared the numbers 8, 5, and 2. He used only these three numbers because they are usually the hardest to identify correctly.

His results for daytime seeing are shown in Figure 82. The stroke width of the letters is shown on the abscissa, and the distance at which the numbers could be read is on the ordinate. These data show that 6

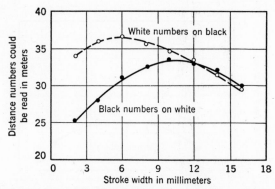

Fig. 82. This figure shows how closely we have to stand to black or white numbers to read them in daylight. The abscissa shows the width of the lines used, and the ordinate shows how close an observer must be in order to recognize the number. The height of the numbers was 80 millimeters. Notice that the white numbers against a black background are more easily seen than the black numbers on a white background. (After Berger, 1944)

millimeters is the best stroke width for white numbers on a black background, but that 10 millimeters is the best width for black letters on a white background. Notice especially that the white numbers on the black background can be recognized farther away than the black numbers on a white background, even when both have the best stroke width.

Numbers at night. In a second experiment, this psychologist compared different stroke widths for numbers seen at night. Some of his numbers were illuminated from behind (luminous), and others were illuminated from the front. Figure 83 shows the best stroke widths for these letters. The luminous numbers can be seen better than those illuminated from the front, but they also need a much smaller stroke width.

After having done all this research, he constructed what he considers to be the best numbers for daylight and night use. The daylight num-

bers are shown in Figure 84, and the luminous numbers for night use
are in Figure 85. The printer did not make a mistake—luminous
numbers are more legible at night if they are thinner.

Angle of viewing. Another factor affecting the legibility of symbols on visual displays is the angle at which they are viewed. As a
principle, applying to visual displays in general, displays should be
placed perpendicular to the line of sight of the people who have to see
them. This is a simple enough principle, but it is very frequently

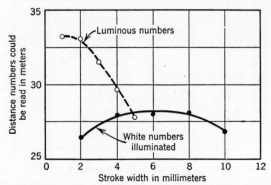

F<small>IG</small>. 83. This figure shows how closely we have to stand to luminous and white
illuminated numbers to recognize them at night. This figure can be interpreted
the same as Figure 82. Notice that the luminous numbers can be recognized more
easily than the illuminated numbers, but that they require a smaller stroke width.
(After Berger, 1944)

overlooked. There are three reasons for following this rule: (1) Displays that are viewed at oblique angles are seen as distorted. (2)
Parallax errors occur when parts of the display are not in the same
plane. In order to counteract the parallax, high-precision meters have
scales backed with mirrors. The mirror helps the observer to locate
precisely the eye point that is exactly perpendicular to the scale. (3)
Letters and numbers are read most easily when they are viewed per-
pendicularly.

Data on the last point come from the study by Mackworth which
we mentioned a moment ago. In Figure 86 notice that Mackworth's
improved design of letters and numbers was consistently better than
the old design at all viewing distances and at all viewing angles. Notice, however, how the reading errors increase for both designs as the
viewing angle changes from 90 to 35 degrees. All the advantage of
the improved letter design is lost when the letters are seen at an angle

as small as this. The conclusion, therefore, is clear: We get best legibility when the display we are looking at is perpendicular to the line of sight.

Further research needed. The problem of legibility of single numbers and letters is by no means solved. We have just begun to make some progress in this direction. The results of the studies we have

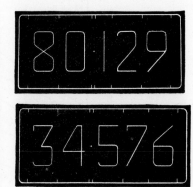

FIG. 84. The most legible kinds of numbers for day vision. (From C. Berger, Strokewidth, form and horizontal spacing of numerals as determinants of the threshold of recognition, *J. appl. Psychol.*, 1944, **28**, 208–231, 336–346)

FIG. 85. The most legible kinds of luminous numbers for night vision. (From C. Berger, Strokewidth, form and horizontal spacing of numerals as determinants of the threshold of recognition, *J. appl. Psychol.*, 1944, **28**, 208–231, 336–346)

been able to summarize are all too restricted in scope. They have not varied enough of the critical factors to enable us to emerge with some really basic generalizations. We need to have more basic studies, for example, in which the height of symbols is kept constant while the width and stroke width are varied in different combinations. It is possible that there are some important interactions here that we do not know about. It may be, for example, that one stroke width is best for a particular overall width of a letter but that another stroke width would be better for another overall width. None of the studies we mentioned tried varying the width of the letters or numbers.

We need to have more basic studies on the effects of things like emphasizing certain parts of letters or numbers. Most of the symbols that have been used so far have the same stroke width all over. Maybe the vertical lines need to be heavier than the horizontal ones.

Or vice versa. We need to have more research on the influence of "overhangs" on certain letters, like the B and D, and on the width of the white space in such letters as the C and G. And, finally, we

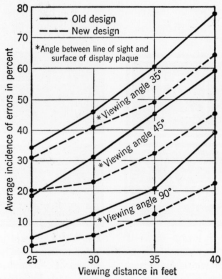

Fig. 86. These curves show how many errors are made in reading letters at different viewing distances and angles. The old and new designs are those shown in Figure 80. Notice that the new design gives consistently fewer errors but also that errors increase a great deal when we view the letters from the side instead of from the front. (After Mackworth, 1944)

need to have basic research on symbols other than letters and numbers, like arrows, dashes, plus marks, and so on. This is a big order. But until we have this information we will not be able to tell you how to design the best possible symbols for visual displays.

TABLES, GRAPHS, AND SCALES

In many man–machine systems, the operator must be able to get precise numerical data of various sorts. The flight engineer, bombardier, and navigator frequently need different mathematical functions in order to perform their flight duties. Engineers and inspectors in high-production manufacturing plants must also refer to numerical data frequently. Presentations of numerical functions constitute visual displays just as much as any of the other types of displays we have been discussing. And they constitute legitimate questions for our research men. Is a table better than a graph for presenting numerical data? What is the best design of graph or table to use? And so on.

THE DESIGN OF GRAPHS

The ruling of graphs. The first question we might ask about the design of graphs is: Does it make any difference how many lines we put on the graph? In Figure 87, for example, are two graphs of the equation, $Y = X^2/C$, where $C = 60, 70, 80, 90$, and 100 degrees. Although it is not essential for our understanding of the problem, we might explain that X represents indicated stress, Y indicates actual stress, and C represents various parameters of temperature in degrees centigrade. The graph on the top was drawn on 20 x 20-lines-to-the-inch graph paper. The graph on the bottom was drawn on 4 x 4-lines-to-the-inch paper.

Seventy subjects were asked to solve three different kinds of problems on these graphs. First, they had to solve problems in which the X and Y values fell exactly on one of the curves shown in the graph. The second type of problem required single interpolation: Either the X or the Y fell exactly on one of the curves, but the other value had to be interpolated. The third type of problem required a double interpolation: The subjects had to interpolate both for the X and Y between curves on the graph. The main result was to show that we can get information just as accurately from one graph as the other, but we can get it considerably faster from the graph with fewer rulings.

We can say, then, that a large number of rulings on a graph will not improve the speed and accuracy with which we can use it. It is interesting to note that this is pretty much the same kind of result we discovered when we studied dials. It looks as though too many lines or markers on a scale create more confusion than accuracy. If we have a few more studies like this, we may establish an important general principle.

Coordinates. Another question we can ask about the use of graphs is whether or not it makes any difference if the X of graphs is along the abscissa, that is, the bottom, or along the ordinate. Usually, you enter the graph with a number on the X axis, and read a number from the Y axis. Actually, experiments have shown that it makes no difference whether we read from the abscissa or the ordinate. We can get the information just as rapidly from the bottom or the side.

Bar graphs versus other kinds of graphs. In presenting the data of statistical analyses in financial reports, statisticians have a choice of several different kinds of graphs. They may use bar diagrams, cir-

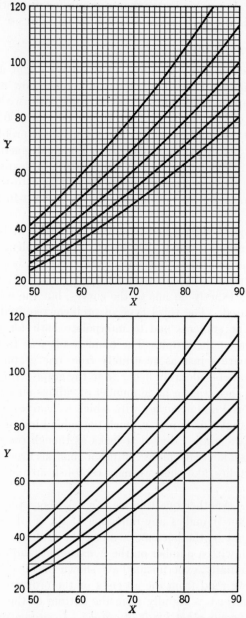

Fɪɢ. 87. These two graphs are exactly the same except that the one above has more rulings on it. The graph below allows us to read the curves faster than, and with just as much accuracy as, the graph above. (After Carter, 1946)

cles, squares, or cubes. These different possibilities are shown in Figure 88. Circles, squares, and cubes are frequently used because they look nicer and make a more interesting report. But, if we are interested in the accuracy with which we can read different kinds of statistical data, then the bar diagram is easiest and most accurate to interpret. Circles and squares are about equally suitable, but both are inferior to bars. Cubes are the worst of the lot. The reason is that

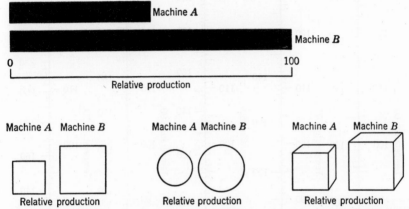

Fig. 88. These four methods of presenting data all tell the same thing: Machine *B* produced twice as much as machine *A*. Does the square, circle, or cube for machine *B* look twice as big as the one for machine *A*? Research shows that the bar diagram at the top is the best way of enabling us to see relative magnitudes accurately. (After Croxton and Stein, 1932)

we have a hard time judging the relative sizes of circles and squares. A circle which has half the area of another circle does not look as if it is one half as large. Of course, if you are the president of a large concern, and want to impress your stockholders with a nice-looking report, you may still want to use circles or squares, rather than bar diagrams. Bar diagrams do not look so pretty as circles or squares, even though they do present the data more accurately.

TABLES VERSUS GRAPHS VERSUS SCALES

Another question we might ask about the presentation of numerical data is this: Does it make any difference if we present the data in a graph or a table? Still a third possibility, shown in Figure 89, is to use a series of scales. How do the scales rate in comparison to the graph or table? The table, graph, and scales all present the same in-

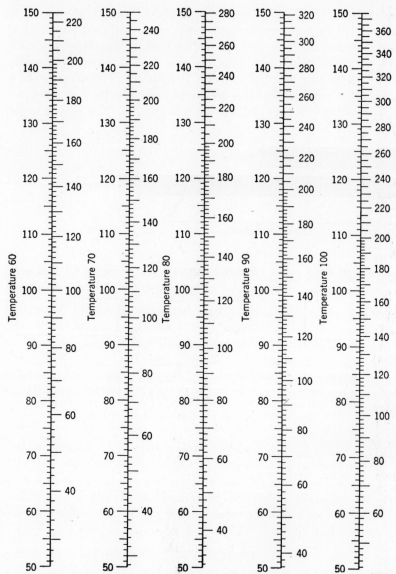

Fig. 89. This figure illustrates how curvilinear relations can be presented on scales. Each scale is for a different temperature as indicated. The numbers on the left side of the scales show the indicated stress, and the numbers on the right side show actual stress. (After Connell, 1947)

formation, and the question is: Which one enables us to get the information fastest and most accurately?

Tables and graphs. The results of research [5, 6, 8] on this problem are fairly clear-cut. The conclusion is that it is a lot better to use a table than a graph, providing we can get all of our data into the table. In general, a large table, even if it runs to several pages, is much better to use than a complicated graph with a large number of curves on it. This conclusion is valid *so long as the table contains all of the values that will be used in normal practice.* If, on the other hand, we have to make a large number of interpolations, the graph works better. If, for example, the temperatures come at odd numbers which do not appear or which cannot be tabulated in the table, then it is a lot more efficient to use the graphic type of presentation.

Scales. Likewise, scales are better than graphs if we do not have to interpolate. If we must interpolate between markings, then there is no difference between scales and graphs in terms of speed and accuracy. In such a case, whether or not we use a scale or graph must depend on other things such as the amount of space we have or the convenience of using one or the other. As a general rule, however, both scales and graphs are better than tables whenever we have to interpolate.

WARNING LIGHTS

In the last chapter, we talked about different functions that instruments serve. We pointed out that, in the simplest case, instruments present us with either–or information: Is something working, or isn't it? Everything is working fine, or wake up and do something. In presenting either–or information, we could have a light change its color, its position, its size, and so on. In one position, or with one color, the indicator would mean one thing; in the other position, it would mean something else. A much simpler arrangement, and in most cases a completely satisfactory one, is to have a light simply stay off for one kind of information, and go on for the other kind of information. Although we have labeled this section "warning lights," we are talking about the presentation of two-category information in general.

You might suppose that we would have a lot of useful information for telling us how to design the most effective warning light. Actually, this is not the case. We can point to only one very small study at the University of Maryland.[15]

The psychologist who did this study was interested in finding out what kind of a light would be most effective in attracting an operator's attention when the operator was doing something else. The operator, in this case, was required to work a complicated gadget used to select aviation cadets. From time to time, a light would go on in the edge of the subject's field of view. As soon as the operator spied the light, he had to flip a switch. There were three differently colored lights, red, green, and amber, located at 30, 45, and 60 degrees from the subject's line of sight. Experiments were done under both daylight and night conditions, with steady and flashing lights.

Results. First, it was found that subjects respond faster under night conditions than under day conditions. This is reasonable since there is a lot more contrast between lights and their backgrounds at night. And, as we saw in Chapter 4, speed of vision and brightness contrast are directly related.

The second finding was that red lights are more effective than green lights, and green lights, in turn, are more effective than amber lights. These differences hold up under both day and night conditions.

Third, lights in the 30-degree position are better than lights at 45 degrees, and lights in the 45-degree position are also better than those at 60 degrees. It looks as though the best warning light should be close to the central line of sight. This study, unfortunately, did not try any lights closer than 30 degrees, and so we are not sure that 30 degrees is the best position.

The final point of interest is that steady lights are more effective than flashing lights. At first glance, this seems to contradict a basic law of attention: moving or changing stimuli are more effective in getting our attention than steady stimuli. It is also generally known from psychological experiments that, if we use certain rates of flashing, we can make a light seem downright annoying. We must not feel, therefore, that the question of steady versus flashing lights has been completely answered. Perhaps with a more strenuous experiment, with the subjects very drowsy, and with the right kind of flashing light, this part of the experiment might have resulted differently.

Patterning of lights. When we were talking about dials in Chapter 5, we found that patterning could be useful in helping us size up a complex display rapidly. The same principle should also be helpful in using large groups of signal lights or warning lights.

The commander on a submarine has to be sure the sub is rigged for diving before he gives the command to "Take 'er down!" He has to be sure that the hatches are closed, that the Diesel engines are turned off, that the ballast tanks are just right, and so on. To help get this information to the commander, submarines are equipped with what is known as a submarine-hull-opening indicator board, more popularly termed the "Christmas tree." When the sub is lying on the surface with all hatches open, two strings of red lights are on at the control station. As each specific part of the job gets done, the red lights turn off, one by one, and green lights come on instead. The patterning is simple enough, the red lights are lined up in two rows, and the green lights are lined up underneath the red lights. When the ship is rigged for diving, the commander sees two rows of green lights and no red lights. A simple but apparently effective display system.

SUMMARY

It is a bit difficult to write a neat summary of a chapter as diverse as this one. Here we have discussed several different problems we find in various visual display systems. The displays themselves are so varied that there are few general principles we can cite—principles that cover all display problems. But, even though basic research in this area is definitely limited, we can still see that there are ways of handling problems of visual displays. We know that pictorial displays are sometimes better than symbolic displays. Some combinations of numbers on displays are better than others. Letters and numbers can be designed for best readability or legibility. And last, but not least, how good a warning light is depends on where we put it, what its color is, and whether it is flashing or steady. Even though we still need a lot of information, we can design visual displays in terms of the ability of the human operator who uses the display.

SELECTED REFERENCES

1. ADAMS, P. R. Analysis of realism as applied to display of air traffic navigation information. Federal Telecommunication Laboratories, Inc., 67 Broad St., New York 4, New York, Technical Memorandum No. 275, May 1947.
2. BARTLETT, N. R., REED, J. D., and DUVOISIN, G. Estimations of distance on polar coordinate plots as a function of the scale used. Systems Research, The Johns Hopkins University, Report No. 166–I–44, 20 April 1948.
3. BECK, C. S. Solution to the proplem of reversed sensing of directional indicators. United Air Lines, Inc., Engineering Department, Report No. R-169, 26 May 1947.
4. BERGER, C. Stroke-width, form and horizontal spacing of numerals as determinants of the threshold of recognition. *J. Appl. Psychol.*, 1944, **28**, 208–231, 336–346.

5. CARTER, L. F.   Relative effectiveness of presenting numerical data by the use of tables and graphs.   Aero Medical Laboratory, Air Materiel Command, Dayton, Ohio, Report No. TSEAA–694–1, 17 April 1946.

6. CARTER, L. F.   A study of the best design of tables and graphs used for presenting numerical data.   Aero Medical Laboratory, Air Materiel Command, Dayton, Ohio, Report No. TSEAA–694–1C, 24 September 1946.

7. CHAPANIS, A.   Accuracy of interpolation between scale markers as a function of scale interval number.   *Amer. Psychologist,* 1947, **2,** 346.

8. CONNELL, S. C.   The relative effectiveness of presenting numerical data by the use of scales and graphs.   Aero Medical Laboratory, Air Materiel Command, Dayton, Ohio, Report No. TSEAA–694–1M, 22 December 1947.

9. CROXTON, F. E., and STEIN, H.   Graphic comparisons by bars, squares, circles and cubes.   *J. Amer. Statist. Assoc.,* 1932, **27,** 54–60.

10. FORBES, T. W., and HOLMES, R. S.   Legibility distances of highway destination signs in relation to letter height, letter width, and reflectorization.   *Proc. Highway Res. Bd.,* 1939, **19,** 321–335.

11. GRETHER, W. F.   Discussion of pictorial versus symbolic aircraft instrument displays.   Aero Medical Laboratory, Air Materiel Command, Dayton, Ohio, Report No. TSEAA–694–8B, 4 August 1947.

12. LOUCKS, R. B.   An experimental evaluation of the interpretability of various types of aircraft attitude indicators.   In FITTS, P. M. (Ed.).   *Psychological research on equipment design.*   U. S. Government Printing Office, 1947, 111–135.

13. LUCKIESH, M., and MOSS, F. K.   *Reading as a visual task.*   New York: D. Van Nostrand, 1942.

14. MACKWORTH, N. H.   Legibility of raid block letters and numbers.   Psychological Laboratory, University of Cambridge, England, Flying Personnel Research Committee Report No. 423(s), April 1944.

15. MATHENY, W. G.   An evaluation of signal lights for use as warning devices.   Unpublished report, Psychology Department, University of Maryland.

16. PATERSON, D. G., and TINKER, M. A.   *How to make type readable.*   New York: Harper, 1940.

17. ROBINS, N. B.   Functional test of modified methods of directional gyro indication.   Air Proving Ground Command, Eglin Field, Florida, Project No. E4818, 5 September 1946.

18. UHLANER, J. E.   The effect of thickness of stroke on the legibility of letters.   *Proc. Ia. Acad. Sci.,* 1941, **48,** 319–324.

19. VERNON, M. D.   Scale and dial reading.   Medical Research Council Unit in Applied Psychology, University of Cambridge, England, Report No. APU 49, June 1946.

20. YULE, G. U.   On reading a scale.   *J. Roy. Statist. Soc.,* 1927, **90,** 570–587.

7. How We Hear

IN THE PRECEDING THREE CHAPTERS WE SAW HOW IMPORTANT OUR EYES are in telling us what goes on in the world. Our ears, however, are almost as important, because they make it possible for us to communicate with other people, for other people to communicate with us, and even for machines to communicate with us. If people are going to get along in this world, they must be able to hear each other and to act accordingly. Perhaps when we tell somebody else to do something, he will not want to act accordingly, but at least he will be able to if he wants to. The problems of communication, of what and how we hear, are our problems for this and the next two chapters.

WHAT IS SOUND?

If you ask the physicist what sound is, he will tell you that it consists of pressure waves in the air. Sound is physical energy. The psychologist, however, will tell you that it is what we hear. Sound is sensation. He will agree that most of the time we hear things because of the pressure waves in the air, but he will still insist that sound is what we hear. Who is right?

Both are really right, because the word sound has been used to mean both the physical energy and the sensation the physical energy causes when it hits our ears. Unfortunately we do not have two different words to mean these two clearly different things, and so we shall have to use the same word to mean both things just as everybody else does. But the distinction is important to keep in mind, because the sound sensations do not always change in the same way as the physical sounds do.

What Is Physical Sound?

We have all read about molecules, and we know that there are molecules of air that move and bounce around all the time and are not packed together very tightly. The movements of molecules are very small and random and not all in the same direction at the same time, so that the molecules are not packed together any more tightly at one place than at another.

Any object more solid than the air can push these molecules around or squeeze them together. If a solid object, such as a piece of metal, begins to vibrate, it will create changes in the density or pressure of the air which correspond to the movements of the vibrating object itself. As the object moves back and forth, the air pressure changes from higher to lower than that of air. When the air pressure is greater than the normal pressure, we speak of a positive pressure, and, when it is less than the normal pressure, we speak of a negative pressure. Thus the vibrating object creates alternations of positive and negative pressure.

These pressure variations move through the air at the speed of sound, about 760 miles per hour at sea level. The molecules of air themselves move very little from their original positions, since any particular molecule gets pulled back by the negative pressure almost as soon as it is pushed forward by the positive pressure. The only thing that really moves is the pressure wave itself.

When these pressure waves hit the eardrum, they cause the eardrum to move too. This movement in turn is transmitted into the inner parts of the ear and eventually determines what we hear. The eardrum, then, is constantly moving in and out whenever we hear a sound. How much it moves in and out determines how loud the sound is, and how fast it moves in and out determines the pitch of the sound. There are, then, two things we want to know about a sound. How fast do the changes in pressure occur (the frequency), and how great are the changes in pressure (the intensity)?

Frequency. How often does the vibrating object move back and forth? How many times in a second does the pressure in the air change? How frequently does the eardrum move in and out? These are all ways of asking what the frequency of the sound is.

Most vibrating objects move back and forth in a very regular manner. It takes just as long to move in one direction as in the opposite direction. Tuning forks have a very characteristic way of vibrating, just as a pendulum has a particular way of swinging back and forth. If *any* single vibrating object moves back and forth freely as a whole unit, the pressure in the air which this movement causes will change in a manner shown in Figure 90. The abscissa in Figure 90 represents time, and each of the pressure waves shown tells us how pressure changes in successive moments of time. When the line drawn is high, the pressure is great, and when the line is very low, pressure is very low and is more like a vacuum. The pressure changes fastest when it is near the normal pressure of the air and changes very slowly when it is either maximal or minimal.

These regular changes in pressure, which occur whenever we have only a single vibration, we call *sine waves*. The sound produced by such changes in pressure we call a *pure tone,* because it is generated by only a single vibration. The frequency of a pure tone is determined by the number of times the pressure changes from positive to negative in a given period of time. For convenience, we measure the number of changes of pressure occurring in a second. If, for example, the pressure changes from positive to negative and back to positive again 500 times in one second, we say that the frequency is 500 cycles per second, and we usually abbreviate this as *cps.* The two top sine waves shown in Figure 90 both have the same frequency, because they both go through the same number of complete cycles of pressure change in the same amount of time. The bottom sine wave, however, has a higher frequency, because it makes more complete cycles in the same period of time.

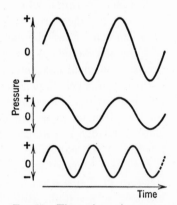

FIG. 90. These three sine waves represent the pressure changes in three pure tones. The top and middle sine waves represent tones of the same frequency but different intensities. The middle and bottom sine waves are for tones with the same intensity but different frequencies. The bottom sine wave has a higher frequency, since more complete cycles occur in the same time period.

Intensity. The other thing we need to know about a pure tone, or any sound, is its intensity. We can again ask how big the movement of the vibrating body is, how great are the changes of pressure in the air, or how far in and out does the eardrum move. These are all ways of asking about the intensity of the tone. All of these questions, you will see, ask about the amount of movement, or the amount of pressure. We are not now concerned with how many times the movement occurs, but only how big it is when it does occur.

Intensity, in Figure 90, is shown as the amplitude of the sine wave. The top and middle sine waves have the same frequency, but the intensity of the middle sine wave is less than that of the top sine wave.

The intensity of the middle and bottom sine waves, however, is the same even though the frequencies are different.

PSYCHOLOGICAL CHARACTERISTICS OF SOUND

Frequency and intensity, then, are two things we want to know about a pure, or sine-wave, tone. The frequency and intensity of a pure tone determine what we hear, but it is important to remember that they are measures of physical sound, not the sensation of sound. Even though we use the one word sound to mean both physical energy and the psychological sensation, we have different words to use for the psychological characteristics of a tone.

Pitch is a psychological term. It refers to the tonal quality, whether it is high or low. Frequency, the physical term, is largely responsible for the pitch we hear, but not altogether. A change in intensity can cause a change in pitch, even though the frequency is the same. We must, then, be careful to distinguish the two terms.

Loudness likewise is a psychological term. Loudness refers to the strength of a sensation, and loudness is determined primarily by the intensity of a sound. But just as a change in intensity can produce a change in pitch, so can a change in frequency produce a change in loudness. We shall see in just a moment how much change in loudness can be caused by a change in frequency. For now it is important to remember that pitch and loudness are psychological terms and that frequency and intensity are the important physical measurements to have.

THE MEASUREMENT OF PHYSICAL SOUND

Whenever a science becomes highly developed, the scientists make up many terms to refer to certain things. These terms are often so much Greek to anyone who has not specialized in that particular science. These specialized terms crop up because it is convenient to have a common terminology and to have measures which everybody will agree mean the same thing. It is almost impossible to learn much about a new science without at least becoming familiar with many of these specialized terms, and so in this section on the measurement of sound we will discuss some of these terms.

INTENSITY

Sensitivity of the ear. The human ear is a very sensitive instrument. It can hear sounds that are so weak that it is almost impossible to distinguish them from the random movements of the air molecules themselves. In fact, if the ear were any more sensitive, we would hear these random movements all the time, and this could become quite annoying. When the ear is stimulated with the faintest tone that can be heard, the movement of the eardrum is too small to see even under a microscope.

Even though we can hear such very faint sounds, we also can hear sounds that are many many times as intense. In fact, some of the sounds we hear have an intensity 10,000,000,000,000 times as great as the intensity of the weakest sound we can hear. This is a tremendous range of sound intensities. Also, the numbers we use to measure such a range of intensities would get either very large, or very small, unless we used some special number scale to measure intensities. Such a special number system is used for measuring sound intensities.

The decibel. Sound intensity is measured in decibels, which is a term coming into greater and greater popular use. Actually, the *bel* is the unit of measurement, and the *deci*bel is simply one tenth of a bel. The bel is named after the famous inventor of the telephone, Alexander Graham Bell.

The decibel, usually abbreviated *db*, is not like most units of measurement, because it is a ratio measure. But for most practical purposes, the decibel can be thought of just as we think of most measures: It is a number that indicates a certain intensity of sound, and, the higher the number, the more intense is the sound. The numbers go from 0 to about 130, depending a little on where the decibel is used.

Mathematically speaking, the bel (ten decibels) is the logarithm of the ratio of two intensities. For example, one bel means that one intensity is ten times another intensity, since the logarithm of 10 is 1. If the ratio of intensities is 100, then the number of bels is two. Since there are 10 decibels in 1 bel, in these two cases we would have 10 and 20 decibels. And, if the ratio of two intensities is 1,000,000,000,000 to 1, then the number of decibels is 120. The number of decibels tells us how many zeros there are in the ratio number.

There is one unfortunate complication of the decibel scale which is not too serious here. Decibels are defined in terms of energy, whereas many of our measurements are actually made in terms of pressure. Since energy increases as the square of pressure, we have to make a correction if we want to convert from pressure measurements to the decibel scale. This is very simple with logarithms, since a squared term simply means multiplying by 2. Thus if the ratio of two *pressures* is 10 to 1, the number of decibels is now 20, instead of 10.

The rule, then, is very simple. If we have a ratio of energies, the logarithm of the ratio is the number of bels. Ten times that number is the number of decibels. If we have a ratio of pressures, we multiply the logarithm of the ratio by 2 to get the number of bels, and again by 10 to get the number of decibels.

Intensity level. In order to provide decibels with an absolute meaning, engineers have agreed to use a common reference intensity, a common anchor. That reference is 0.0002 dyne per square centimeter of pressure, which is equivalent to 10^{-16} watts per square centimeter of energy. *Now* when we say that we have 40 db of sound, we mean that our intensity is 40 db greater than this reference intensity. We have thus provided the numbers with some absolute meaning.

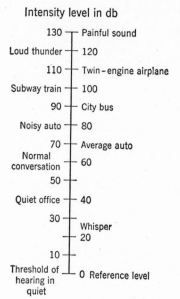

When the decibel scale is used with this reference, we say we are measuring *intensity level* to indicate that we are using this common reference. Sometimes, when measurements of pressure are made, we use the term *sound-pressure level* (SPL). It makes no difference whether we measure energy or pressure when we use the decibel scale, and for all practical purposes intensity level and sound-pressure level are the same thing.

Fig. 91. Illustrations of the intensity levels of various familiar sounds.

The reference energy or pressure used for intensity level measures is, by the way, just about the minimum intensity the ear can hear under ideally quiet conditions. This is very convenient, for we know that an intensity level of 0 db is the lowest intensity that can ever be heard, under any conditions.

Other examples of intensity levels are shown in Figure 91. A whisper has an intensity level of about 25 db; normal conversations are between 50 and 70 db. The average automobile produces about 70 db of noise, whereas a heavy city bus makes about 90 db. A subway train roaring into a station has an intensity level of 100 db, and a twin-engined airplane about 110. When intensity levels reach 130 db, the sounds are definitely painful. Fortunately, we do not often listen to sounds as intense as that.

Sensation level. The intensity level measures use a common physical anchor for the decibel scale. Sometimes psychologists and sound engineers use the ear as a reference point or anchor. When they do this they use the term *sensation level*, rather than intensity level, to distinguish the two uses of the decibel scale. When sensation levels are used, the number of decibels tells how much more intense the sound is than the weakest sound that can just be heard. The main difficulty with this measurement is that the sound that can just be heard varies a great deal, depending on the frequency of the sound, the amount of noise around, and so on.

COMPLEX SOUNDS

As we have pointed out, the frequency of a pure tone is measured in cycles per second. Most sounds that we hear, however, are not pure tones. Usually we hear many pure tones all at once, and these many pure tones can be different in both frequency and intensity. If we hear only a few pure tones, and these tones are octaves apart, we would still describe the sound as a tone. But, if we have a great many pure tones all mixed together, without any consistent relation between them, we would call the sound a noise. The main difference between noises and tones is only that noise consists of more pure tones all sounding at once. We can, however, describe *any* sound by describing the frequencies and intensities of all the pure tones that make up the sound.

Complex tones. When a sound is a tone, but not a pure tone, we call it a complex tone. Complex tones consist of several pure tones, and the pure tones have frequencies that are all some multiple of the lowest frequency. This lowest frequency we call the fundamental or first harmonic. The other frequencies are all harmonics.

Figure 92 shows the intensities of the various pure tones that add together to make the one complex tone we hear when a violin is played. The lowest frequency (the fundamental) is 400 cycles per second, and the other frequencies are 800, 1,200, 1,600, 2,000, 2,400, and 2,800 cycles per second. All these other frequencies are some multiple of the lowest frequency. The 800-cycle-per-second tone is the second harmonic, the 1,200 tone the third harmonic, and so on. Notice that all the tones do not have the same intensity. Changes in the intensities of these pure tones would make the complex tone sound quite different.

When a complex tone is described in this way, we call the graph a *spectrum analysis* because we have broken the complex tone into the various frequencies that make it up.

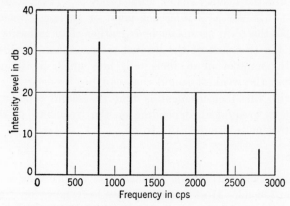

Fig. 92. A spectrum analysis of a tone from a musical instrument. Each solid line shows the intensity of one particular frequency component. A spectrum like this would be obtained from a violin playing a note at 400 cps.

Noises. Many of the sounds we hear in everyday life are not tones, pure or complex, but just plain noises. Any particular noise can be

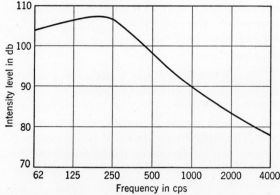

Fig. 93. A spectrum analysis of airplane noise. This curve shows the intensity of the many frequencies involved and is the average of several measured airplane noises. In this type of spectrum analysis so many different tones are involved that it is impossible to show the intensity of each separate tone.

described with a spectrum analysis in the same way a complex tone can, and one such noise is shown in Figure 93. Most noises have so many pure tones in them that we cannot distinguish each separate frequency. As a result, the spectrum of a noise is a continuous line that connects all frequencies together. If the line in Figure 93 were perfectly flat, then all frequencies would have the same amount of energy. We call such noise *white noise,* because it is analogous to white light, and these noises sound more like a hiss than anything else. The noise an air jet makes is a good example of a noise with a flat spectrum.

PSYCHOLOGICAL ASPECTS OF SOUND

Psychophysics of sound. Most of the psychological problems of sound are really problems in psychophysics. Psychophysics asks about the relation between the physical world and the psychological world. How does the audibility of a sound depend on its frequency? How does pitch change with frequency and with intensity? Does a given increase in intensity cause the same increase in the loudness of a tone? How is our ability to hear a difference between two tones related to the frequency and intensity of the tones? All these questions and many more will be asked as we discuss the psychological problems of sound.

FREQUENCY LIMITS OF AUDIBLE TONES

Some tones have a frequency so high that we cannot hear them, regardless of the intensity. Other tones have such a low frequency that they do not sound like tones, but like slow vibrations. The lowest frequency that sounds like a tone is about 20 cycles per second. The highest frequency that can be heard by humans is about 20,000 cycles per second, although this upper limit varies considerably for many people. In general, older people cannot hear high tones so well as younger people, and most adults have difficulty hearing any tone above 12,000 to 15,000 cycles per second. Also, deafness usually affects our ability to hear high tones more than our ability to hear low tones.

Animals are known to have much better hearing at high frequencies than humans. Dogs, cats, and rats can all hear tones that are completely inaudible to humans. That is why we can call dogs with whistles that no human being can hear.

Although not many adults can hear tones as high as 20,000 cycles per second, we generally refer to frequencies between 20 and 20,000 cycles per second as the range of audible frequencies. The term *audio* frequency is used to distinguish them from those frequencies that are physically the same but cannot be heard as tones.

THRESHOLD SENSITIVITY

Even within the range of audio frequencies, all frequencies are not equally audible. Some can be heard at a much lower intensity than others. The ear is most sensitive to frequencies between about 500 and 4,000 cycles per second, and frequencies both above and below these limits must be more intense if we are to hear them. It is fortunate that the ear is most sensitive to those frequencies that are most important in our understanding speech, but we shall deal more with that problem in the next chapter.

The sensitivity of the ear to various frequencies is shown by the lowest curve in Figure 94, which shows how intense a tone has to be so that you can just hear it. You can hear a tone of 1,000 cycles per second when its intensity level is very close to zero, but a tone of 100 cycles per second has to have an intensity level of about 40 db before you can hear it at all. As the frequency gets lower, the just audible intensity increases even more. The same kind of increase occurs for tones above 4,000 cycles per second.

The lowest curve in Figure 94, then, tells us about one type of psychophysical relation: All the tones on that curve are just barely audible. If the intensity of any one of those tones were decreased, we would not be able to hear it any more. But this curve also tells us something more, because, if all tones are just audible, then every tone is just as loud as every other tone.

EQUAL-LOUDNESS RELATIONS

We would like to know more than this. What would happen, for example, if all tones in the lowest curve had their intensities increased by 10 db? Would each tone then be just as loud as every other tone, or would some now be louder than others? And likewise what would happen if all tones had their intensities increased by 40 or 80 db? Would all these tones then be equally loud?

Long ago it was assumed that they would be, but later people interested in these problems decided to find out if it were really so.[3] They did an experiment. First they increased the intensity of a 1,000-cycle-per-second tone by various amounts: 10, 20, 30, and on up to 120 db. They asked many people to listen first to the 1,000-cycle-per-second tone, and then to a tone of some other frequency. Then they adjusted the intensity of the other frequency until that tone was just as loud as the 1,000-cycle-per-second tone. What they found is shown by the curves in Figure 94.

All the tones on each curve are equally loud: Each tone is just as loud as every other tone, but no louder. For example, on the curve marked "20" (the intensity level of the 1,000-cycle-per-second tone), a tone with a frequency of 1,000 cycles per second and an intensity

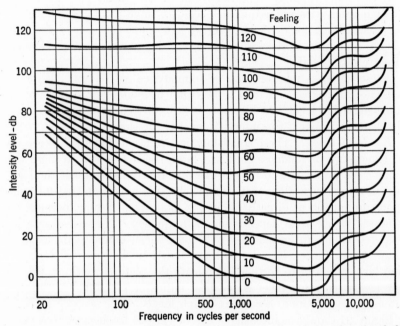

FIG. 94. Equal-loudness relations. The bottom curve shows the threshold intensity levels of the various frequencies. Each tone on that curve is just barely audible, and we can assume that all those tones have the same loudness. The other curves show tones that are just as loud as each other at higher intensity levels; all the tones on any one curve have the same loudness. The number on each curve is the intensity level of the 1,000-cps tone, and that number is used to indicate the *loudness level* of any tone that is on that particular curve. Notice that the curves flatten out at higher intensities, telling us that all tones tend to have the same loudness at high intensities if they have the same intensity. (From Fletcher and Munson, 1933)

level of 20 db is as loud as a tone of 100 cycles per second with an intensity level of 51 db. And on the curve marked "60," a tone with a frequency of 2,000 cycles per second and an intensity level of 60 db is as loud as a 200-cycle-per-second tone with an intensity level of 65 db. Any two points falling on the same curve represent tones that are just as loud as each other.

These curves are the answer to our question. If we add the same intensity to two tones that are as loud as each other at threshold, these two tones will no longer be equally loud. At some frequencies, loudness increases much faster than at other frequencies. In general, the frequencies to which the ear is the least sensitive increase in loudness most rapidly. The net result of this faster increase is that at high intensities all frequencies seem to have the same loudness if their intensities are the same. As we saw, some frequencies are completely inaudible at the same low intensities at which other frequencies are quite loud.

These loudness relations can be summarized as follows: At low intensities, all frequencies tend to be equal in loudness if they have the same sensation level. At high intensities, all frequencies tend to have the same loudness if the intensity level is the same.

Loudness levels. These equal-loudness relations have led to the use of a measure of loudness that has lately been resorted to more and more. We would like to have a measure that tells us about the loudness of a tone regardless of its frequency. We have seen that intensity levels do not tell us directly about the loudness of a tone, because the loudness of the tone depends on its frequency. Nor does sensation level tell us about the loudness of a tone, because here again we must know the frequency in order to know how loud any particular sensation level is. And to further complicate the picture, we know that at low levels sensation level is the best indicator of loudness, although intensity level is more accurate at high levels.

Figure 94 shows the intensity levels of various frequencies that make all tones equally loud. If we give the same number to all tones that are as loud as each other, then we have a single measure which indicates the loudness of a tone, and we no longer have to worry about what frequency the tone is. For the sake of convenience, the numbers we use to do this are the intensity levels of the 1,000-cycle-per-second tone. Those are the numbers marked on the various curves in Figure 94, and all the tones on any one curve have a *loudness level* indicated by that number. For example, all the tones on the curve marked "40" have a loudness level of 40 db, and all the tones on the curve marked "80" have a loudness level of 80 db.

The loudness level of any tone, then, is the intensity level of a 1,000-cycle-per-second tone that is just as loud as the tone in question. When we use loudness-level measures, we no longer have to specify the frequency if we are concerned solely with the loudness of the tone. In practice, if we know the intensity level and the frequency of a tone, we can determine its loudness level by reading it from the curves in Figure 94. Or, if the facilities are available, the loudness of a 1,000-cycle-per-second tone can be matched directly to the tone in question, and the loudness level of the tone would then be the intensity level of the 1,000-cycle-per-second tone.

In order to distinguish this measure from the other measures of loudness and intensity, the term *phon* is frequently used. We say, for example, that a tone has a loudness of 40 phons, which means that the tone is just as loud as a 1,000-cycle-per-second tone with an intensity level of 40 db.

THE LOUDNESS FUNCTION

Equal-loudness relations are one step in the measurement of the psychological rather than the physical aspects of a tone. These relations tell us which tones have the same loudness. But they do not tell us whether one tone is twice as loud, or half as loud, as another tone. Nor do they tell us if the difference in loudness between a loudness level of 20 and 40 phons is equal to the difference in loudness between loudness levels of 80 and 100 phons. It has been possible to build a loudness function that tells us just how the psychological loudness changes with loudness level, but another experiment was necessary to do it.[3]

Observers were asked to listen to tones, one tone following the other. One of the tones had a fixed loudness level, and the observer himself could change the loudness level of the second tone. He was asked to adjust the loudness of the second tone until it sounded twice as loud, or half as loud, as the tone with the fixed loudness level. After many judgments like this were made, at many different loudness levels, it was possible to construct the loudness function, which is shown in Figure 95. The units of loudness are arbitrary, but we can see from this figure how loudness increases when we increase the loudness level.

At low loudness levels, loudness increases just as much as loudness level increases: there is a one-to-one relation between them. As loudness level gets greater and greater, however, the change in loudness is much less than the change in loudness level. Regardless of the loudness level, the relative loudness of any two tones can be determined from Figure 95. If the number for the loudness of one tone is twice as great as the number for the loudness of the second tone, then the first tone is twice as loud as the second tone.

If we want to determine the loudness of any tone of a given frequency and intensity level, we first look up the loudness level in Figure 94, and then the loudness of that loudness level in Figure 95. If we have two such tones, we can determine the relation between the loudnesses of the tones. Remember, however, that Figure 95 shows the logarithm of loudness. The logarithm must be converted to a real number to determine relative loudnesses.

The particular units of loudness we choose to use can be, of course, completely arbitrary. It has been suggested, however, that a loudness level of 40 db be chosen as the unit of loudness, and that this unit be

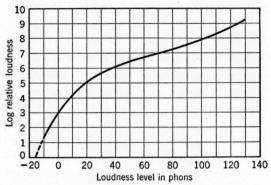

Fig. 95. This curve shows how loudness increases with an increase in loudness level. If the loudness level of any tone is known, its loudness can be determined from this curve. Loudness is plotted logarithmically here, and so the antilogarithm of the numbers shown here must be used to determine actual loudness. The term *sone* has been used as the unit of loudness, where one sone is the loudness of a tone with a loudness level of 40 db.

called a *sone*.[6] Thus, a tone with a loudness level of 40 db would have a loudness of 1 sone, and a tone twice as loud would have a loudness of 2 sones. We mention this particular terminology because it will probably become more common in the future.

MASKING

It is all well and good to know what we can hear in a nice quiet room in the laboratory. But that tells us very little about what we ordinarily hear. How well we can hear in everyday life depends very much on where we are. We can hear a very quiet whisper if we are 10 miles out in the woods, but we could not hear that same whisper if we were in a noisy night club. There is far too much noise in most night clubs for us to hear anything less than a good healthy shout. Noises can make it hard for us to hear. And tones can also make it hard for us to hear, as you know if you have ever tried to carry on a conversation next to a fire siren.

How well we can hear depends on the amount of noise and the kind of noise we have to listen to. And it also depends on what we are trying to listen to. In order to study these effects systematically, much laboratory work has been done to determine just what kinds of tones and noises make it hardest for us to hear certain other kinds of tones and noises.

The effect of one tone or noise on our ability to hear another tone or noise we call *masking*. By masking we mean that the presence of certain noises makes it hard or impossible to hear other noises, just as a mask on a woman's face makes it impossible to see her face. And in order to keep straight which tone or noise we want to hear and which we do not want to hear, we use two different terms. The signal we do *not* want to hear is the *masking signal;* it is what prevents our hearing something we want to hear. The signal we *want* to hear we call the *masked signal;* it is the one that the masking signal prevents our hearing.

Once again, to understand best the nature of the masking process, we determine first of all the effect of certain tones and noises on our ability to hear pure tones. We shall discuss first how pure tones mask other pure tones and then how noise masks pure tones.

Masking by pure tones. There are two ways to measure masking effects. One is to determine the threshold under the masking conditions in terms of intensity level—just as we measure the absolute threshold in intensity level. The other is to determine how much the threshold was increased by introducing the masking signal. If, for example, the threshold in quiet is 20 db, and the threshold in the presence of the masking signal is 80 db, we know that the threshold has been increased 60 db. The amount of masking produced is then 60 db. This latter method is more common in measures of masking.

The two graphs in Figure 96 show masking effects in these terms. Figure 96A shows how a pure tone of 400 cycles per second affects our ability to hear other pure tones.[2] The numbers on the different curves are the sensation levels of the masking tone. With a sensation level of 100 db, the 400-cycle-per-second tone makes many other pure tones much harder to hear, and even a 4,000-cycle-per-second tone has to be 70 db more intense in order for us to hear it. At lower sensation levels, the masking effect covers a narrower range of frequencies.

Figure 96B shows how much masking a pure tone of 3,500 cycles per second can produce on other pure tones. Here again, the 3,500-cycle-per-second tone at a sensation level of 100 db makes frequencies near

3,500 cycles per second hardest to hear. But the masking effect of this tone on low frequency tones is very small.

That difference between the effect of low tones and of high tones on other frequencies is the most important point to remember about the masking of pure tones on pure tones. *Low frequencies make high frequencies very hard to hear, but high frequencies have very little effect on low frequencies.* If we want to listen to low tones, high ones will

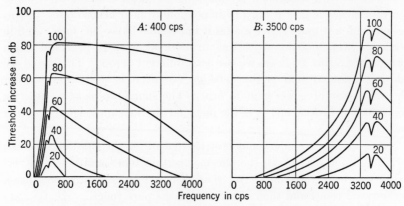

Fɪɢ. 96. This figure shows how one pure tone makes other pure tones harder to hear. In *A*, the *masking* tone is 400 cps; in *B* it is 3,500 cps. The sensation level of the masking tone is shown for each curve, and the ordinate tells how much the intensity of the different frequencies has to be raised in order for the tone still to be heard. Notice that the 400-cps tone makes other tones much harder to hear than the 3,500-cps tone. (After Fletcher, 1929)

not bother us. But if we want to listen to high tones, low ones will bother us. And if we want to prevent somebody else from hearing any tones, low tones are more useful than high tones.

Masking by noise. In most situations, however, it is not the tones that bother us, but noise. What happens to our ability to hear tones when there is a lot of noise in the background?

Figure 97 shows how our threshold for pure tones increases as more and more noise is introduced into the listener's background.[4] The noise used in these experiments was a hiss—white noise. It had energy at all frequencies from 0 to 10,000 cycles per second, and in equal amounts. That is to say, there was no more noise at the low frequencies than at the high frequencies, or vice versa.

When there is a small amount of noise present, the threshold curve for pure tones still looks much like the quiet threshold curve shown in Figure 94. Tones in the middle frequencies are heard most easily, and tones at higher or lower frequencies must be more intense if we are to hear them at all. Even with as little as 40 db of noise, however, the high frequencies do not require as much intensity as when there is no noise. With greater amounts of noise, the threshold curve flattens out until at 100 db of noise the low frequencies can be heard slightly better than the high frequencies. In general, then, the threshold curve for pure tones tends to be flat when there is a lot of noise in the back-

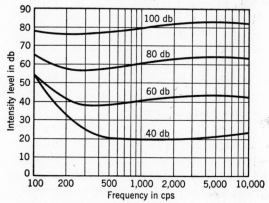

FIG. 97. These curves show how noise makes pure tones harder to hear. The threshold intensity level of the pure tone is shown on the ordinate for the various frequencies indicated on the abscissa. Each curve is for a different intensity level of the noise as indicated, and the noise had equal energy at all frequencies up to 10,000 cps. Notice that all tones are nearly as audible as other tones at high levels of masking noise. (After Hawkins, 1945)

ground, although when there is no noise both high and low tones need a lot more intensity than the middle frequency tones if they are to be heard.

You probably have noticed that these curves are very similar to the equal-loudness relations shown in Figure 94. That similarity is important. As intensity is increased, all tones tend to have the same loudness, regardless of their frequency. And all tones tend to have the same threshold as the tones become more intense, again regardless of the frequency. It would seem, then, that all tones act pretty much alike at high intensities, although at very low intensities the ear can detect some frequencies much more easily than it can others.

These masked threshold relations do not change the nature of the equal-loudness relations. The intensity of the tone, whether or not it is masked, primarily determines the shape of the equal-loudness curve. In fact, as we can see from Figure 97, the masking curve for 100 db of noise shows that tones of all frequencies are just as loud as one another, because they can all just be heard at approximately the same intensity. The equal-loudness curves show that they are just as loud as one another whether or not there is any masking noise in the background.

How Sounds Have Meaning

Sound and our sense of hearing are a means of communication among various persons, or between a machine and a person. We are interested in the psychology of hearing only because different sounds can tell us different things. When we use speech, many different meanings and ideas are conveyed from one person to another. The chime of the clock at midnight tells us what time it is. Morse code is another means of transmitting information from one person at one place to another person some distance away.

It is in our interest, then, to ask how sounds can transmit information, whether the information be words, ideas, directions, or the time. If we know what it is about sounds that have meaning, then we can decide what kinds of instruments are needed to convey the information correctly. All instruments, particularly electronic instruments, do not give a perfect reproduction of the sound wave. We would like to know what aspects of the sound wave must be preserved and what aspects of it may be destroyed without destroying the meaning in the sound.

There are many aspects of a sound that can produce meaning. We have already seen that sounds can be different in intensity, frequency, and frequency spectrum. That is to say, the mixtures of various pure tones can be different for different sounds. There are other ways in which sounds can be different. The chime of a clock, for instance, tells us the time because a certain *number* of tones means a certain time. Some clocks also make use of our ability to hear differences in pitch. The quarter-hour, as an example, may give one pattern of pitches, whereas the half-hour has another pattern. These differences in pitch pattern tell us whether it is quarter-past the hour, or half-past the hour. Sometimes the rhythm of a sound conveys information, although we do not usually depend on rhythm except in music.

The change of sounds. Pure tones, heard in isolation, have very little meaning. A pure tone of 1,000 cycles per second, at an intensity level of 70 db, does not have an absolute meaning, the way the number "7" printed on a sheet of paper has. It is very hard for us to tell one tone from another, and it would be almost impossible for us to know that a 1,000-cycle-per-second tone means one thing and a 1,500-cycle-per-second tone another thing. We probably could not tell one tone from the other anyway, unless they were heard in succession. Then we would know whether the first or the second tone was higher in pitch. We have the same sort of problem with intensity. It is very hard for us to identify the absolute intensity of a tone (without physical instruments), although it is relatively easy to know that one tone is louder than another.

In order for tones to have meaning, then, there must be at least two tones so that one can be compared to the other. We must, in other words, have an anchor or reference tone. The reference tone need not be always the same; if many tones are heard in succession, each tone can be the reference for the next one. Tones can change, as we have mentioned, in intensity, frequency, or spectral composition. As these changes occur, through a period of time, meaning is produced. Music is understood, for example, not by the absolute pitch and loudness of the tones heard, but rather by the changing frequency and intensity which gives us a pattern we can understand. In speech it is not the pitch of a voice that makes words intelligible but rather the changing frequency and intensity pattern over a period of time.

What we recognize, then, and what provides meaning is the changing pattern of frequency, intensity, and spectral composition during a period of time. Occasionally we recognize the time sequence itself, but not very often. If what we recognize is the change in frequency and intensity (changes in spectral composition are really combined frequency and intensity changes), then we need to know how well the ear can detect these changes. We have already discussed how well the ear hears tones in the quiet and in noise. Now we are concerned with how well the ear can distinguish one tone from another—either in intensity or frequency.

Changes in intensity. Figure 98 shows how much difference in intensity two tones must have if we are to hear them as two different tones. The difference in intensity is not the same for all tones. The abscissa of the graph shows the intensity of the tone (really sensation level), and each curve in the graph is for a different frequency. The ordinate scale (on the left) shows how much greater in intensity level one tone must be if it is to be heard as louder than another tone. The scale on the right shows the increase as a ratio of intensities. Both scales are equivalent since decibels are a ratio measure.

As intensity is increased the difference in intensity between two tones can be decreased, if we are to hear the tones as different. For example, a tone of 1,000 cycles per second at 20 db must be increased by 1½ db before the difference will be noticed. If two tones were compared and one was only 1 db more intense than the other, then they would sound equal in loudness. If the difference were 2 db, then it would be clearly heard. At higher intensities, however, differences as small as ⅓ db can be heard.

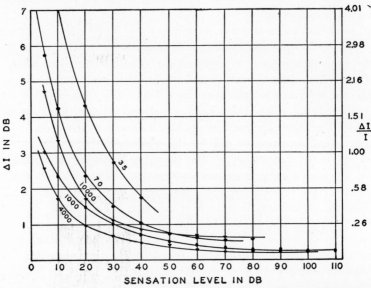

Fig. 98. These curves show how much the intensity of a tone must be increased in order for us to hear the increase. Each curve is for a different frequency as indicated. The scale on the left shows the necessary increase in decibels; the one on the right shows the increase as a ratio of the two intensities. (Reproduced by permission from *Hearing* by S. S. Stevens and H. Davis, published by John Wiley & Sons. 1938)

How easily we can hear differences in intensity depends on the frequency of the tone. In the middle range of frequencies we can hear differences much better than at high and low frequencies. This is the same range of frequencies that we can hear best at threshold as well.

We should point out that the sensitivities shown in Figure 98 are really the best sensitivities. These measures were obtained in a sound-deadened room in a laboratory where listening conditions were best. Under noisier and more distracting conditions, slightly larger differences would be necessary. At higher intensity levels and in the middle range of frequencies, we usually can hear about a 1-db change in intensity. In fact, the decibel unit was chosen because it is a fairly good approximation to the least change in intensity that can be noticed.

Changes in frequency. Figure 99 shows how well we can hear changes in frequency. The ordinate scale shows the least perceptible change in frequency divided by the frequency itself. In other words,

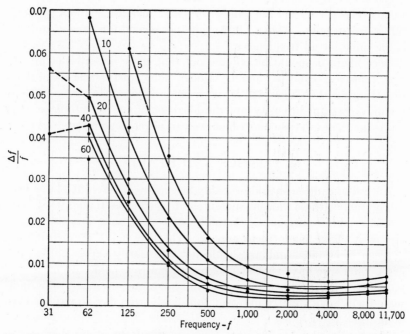

FIG. 99. These curves show how much the frequency of a tone must be increased in order for us to hear the increase. Each curve is for a different sensation level as indicated. The ordinate scale shows the necessary increase as a percentage of the frequency shown on the abscissa. (After Shower and Biddulph, 1931)

the ordinate scale shows the lease percentage change in frequency that can be detected by the ear.

The abscissa scale shows frequency, and once again we see that sensitivity is dependent on frequency. We can hear changes in frequency best in the middle and upper ranges. Each curve is for a different intensity, and it is obvious that we can hear differences in frequency better at the higher sensation levels. Above approximately 40-db sensation level, however, intensity has relatively little effect.

Above about 1,000 cycles per second frequency has little effect on our ability to hear differences in frequency, if these differences are measured as percentages. Below 1,000 cycles per second, however, the percent difference in frequency rises very rapidly. At 500 cycles per second the percent change is (for 40 db) 0.5, which is 2.5 cycles. At 250 cycles per second the percent change is 1.0, which is again 2.5 cycles. At 125 cycles per second, the cycles change is 3.2, and at 62 cycles per second the cycles change is 2.7 cycles. So we see that below 1,000 cycles per second the *number of cycles* increase is about the same for all frequencies. Above 1,000 cycles per second the *percent* increase is the same for all frequencies.

Once again it should be pointed out that these sensitivities are the best that will ever be found. Under noisy distracting conditions, slightly greater changes will be necessary. These measures and those for differences in intensity are the ideal maximum sensitivities; they represent the limits beyond which we can never hope to go.

STATISTICS AND HEARING

A word of caution should probably be expressed here. We have been talking about these various measures of hearing as though they were absolute precise measures. Actually, of course, they are not so precise as we have made them appear. The thresholds we mention are *average* thresholds, and we should not necessarily expect to find the exact values we have shown if we measure a threshold only once. All individuals do not have the same threshold, and even the same individual will have slightly different thresholds from day to day, or even before and after lunch.

Absolute thresholds for pure tones, particularly at the higher frequencies, will vary greatly between individuals. One individual may hear tones as much as 15 db weaker than tones that another individual can just hear, even though both individuals can be considered normal. Masked thresholds, on the other hand, are much more consistent, and most individuals will have essentially the same threshold here. You should remember, however, that even though we do not keep mentioning the statistical problems of measurement in hearing, the problems are still here. We can never ignore the statistics that were discussed in Chapters 2 and 3.

SUMMARY

In this chapter we have seen that all physical sounds can be described by describing the intensities and the frequencies of the various pure tones that make up the sound. Intensities are usually measured in decibels, and frequencies in cycles per second. The ear can hear tones in the middle range of frequencies more easily than higher or lower frequencies, and these middle frequencies are louder except at very high intensities. Equal-loudness relations tell us whether any two tones are as loud as each other, and the psychological loudness function tells us about the relative loudness of any two tones: which one is louder and how much louder.

Hearing provides us with a means of communication because we can hear relative differences between tones and because tones can change through time. There are, however, certain minimal limits of change which can be detected, and these limits in a sense determine the maximal precision for communication. The next problem is to see how these characteristics of the ear and hearing affect communication and particularly how they affect the design of communications equipment.

SELECTED REFERENCES

1. DAVIS, H. (Ed.). *Hearing and deafness.* New York: Murray Hill Books, 1947.
2. FLETCHER, H. *Speech and hearing.* New York: Van Nostrand, 1929.
3. FLETCHER, H., and MUNSON, W. A. Loudness, its definition, measurement, and calculation. *J. Acoust. Soc. Amer.,* 1933, **5**, 91–108.
4. HAWKINS, J. E. Masking of pure tones and of speech by white noise. Part I in: The masking of signals by noise. Psycho-Acoustic Laboratory, Harvard University, OSRD Report No. 5387, 1 October 1945. (Available through the Publications Board, U. S. Department of Commerce, Washington, D. C.)
5. SHOWER, E. G., and BIDDULPH, R. Differential pitch sensitivity of the ear. *J. Acoust. Soc. Amer.,* 1931, **3**, 275–287.
6. STEVENS, S. S. A scale for the measurement of a psychological magnitude: Loudness. *Psychol. Rev.,* 1936, **43**, 405–416.
7. STEVENS, S. S., and DAVIS, H. *Hearing.* New York: John Wiley, 1938.

8. *Speech*

MANY SOUNDS MEAN SOMETHING TO US, AND DIFFERENT SOUNDS MEAN different things. But the variety of sounds produced by our vocal cords gives us more different meanings than all other sounds put together. In fact, there is a vocal sound, or combination of sounds, to use for any idea known to man. The really interesting thing about speech is not so much that we can produce so many different sounds, but rather that we can hear and understand them.

Speech as communication. Our civilization is a wordy civilization, and for good reason. Some human activities happen without verbal communication, but speech seems to get involved in most situations. Speech lets one person in one place know about another person somewhere else—what the other is doing, saying, and thinking. Information is transmitted, and the nature of the speech sounds make the vocal noises have meaning.

How we look at the problems of speech. There are many ways of looking at the psychological problems of speech and speech transmission. You can judge speech, or any communications device, from an aesthetic or utilitarian point of view. If you are buying a phonograph so you can listen to Fats Waller or Lily Pons, you choose on the basis of quality of tone; you do not like it if Lily Pons comes out sounding like Fats Waller, or vice versa. But if you are selecting an intercom system for use in an office, or a radio for directing aircraft, you ask the very practical question: How well does it work? You do not care about the prettiness of the sound; you are interested solely in the ability of the system to produce the results you want. Do messages get across? This is the criterion for a good communications system—the sort of thing we are interested in.

SYSTEMS OF TRANSMITTING SPEECH

Air. There are many ways of transmitting speech so that one person in one place can say something to somebody in another place. Obviously the simplest medium for transmitting speech is the air. One man talks, another listens, with air forming the link between them. One voice and one ear can get the job done. With such a system of speech communication—the oldest and most reliable—the number of problems involved are relatively small. To be sure, we are concerned with the amount of noise in the environment, with how loud a man has to shout, and a few things like that. But relatively speaking, the problems are pretty simple.

Sound-powered telephones. When a man has to speak to somebody 5 or 500 miles away, he must call in some electrical or electronic help. Our real problems occur when these gadgets must be used. One of the least complicated of these devices is the sound-powered telephone. The sound-powered telephone changes acoustic energy into electric energy, and, even though the electric energy is not amplified, it is transmitted over some distance to a receiver. The receiver reconverts the electric energy to acoustic energy so that we can hear what is said. The old-fashioned home telephone is one of the simplest forms of sound-powered instruments. Those of you who have listened on such telephones will agree, we are sure, that what comes out does not sound exactly like what went in. The speech is distorted, and that distortion is one of our main problems.

Intercom systems. A slightly more complicated device is the intercommunication system. In an intercom system, the acoustic energy of the voice is converted to electric energy, but this electric energy is now amplified before it is passed along. Energy can be transmitted over greater distances with the amplification than without it. With intercom systems, however, the amplifier provides a new source of distortion which we did not have with the sound-powered instrument.

Radio. When the distance between two persons becomes so great that the use of wires becomes awkward, we go to the wireless radio. With a radio, the problems of distortion are the same as with other systems, but we have a few new sources of distortion. There are more amplifiers, and the use of high-frequency modulation introduces all sorts of new problems. Furthermore, the voltages in radio are very small, and the problem of static in the atmosphere becomes severe because the static energy is often greater than the radio energy.

The human element. Generally at least two human beings are involved when these communication devices are used. But, as mentioned previously, we will not concern ourselves much with the human element *per se*. We are interested in the design of the instruments and how the design affects the intelligibility of speech. Even though we disregard the human element, we must always remember that it is there. The talker and the listener, being human, have limitations which we must take into account at every turn.

VISIBLE SPEECH

Scientists, working at the Bell Telephone Laboratories, have recently made it possible for us to see as well as hear speech.[6, 12] This development has many important applications. Visible speech can be used for instruction, particularly of the deaf, who cannot hear speech. But this development is important also because it has given us some insight into the nature of speech and what makes it intelligible.

How speech is made visible. First, let us see just how it is possible for us to see speech. The technique is relatively simple. A talker talks into a microphone, and from that point on all the frequencies in his speech are sorted out into 12 different bands by 12 filters. Twelve little lights are lined up, and the energy from each filter controls the intensity of one light. Across this stack of lights a phosphor screen is drawn at a constant speed. As the phosphor screen moves across the lights, it begins to glow when one or more of the lights is lit. The amount of glowing and which part of the screen glows are determined by the amount of energy in each of the 12 bands of frequencies. The glowing of the phosphor does not stop as soon as the screen is past the lights, but continues for a little while, so that the whole pattern for a spoken word lasts 2 or 3 seconds. We can then literally see what a word or phrase "looks like."

How different voices look. Figure 100 shows the visible speech patterns of four different voices uttering the same phrase. The voices range from low to high, all different in basic pitch range. In this figure, the vertical scale represents frequency or pitch, and the darkness of the figure shows the intensity of the frequencies in the various bands. The abscissa of the figures is time, starting from the left to right. There are general differences in the speech patterns shown here: Some voices use a greater range of frequencies than others do, and some show a clearer pattern than others. But in spite of differences, it is clear that the general shape of the patterns is very much the same. All of them show a frequency spread to start, which narrows down and then spreads out again, and these changes take place at the same time for each voice.

How different accents look. Figure 101 shows the visible speech pattern for four different sectional accents, ranging from a general

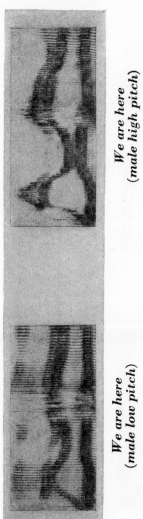

We are here
(male high pitch)

We are here
(male low pitch)

We are here
(female high pitch)

We are here
(female low pitch)

Fig. 100. These visible speech patterns show the nature of the differences between different voices saying the same phrase. The abscissa of these figures represents time, and the ordinate represents frequency. The darkness of the trace gives some indication of relative intensity. Notice that, even with these widely different voices, the general frequency pattern remains the same. (From R. K. Potter, G. A. Kopp, and Harriet C. Green, Bell Telephone Laboratories, *Visible speech*, Van Nostrand, copyright 1947)

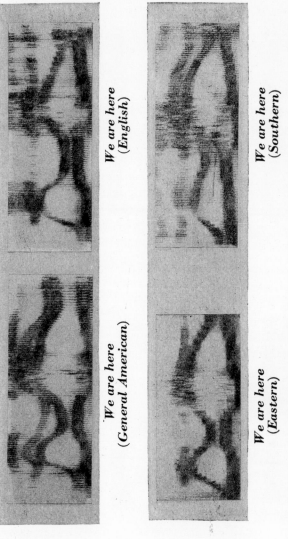

We are here
(English)

We are here
(General American)

We are here
(Southern)

We are here
(Eastern)

Fig. 101. These visible speech patterns show similarities and differences of sectional accents. They are similar to those shown in Figure 100. Notice again that the general frequency pattern is quite similar for the different accents. (From R. K. Potter, G. A. Kopp, and Harriet C. Green, Bell Telephone Laboratories, *Visible speech*, Van Nostrand, copyright 1947)

American accent to a real southern accent. Once again there are differences between the accents in the intensities of the various bands of frequencies. But notice that the general pattern of the speech is still the same. There is a common recognizable pattern for all the accents and for all the voices.

This pattern is really a time–frequency–intensity pattern, a change in the intensity–frequency relations through a period of time. The frequencies are not always the same, but the *pattern* of the frequencies is the same. Although we are not sure just how the ear is able to comprehend these relations, it seems pretty clear that speech intelligibility resides in the pattern of frequencies, rather than in the frequencies themselves. In other words, the absolute frequencies involved in speech are not nearly so important as the relative frequency pattern. The whole pitch of a voice could be changed an octave, but, if the frequency pattern did not change, we could understand the speech.

The importance of this concept will become clearer as we discuss the factors that affect speech intelligibility. There are many ways in which speech can be distorted, but as long as the frequency patterns are not destroyed, the speech will be intelligible, even though it may not sound very pretty.

HOW WE MEASURE INTELLIGIBILITY

We mentioned before that we are not concerned with the prettiness of sounds. We are concerned only with the efficiency of a system, efficiency in terms of communication. There are many ways, however, of measuring the efficiency of a system.

Does it produce results? There is little or no point to communication unless you want something to happen. Thus the most realistic way of scoring a communications device would be to count the number of times that the correct action took place on the other end. In many cases, however, it is very hard to measure the correctness of the action. Many times you do not intend to produce a specific action; no action may occur until several messages have come through. Much communication is solely for the purpose of providing information which a person stores up in the back of his mind for future reference, and it is difficult to determine whether the correct action occurred. In the laboratory we try to short-cut any long-drawn-out methods of measurement, and so we use other ways of measuring the efficiency of communication.

How often is it repeated? Another way of measuring the efficiency of speech communication is to determine how often it has to be repeated before it is correctly heard. This would be a good measure, but it would take a little longer than we would like, and there are still better methods.

How long does it take? The time required to provide a specific bit of information is important in many circumstances and is related, of course, to the number of repeats required. Many times, it may be worth our while to give less precise information because we can give it faster. This criterion for the efficiency of a communications device is a useful one, although it will prove more useful in relation to the problems in the next chapter, where we discuss communications devices other than speech.

How many items are heard correctly? The simplest way of scoring the efficiency of a communications system is to measure the number of items heard correctly. This is certainly the most efficient laboratory technique, and it turns out that most of the other criteria are related to it. We put a number of words into the system and measure how many were correctly understood at the other end. The greater the number of items heard correctly, the more efficient the system, and vice versa.

THE SCORING OF LISTENING TESTS

Determining how many items have been correctly understood is not always so easy as it seems. The Bell Telephone Laboratories and more recently the Psycho-Acoustic Laboratory at Harvard [2] have developed many elaborate techniques for scoring the efficiency of a communication system. These techniques were developed over a long period of time, and we now know the interrelations between the various possible techniques that can be used. In other words, we now can score the efficiency of a communications system in the most efficient manner for any particular case.

Nonsense syllables. In the first place, in our testing situation, we can use nonsense syllables like *guk, mip, og, oit,* and *aug*—monosyllabic noises that have no English meaning. With such material we can construct a test containing all the sounds and all the possible combinations of sounds found in the English language. The particular value of using nonsense monosyllables is that they have no meaning, and one word will not be recognized more frequently than another simply because the listener is more familiar with it. These nonsense syllables also allow us to find out which sounds are most often and least often understood. In establishing any code vocabulary, we can avoid those sounds that are most frequently misunderstood.

Monosyllabic words. We can also use monosyllabic words, which are like nonsense syllables except that they have meaning. Their particular advantage as test material is that they make possible the speedy attainment of articulation scores. Less training time is required for the listener because he is already familiar with all the words ordinarily used for this purpose.

Spondees. A third type of material used in articulation testing is the spondaic word. Spondees, as they are called, are words of two syllables with no primary accent on either syllable. Words like *beehive, blackout, hotdog,* and *whizbang* are spondees. Spondees are useful because they have no primary accent on either syllable, and thus both parts of the words are equally stressed in the speech. If one part of a word is unstressed, we are apt to miss it under poor listening conditions.

Sentences. If we want, of course, we can use whole sentences in our intelligibility test, for example, "Ring twice, and batter down the door," or "If a man answers, hang up." In scoring these sentences we usually score only those words found by other tests to be key words. In the first sentence we would score *ring, twice, batter, down* and *door.* If you hear these words correctly you usually get the meaning of the whole sentence. This type of scoring, of course, emphasizes the fact that relatively few words are actually needed to carry information. Many of the words used in ordinary speech have no value except to make the grammar correct. In testing the efficiency of a communication system, we are not particularly interested in good grammar.

The articulation score. Regardless of the type of material, we use one common measure in scoring listening tests. This measure we call the articulation score, the percentage of words that are correctly heard. Usually, in the test situation, the listener has to write down the words as he hears them. Later on it is possible to score how many words he heard correctly. If he heard 75 out of 100 words correctly, his articulation score would be 75 percent. If he heard all the words correctly, of course, his articulation score would be 100 percent. If he understood none of the words correctly, his articulation score would be 0.

The articulation score can be used to score two systems against each other or to compare two different conditions using the same system. If the articulation score is higher under condition *A*, for example, than under condition *B*, we can say that condition *A* is a more efficient condition to use in communication. And, if the articulation score is higher for system *A* than for system *B,* then we can say that system *A* is better to use for communication purposes.

FACTORS INFLUENCING SPEECH INTELLIGIBILITY

When we study speech from the point of view of the communications equipment, we find a rather amazing and alarming number of factors that are specific to each system. One communications system, for example, may have as many as 40 identifiable factors, each of which has some effect on the intelligibility of the system. In a microphone alone, such things as its frequency response, nonlinear distortion, efficiency and impedance, and directionality affect its performance. Many other factors, each of which can be changed in the design of the equipment, are important. Fortunately, however, many of these factors act the same in different parts of the system, and we do not have to study each single instrument of a total system.

General principles. In discussing some of these factors, we will rarely refer to specific types of communication equipment. Seldom will we refer to a specific earphone, a specific microphone, or a specific radio transmitter. We now have so much information about communication systems that it is no longer necessary to discuss specific cases. We can make valid general statements with complete assurance that they will apply to any given specific case.

INTENSITY

Obviously, one of the prime determiners of speech intelligibility is the intensity of the speech. If we cannot hear speech, we cannot understand it. The exact relation between intensity and intelligibility, however, is not quite so simple as we would expect.[2]

In quiet. Figure 102 shows us how the word articulation score varies as a function of the intensity of speech. The curve on the left shows how intelligibility, or articulation, increases with intensity when there is no noise in the environment. Notice that intelligibility increases very rapidly, reaching almost its maximum within a range of 30 db, but not reaching its real maximum until approximately 60 db above threshold. One very interesting thing about this curve, however, and about all such curves, is that, as speech intensity is increased to very high levels, speech intelligibility decreases rather than increases. This means that there is an optimal intensity for intelligibility. If the intensity is decreased below that optimal level, or increased above that optimal level, speech intelligibility will be poorer.

In noise. The curve on the right shows how intelligibility increases with intensity of speech when there is a very loud noise in the environment. You can see that this curve is roughly the same as the curve for the quiet condition, although the rise is much steeper, and intelligibility never reaches 100 percent. In most situations intelligibility never does reach 100 percent as measured by an articulation score. This is of no serious concern, however, because, if 80 to 90 percent of the words are understood, we can get the meaning of a total

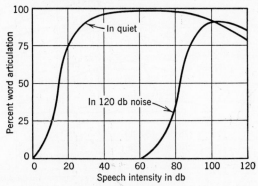

Fig. 102. The relation between speech intelligibility and intensity. In the quiet, speech intensity must be about 40 db before maximum word articulation is obtained. With 120 db of noise in the listener's background, the usable range of speech intensity is reduced about 70 db. Notice that both in noise and in quiet, articulation decreases again when intensity becomes too great. (After Egan, 1946)

paragraph quite well. It should be clear from the curve on the right-hand side of the illustration that intensity alone is not the prime determiner of speech intelligibility. Rather it is the ratio of speech energy to noise energy. Intelligibility of speech is determined primarily by how much more speech energy than noise energy there is in the listener's environment.

This problem of the masking effect of noise in the environment is a very serious one. Furthermore, it becomes more serious the more electronic links there are in the communication system. For example, in straight voice-to-ear talking, the only noise that can interfere with the speech is the noise in the air. When, however, intercom systems are used, we have to contend with not only the noise surrounding the speaker and the noise surrounding the listener, but also all noise that is introduced in the amplification process. Vacuum tubes themselves generate a certain kind and amount of noise. The more noise they generate, the harder it is to understand the speech. In a radio system of communication noise may also be introduced in the RF amplifiers and in the air. Electric static is well known to all of you. Static not only is very annoying but also makes speech hard to hear. Figure 102 tells us how important these noise problems are.

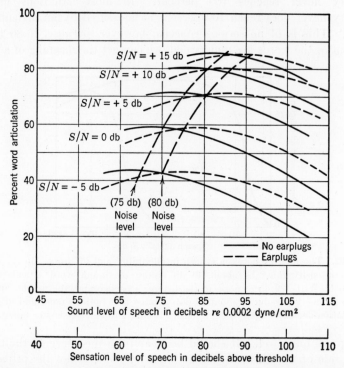

Fig. 103. These curves show how speech intelligibility is related to overall intensity of speech with different speech-to-noise ratios. The solid curves are for listening in an open room. The dashed curves are for listening in an open room, but with earplugs inserted in the ears. Notice that there is an optimal intensity level for each *S/N* value and that the optimal levels are shifted to the right (higher overall intensity) when earplugs are worn. (After Kryter, 1946)

Speech-to-noise ratio. Intensity *per se* is not nearly so crucial as we would first suspect. Since the ratio of the speech energy to the noise energy is so important, we frequently use the *speech-to-noise* ratio, or just *S/N* ratio, as a measure of effective speech intensity. This ratio is easily expressed in decibels. If the *speech-to-noise* ratio is held constant, articulation is reasonably constant, regardless of the overall level of speech.

Figure 103 shows us percent articulation as a function of overall intensity, for various speech-to-noise ratios. You can easily see that the speech-to-noise ratio has more effect on word articulation than does the overall level of the speech. The intensity of the speech still has some effect, however. There is an optimal overall intensity for every speech-to-noise ratio.[7]

Optimal speech-to-noise ratio. These general relations contain direct and helpful hints about the best way to operate a radio receiver. If all the noise in a particular instance is coming from the radio receiver, then changing the gain level on the receiver does nothing at all to the speech-to-noise ratio. It simply changes the overall level—giving a stronger speech signal but at the same time feeding more noise. When this is the case, the optimal gain is not always the maximum gain. If, for example, the speech-to-noise is about +5 db, then we will get best intelligibility around 70 db intensity level for the speech.

The importance of gain. If, on the other hand, the main source of noise is outside the receiver, then the situation is entirely different. For example, if the receiver itself is relatively quiet but there is a lot of noise in the air—as in an aircraft—then the best gain is the maximum possible gain, since we would want to get as much speech intensity as possible relative to the noise intensity. When we turn up the gain, we increase the speech without increasing the noise. That is good. It gives us a better speech-to-noise ratio and better intelligibility.

The advantage of earplugs. We have not mentioned anything about the dotted lines on these curves, but they, too, make a rather interesting story. If we have a fixed speech-to-noise ratio, it is still possible to increase speech intelligibility. Let us take the case we just mentioned—in which all the noise is produced by an aircraft. In this instance we would want to push up the speech energy as far as possible above the noise energy and thus get the best possible speech-to-noise ratio. But we know that any given speech-to-noise ratio will give us the best intelligibility if the overall level of the speech and noise is right. If we increase the gain to maximum, the overall level may be too high for best intelligibility.

Now, when the noise is primarily in the air, we cannot decrease the overall level of both signal and noise by changing the gain of our receiver. We can, however, effectively change the overall level at our eardrums by inserting some kind of a stop in the eardrum—an earplug, or even a wad of cotton. Either will do the same thing, except that the earplug will do it better. We essentially decrease the overall level and thus increase speech intelligibility. What has happened in the dotted curves of Figure 103 is that the insertion of an earplug in the listener's ear has shifted the whole curve. Remember that the speech-to-noise ratio was already determined by the amount of noise in the environment; that is fixed. But, if we can change the overall level by changing the amount of noise and speech hitting the eardrums, then we can improve speech articulation, or intelligibility. In such noisy places as aircraft, factories, and cocktail lounges, the use of earplugs, paradoxical though it may sound, will increase a person's ability to hear what is being said.

In summary then, the intensity of speech is a prime determiner of the intelligibility of speech. The speech-to-noise ratio, however, is more important than the overall intensity of the noise. But, even with a constant speech-to-noise ratio, speech intelligibility can be improved if the overall system is operated at a proper gain level. Under conditions where the noise and speech are coming from the same source, this overall level can be set with a simple gain control. However, when the noise and the speech are coming from different sources, then the overall level can be changed only by decreasing some of the sound at or near the eardrum. Earplugs do this.

FREQUENCY CHARACTERISTICS OF SPEECH

Intensity is not the only thing that determines speech intelligibility. The spectrum of the speech—the patterned distribution of energy among the various frequencies in speech sounds—also has a lot to do with the intelligibility of speech. We have pointed out previously that the frequency pattern is what makes it possible for us to understand speech. If we destroy this pattern, we will seriously affect our ability to understand words.

Here we immediately encounter the problem of frequency distortion —the problem of infidelity on the part of communications devices. Frequency distortion consists in not transmitting all the frequencies with the same amplitude, so that the spectrum coming out of an instrument is not the same as the one that went in. The most usual type of distortion consists of not transmitting some frequencies at all. In AM radio, for example, no frequencies above 5,000 cycles per second are transmitted. This is a form of frequency distortion that, fortunately, is not too serious, because most of the speech energy occurs at frequencies below 5,000. Other types of frequency distortion occur when we have a very small speaker in an intercom system, because a small speaker does not transmit the low frequencies very well. Almost any electronic system, or any telephone system, has some frequency distortion. The main problem lies in determining how much frequency distortion can be tolerated for a given level of intelligibility. But before we get involved with these problems of frequency distortion, let us look at the normal speech spectrum.

The speech spectrum. Figure 104 shows the distribution of energy at various frequencies in normal human speech. This spectrum was

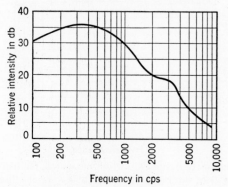

Frequency in cps

Fig. 104. The normal speech spectrum. This curve shows how speech energy is distributed among the many speech frequencies. The intensity shown for each frequency range is the average over a long period of time. The curve drawn here is the average of many measured spectra, both male and female.

obtained by averaging measurements made by different investigators for both male and female voices. We see in Figure 104 that speech energy decreases more and more above 600 cycles per second and that there is almost no energy above approximately 7,000 cycles per second. The speech spectrum tells us that, if our communications system cut out all the frequencies below 2,000 cycles per second, we would not have so much energy left as if we lost all the frequencies above 2,000 cycles per second. But we shall see in a moment that it is more important to know which frequencies are cut out than to know how much energy is lost when they are cut out. Some frequencies are more important than others, even if they have less energy.

Frequency distortion. Almost every known electronic or electric device produces some frequency distortion. If distortion must occur, and apparently it must, then we at least should be diligent in our efforts to make it happen where it matters least. Figure 105 shows what happens to the articulation score as we cut out either the high or the low frequencies.[5] One of the curves, the one that rises with increased frequency, shows what happens when the high frequencies are cut out and the low frequencies are transmitted. That particular curve shows that, if all the frequencies below 1,000 cycles per second are transmitted—but none above 1,000 cycles per second—the articulation score is less than 30 percent. If, on the other hand, all the frequencies below 10,000 cycles per second are transmitted, then our articulation score is nearly 100 percent. The other curve shows what

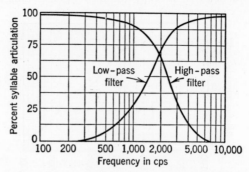

FIG. 105. The effect of frequency distortion on speech intelligibility. The "low-pass" curve shows how word articulation increases as the band of transmitted frequencies increases. For that curve, all frequencies below the frequency indicated on the abscissa are passed through the system, and all higher frequencies are rejected. The "high-pass" curve indicates word articulation when all frequencies above a given level are transmitted and all lower frequencies are rejected. The two curves cross just below 2,000 cps, and so we can consider that the frequencies above 2,000 cps contribute as much to intelligibility as the frequencies below 2,000 cps. (After French and Steinberg, 1947)

happens if we cut out the low frequencies but transmit the high frequencies. For example, if we cut out all the frequencies below 1,000 cycles per second then our articulation score is approximately 90 percent. If we cut out all of the frequencies below approximately 7,000 cycles, then our articulation score is 0.

There are two very interesting things to be noted about this particular set of curves. In the first place, we pointed out in the preceding section that most of the speech energy occurs at frequencies below 1,000 cycles per second. But if we cut out all the frequencies below 1,000 cycles per second the articulation score is not seriously affected. It drops to 90 percent, which is still pretty good. In fact, we still have much better than 50 percent articulation when all of the frequencies below 2,000 cycles are cut off. Thus, although most of the energy in the speech spectrum is in the low frequencies, the high frequencies are much more important in making speech intelligible. This makes sense when we consider once again the fact that speech intelligibility is determined by our recognition of the frequency pattern, rather than our ability to hear the low frequencies. In speaking, there is always some fundamental frequency which tends to be very low—500 cycles or less. This fundamental is not nearly so important as the overtone structure which gives us the frequency pattern. If we destroy the overtones we also destroy the frequency pattern and decrease intelligibility. For this reason, it is much more important to keep the frequency pattern than to keep the frequencies that have the maximum energy. Maximum energy does not necessarily imply maximum intelligibility.

The second important thing to note is that, when these curves cross (at approximately 2,000 cycles per second), the articulation score is better than 50 percent. If we cut out all the frequencies above 2,000 cycles per second we have approximately 67 percent intelligibility. Likewise if we cut out all the frequencies below 2,000 cycles per second we still have approximately 67 percent intelligibility. In other words, all the frequencies above 2,000 cycles per second contribute as much to intelligibility as all the frequencies below 2,000 cycles per second, but when either group is present by itself intelligibility is better than 50 percent. This means that both the higher and the lower frequencies are contributing more to intelligibility than is actually necessary. Although all the frequencies above or all the frequencies below 2,000 cycles per second would by themselves produce 67 percent intelligibility, the addition of all the frequencies together produces only 100 percent articulation. In a sense, then, when all frequency components are present, we have more intelligibility than we really need.

Effect of intensity. Figure 105 shows only one set of curves relating speech intelligibility and frequency distortion. The particular shape of these curves and how high they will get depend to a large extent on the intensity of the speech. And, to a large extent, any given amount of frequency distortion can be offset by increasing the overall gain level: An increase in intensity partially offsets the deleterious effects of frequency distortion.[3] Many curves of the type shown in Figure 105 are necessary to get the complete picture, and we do not have the time or the space to show all of them here. It is possible, however, to work out all the relations between intelligibility and frequency distortion and to determine how much intelligibility can be restored by increasing the intensity. Obviously there is a point beyond which no increase in intensity could compensate for frequency distortion. If none of the frequencies below 7,000 cycles per second, to take the extreme example, were transmitted, then we could not possibly get any intelligibility even though we increased the gain a tremendous amount.

Knowing, however, what the relations are between frequency distortion and gain to produce any given amount of intelligibility, we can determine the optimal design of any electronic or electric system. In many systems, it is much simpler to increase the gain than it is to provide a perfect response.

It should be pointed out further that these generalized functions apply regardless of where the frequency distortion occurs in any given system. Frequency distortion may occur in the microphone, in the electric components, in any of the amplifier systems, and in the speaker or the earphones. Regardless of where the distortion comes from, the effect is the same. That is why we do our experiments with general effects rather than in terms of any specific type or unit of a total communication system.

FREQUENCY CHARACTERISTICS OF THE MASKING NOISE

The frequency characteristics of the transmitted speech are, to be sure, important. The frequency characteristics of the noise which makes it hard to hear speech, however, are probably just as important. The particular type and quality of the masking noise, or signal, determines to a very large extent the amount of masking that will be produced and, in turn, the amount of intelligibility we can get through any particular system. Once again, it does not matter whether the masking noise is in the communication device itself, at the point where the speaker is talking, or at the point where the listener is listening. Regardless of where the noise comes from it has the same effect.

Figure 106 compares the masking of pure tones to the masking of noise.[10] The intensity of the masking sound is plotted on the abscissa. On the ordinate we have shown how much the intensity of the speech has to be increased in order for us still to hear it with the same intelligibility. For example, suppose we are working with articulation scores of 80 percent. In the curve showing the masking effect of noise, 60 db of masking noise makes it necessary to raise speech approximately 25 to 30 db in order still to have 80 percent intelligibility. Of course, any other particular articulation score could be used, and the shape of this function would still be about the same.

Masking by tones. The important thing to notice about Figure 106 is that speech is much harder to hear in the presence of noise than in the presence of tones. Pure tones of 300 and 1,000 cycles per second produce very little masking of the speech even with intensities as great as 70 db. The 300-cycle-per second tone does more masking with still higher intensities, but the 1,000-cycle-per-second tone has only a small effect even with an intensity as great as 120 db. We remember from the last chapter that low tones mask high tones quite well but that high tones have very little effect on low tones. That explains why the 300-cycle-per-second tone has more effect than the 1,000-cycle-

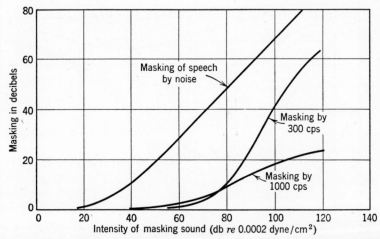

Fig. 106. A comparison of the masking of speech by noise and by tones. The abscissa indicates the intensity level of the masking sound, and the ordinate indicates how much the intensity of the speech had to be increased for it to be heard as well with the masking sound as without it. Notice that noise masks speech much more than the tones do, but that the 300-cps tone has more effect than the 1,000-cps tone. (After Miller, 1947)

per-second tone at high intensities. As the intensity of the low-frequency tone is increased, it makes frequencies near it hard to hear but also makes frequencies as high as 2,000 cycles per second and higher hard to hear. The 1,000-cycle-per-second tone, on the other hand, affects only frequencies above 1,000 cycles per second, and all the lower frequencies can be heard quite easily.

Masking by noise. Noise, however, masks speech much more than either tone does. Noise has many different frequency components, and all these frequencies help to mask both high frequencies and low frequencies. It is, then, much more likely that any particular frequency component of the speech will be masked when there is noise in the listener's background. This is an important point to remember if we want to interfere with other people's communication. Occasionally, although not always politely, we would like to make it hard for two people to communicate with each other. If that is what you want to do, then use noise rather than tones. A pure tone is a great waste of good energy in trying to prevent the communication of others.

Kinds of noise. All noises are not the same, and the masking produced by different kinds of noises is not always the same.[10] Just as

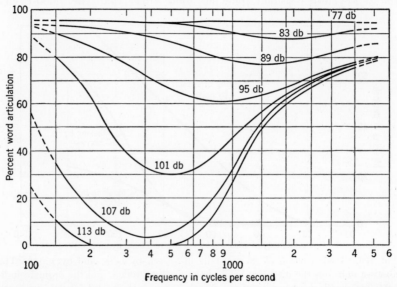

Fig. 107. The masking of speech by various noise spectra. Each curve shows the masking produced by narrow bands of noise frequencies. The abscissa indicates the center of the band of frequencies, and the ordinate is speech intelligibility. Each curve is for a different intensity level of the masking noise. Notice that, as the intensity is increased, the frequencies that mask speech most shift toward the low frequency end of the spectrum. (After Miller, 1947)

the frequency of a pure tone determines how much masking will result, so the frequency spectrum of the noise determines how much masking will happen. Figure 107 shows us that the amount of masking that noise produces depends on the frequency band of the noise. The curves in Figure 107 were obtained by using narrow bands of noise frequencies and measuring the loss in intelligibility when the listener heard these various noises with the speech. The intensity of the noise is indicated on each curve, and the abscissa shows the center frequency of the bands of masking noise. The bands of noise used were: 135–400, 350–700, 600–1,100, 900–1,500, 1,300–1,900, 1,800–2,500, 2,400–3,120, and 3,000–4,000 cycles per second.

We can see from these curves that speech intelligibility is fairly good when the masking level of the noise is relatively low. But, as the intensity gets greater, the articulation score drops quite rapidly. At the more intense noise levels, the best bands of noise frequencies are those below 1,000 cycles per second, if by best we mean the ones that produce the most effective masking. With lower-intensity noises, the bands of frequencies above 1,000 cycles per second have the greatest effect. These differences at low and high intensities are the same kind we saw with pure tones, and the explanation is the same. The most important speech frequencies—although not the most intense— are those above 1,000 cycles per second. At low levels of masking noise, noise frequencies in this area have the greatest effect, because they mask the most important speech frequencies. With more intense masking noises, however, masking effects tend to spread. This spread of masking effect is greatest with low frequencies, however, and thus the low frequencies have more effect on speech intelligibility than the higher frequency noises. And once again we can summarize by pointing out that, at intense masking levels, low frequencies mask higher frequencies; but higher frequencies have very little effect on lower frequencies.

Masking by voices. A pure tone produces some masking, particularly if the tone is low frequency. Noise is still more effective. One type of masking noise we frequently encounter is produced by the human voice itself. Frequently we get interference in communication because more than two people are trying to communicate at the same time and place. For the same total amount of energy, speech is far and away the most effective masker of other speech. This is not at all unreasonable when we realize that the best way to mask any signal is to use another signal just like it, and the most effective masker of any frequency spectrum is an identical masking spectrum. The one best way of getting a masking spectrum identical to the speech spectrum is to use human voices in producing the masking spectrum.

Figure 108 shows how well voices mask other voices. How efficient the human voice is depends on how many different voices are doing the masking. One voice all by itself has much less effect than several voices all talking at the same time. When only one voice is doing the masking, there are holes in the speech because a person does not talk really continuously, even though we think so at times. There are hesitations, and occasionally lapses to allow us to breathe. In between these gaps in the speech we can hear the words we are listening for. When several people talk at once, however, the noise from one person's voice fills in the gaps from another person's, so that there are no gaps left.

It is small wonder, then, that we have the greatest difficulty understanding speech in noisy places like night clubs, where most of the

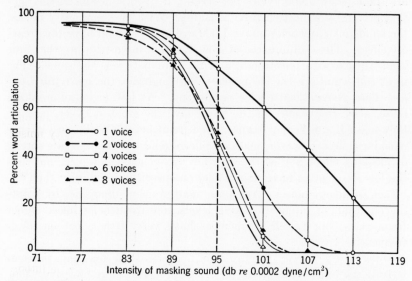

Fɪɢ. 108. The masking of speech by voices. One voice will mask another voice with a high intensity. Several voices, all talking at once, have a much more serious effect than just one voice, because the various voices are not all saying the same thing at the same time, and thus the holes in one person's speech are filled in by another person's. (After Miller, 1947)

noise comes from other people all talking at once. If you want to get really good communication find a nice quiet corner in the woods, where nobody else can talk when you want to talk.

AMPLITUDE DISTORTION

We have not yet mentioned the problem of amplitude distortion. That is, however, a very serious problem and one about which we know a great deal. Amplitude distortion occurs whenever there is some nonlinear relation between the intensities in a system—when the intensity of what comes out of a system is not linearly related to what goes in. The distortion may occur in the amplifiers, in the earphones or the microphones, or in the modulation stages of a radio transmitter.

Types of amplitude distortion. There are many types of amplitude distortion, and different effects occur with different kinds of distortion.[8, 9] Nonlinear amplification may occur at any point along the pressure wave of a tone or complex wave. Center clipping, for example, is one kind of amplitude distortion. In center clipping the area in the center of the total wave form, that is, the intensities around zero pressure, are rejected from the system: Only the big positive and negative pressures come through. When we speak of peak clipping, we mean that the top and the bottom of the wave are flattened off and not amplified at all. These are actually two extreme cases of amplitude distortion. We may have all the intermediate cases. For example, simple linear rectification is a form of distortion. In this case, only one-half the pressure wave comes through. Also we may have symmetrical peak clipping or asymmetrical peak clipping, or the clipping may not be sharp. In other words, we may have linear amplification up to a particular point, beyond which the amplification, although still linear, may have a different slope. In Figure 109 we see two extreme forms of clipping. These two forms of amplitude distortion we call peak clipping and center clipping.

Differences in peak and center clipping. Peak clipping and center clipping produce quite different results on speech intelligibility. The difference between the forms of clipping is due primarily to the nature of speech. All speech is made up of consonants and vowels. Vowels usually have considerably more energy than consonants: The maximum energy of vowels may be five and ten times as great as the energy in the consonants. Thus when we peak-clip, we tend to discriminate against the vowels in favor of the consonants, because we cut out the big pressures, but leave in the small pressures. On the other hand, when we center-clip, we tend to discriminate against the consonants in favor of the vowels, because we cut out the small pressures and leave in the big pressures.

Actually, we can get along much better without vowels than we can without consonants. In rapid speech, vowels sound pretty much alike. We really do not discriminate between vowels at all well. If, however, we are not careful in our consonants, words are very poorly understood. For example, in the following sentence, we have left the vowels as they should be but have made all the consonants alike. "Iv iv vivvivuvv vo veav vviv vevvevve." As you pronounce this sentence it is hardly intelligible. What you have done is simply to make every consonant sound alike, although you have pronounced all the vowels as they should be pronounced.

Now in contrast look at a sentence in which all the vowels are pronounced alike but all the consonants are correctly pronounced. "But thus suntunc luks und sunds sumwhut undurstundubl." This sentence,

unlike the previous one, is fairly intelligible, because all the consonants
are correctly pronounced.   In the center and peak clipping shown here,

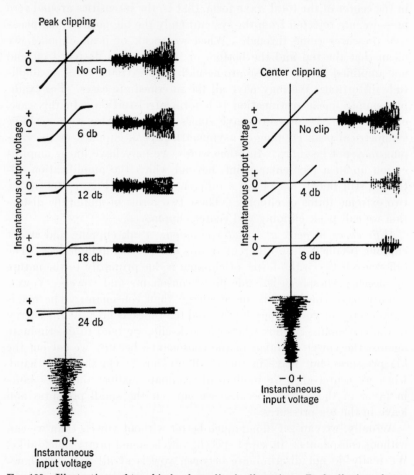

FIG. 109.   Illustrations of two kinds of amplitude distortion.   Peak clipping, shown
on the left, involves rejection of the large-amplitude components, while the small-
amplitude components come through the system.   Center clipping, on the right,
rejects the small-amplitude components and allows the large amplitudes to come
through.   Twenty-four decibels of peak clipping is intelligible, whereas 4 db of
center clipping is unrecognizable.   (After Licklider, 1944)

peak clipping of 24 db gives readily intelligible speech, whereas center
clipping of 4 db makes speech incomprehensible.[9]   Center clipping is
definitely disadvantageous.   Peak clipping, on the other hand, may
have certain advantages.

Advantages of peak clipping. Although it is true that peak clipping makes speech sound unreal—makes it sound distorted—still this peak clipping may offer certain advantages in a communications system. This advantage is due to the fact that, in any system limited by peak energy, we can get greater average power by peak-clipping the signal and then reamplifying it. The most obvious case in which this holds is in radio which uses amplitude modulation where the lim-

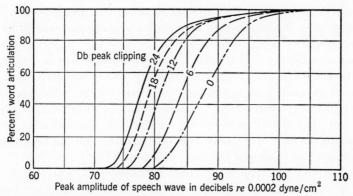

FIG. 110. The effects of peak clipping on the intelligibility of speech. Each curve shows word articulation as a function of speech intensity for different amounts of peak clipping. After the peak clipping, each speech wave has been amplified so that all curves are equated in terms of peak intensity. Notice that the peak-clipped speech is more intelligible than the unclipped speech. This increase in intelligibility is primarily due to the increased average intensity of the speech that we obtain with peak clipping. (After Licklider, 1946)

iting factor is the peak amplitude rather than the average amplitude. Greater average power can be obtained with any given peak power if the speech is squashed down, so to speak, and neatly packaged into a small bundle. We do that when we peak-clip.

With ordinary speech transmission, for example, the peak amplitude may be as much as five and ten times as great as the average amplitude. When, however, the speech is severely clipped, the peak intensity may be as little as 50 percent greater than the average intensity. This is certainly efficient in terms of a power system.

Peak clipping in transmission. The question still remains, however, whether this increase in power actually leads to an increase in intelligibility or whether the distortion introduced has made the speech so unrecognizable that it cannot be used. We have plenty of information on that matter. Figure 110 shows us the relative intelligibility of undistorted and peak-clipped speech, when the speech is equated in terms of peak amplitude. (In a radio-transmission system, the carrier power would be the same, and the percent modulation would be the same for each amount of peak clipping.) We can readily see that an advantage in speech intelligibility is obtained even when the clipping is as great as 24 db. Twenty-four-decibel clipping means that the speech has been cut down to $\frac{1}{16}$ its former amplitude and then amplified so that its peak amplitude is the same as it was when it started. This is an amazing amount of distortion, and it is even more amazing when we realize that articulation scores can actually be improved by introducing such distortion.

We can easily see how clipping can have a good effect in such a circumstance. We have neatly packaged the speech and have increased the average energy at the expense of peak energy. This increased energy has more than offset the disadvantage of distorting the speech. It is true that distortion in speech ordinarily is not desirable, but, as we saw in the case of frequency distortion, distortion can be overcome by means of an increased gain.

Peak clipping in receivers. There is another case where peak clipping is advantageous, although for quite different reasons. Instead of clipping before we transmit the speech in a radio wave, we can do our clipping in the receiver. In Figure 111 we see the effect of clipping at the receiving end of the system. The two curves shown are for clipping and no clipping. With the limiter—the clipper—in the receiver, it is very apparent that word articulation is considerably increased. What has actually happened in this case is that the noise which ordinarily masks the speech has been discriminated against in the clipping. A good portion of the noise that comes through most radio receivers is of the static type. Static noise is very sharp and spiky in appearance, and its peaks may be considerably greater than the peaks of the speech. By clipping this whole signal, both the speech and the noise, the noise is clipped off more than the speech, so that we get a more favorable speech-to-noise ratio.

Premodulation clipping (before radio transmission) is performed before any noise has been introduced into the system. What we do, essentially, by this sort of clipping, is to increase the average power of the speech with respect to the noise. With receiver clipping, we likewise can increase the speech energy with respect to the noise energy because of the differences in wave form of the two types of sound. We know that we can clip speech a great deal and still have good intelligibility of speech. We also know that, if in that clipping process we can get rid of a good bit of the noise, we have gained a twofold advantage. Not only have we increased the average amplitude of the speech but we have also increased the energy of the speech with respect to the energy in the noise.

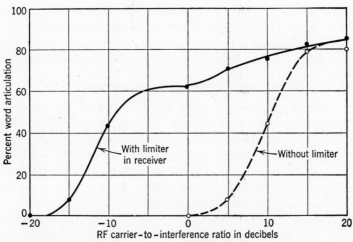

Fig. 111. The effect of peak clipping in a radio receiver. These two curves show word articulation as a function of speech intensity, with speech intensity expressed as the ratio (in decibels) of the radio-carrier intensity divided by the intensity of the interfering noise. With peak clipping in the receiver (the limiter) speech intelligibility is improved, because the limiter discriminates against the interfering noise in favor of the speech. (After Licklider, 1946)

TIME DISTORTION

We should mention, briefly, one further type of distortion which usually does not have a very serious effect. Time distortion consists in not transmitting all of the speech all of the time. Obviously if the radio is turned off every other second, your intelligibility will be decreased to about half. But, if the radio is turned off and on very rapidly, the effect on intelligibility is surprisingly small. Experiments have shown that, if speech is on only 50 percent of the time and is turned off and on at a rate of 8 times per second, speech intelligibility is reduced only to approximately 80 percent of what it would be if the speech were on all the time. In fact, speech can be interrupted at this rate so that it is on only approximately 20 percent of the time, and we will still get an articulation score of approximately 30 percent.[10]

This type of distortion is not too serious because the ear fills in the gaps between the speech, and, as long as the basic elements of the frequency pattern remain, intelligibility is fairly good. If the speech were interrupted at a rate slower than 8 times per second, the effect would be more serious. Most speech sounds last for approximately ⅛ second or less, and at the lower rates we would begin to lose whole speech sounds. If the speech is interrupted at much faster rates, the effect on intelligibility is even less, because every single speech sound is heard at least long enough for us to recognize the speech pattern.

OTHER FACTORS AFFECTING SPEECH INTELLIGIBILITY

The coverage in this chapter of the factors that can affect speech intelligibility has been very cursory. The number of factors that can affect speech intelligibility is so great that we could not possibly cover them all in anything less than a full-sized volume. We should, however, at least mention some of these other factors which we know from experiments affect speech intelligibility. In any system design all these factors must be taken into account.[2]

The speaker and the listener. The ability and the training of the speakers and the listeners who use the equipment are important. There are wide individual differences in performance, and the fact that it is possible to get considerable improvement in performance by proper training and practice emphasizes the need for training and selection programs in any job that requires a great deal of speaking or listening.

The speech sounds. Another factor, which we have mentioned but not discussed, is the inherent audibility or intelligibility of the speech sounds themselves. Some speech sounds can be heard much more easily than others. Some speech sounds are much more easily masked than others. Some speech sounds are more difficult to say than others. There have been many studies on this type of problem, and we know much about the selection of vocabularies in terms of their speech sounds. The relative intelligibility of any word is determined by the intensity of the component speech sounds, the spectrum of the component speech sounds, the number of the component speech sounds, and the relation of a particular speech sound to other sounds in the language. In constructing a code language, these factors must be considered.

Experience. Other psychological variables which determine speech intelligibility are the relation of the dialect or accent of the listener to the dialect or accent of the speaker. There are marked variations of pronunciation of certain sounds, and, although the words usually can be recognized, the facility with which any particular speech sound is recognized is a function both of the normal accent of the speaker and the normal accent of the listener. Also, the educational level of the listener has a great deal to do with the intelligibility score you will obtain. How often you hear a particular word depends on your conversational level. Words familiar to people with college educations are less familiar to people with only a high school education. In selecting any particular vocabulary and in selecting a speaker who will talk to a particular audience, we should consider these differences in familiarity of words.

Context of words. Another psychological factor is the context of the word. By context we mean the set of words that usually occur with the particular spoken word. For example, we are much more apt to recognize the spoken word *river* if we have been talking about houseboats than if we have been talking about duststorms. The word river is much more in context with the word houseboat than it is with the word duststorm. The context is determined by how often a particular word occurs with other words and by certain known relations which are inherent in any particular language. The articles, such as *an, a,* and *the,* very rarely appear all by themselves. They occur in the context of a noun. And some sentences invariably have an article preceding the first noun in the sentence. This problem of context is particularly important when we are working with specialized vocabularies, vocabularies artifically produced to decrease the number of words we need to transmit any particular information.

PRACTICAL APPLICATIONS

Throughout the discussion in this chapter we have said relatively little about actual practical applications. How do we go about using all the information that we have presented here, and that we have indicated is present in other places? Unfortunately, as we have mentioned before, the number of facts and the number of factors operating are so many that it is impossible to get a complete discussion of all of them in one short chapter. It is certainly not possible to make a perfectly designed communication system with the information presented in this chapter. At best, we hope that this has acquainted you with the most important factors affecting intelligibility so that you can recognize where the most serious effects occur, and how to correct them.

Acoustical treatment of rooms. Practical applications occur in almost any area where speech communication occurs. Even in direct voice-to-ear communication, something can be done about controlling the amount of masking noise in the environment. Such things as acoustical treatment of rooms and the insulation of one room from another can be used to increase the efficiency of the communication between two people.

Electronic equipment. Whenever we become involved in problems of electronic or electric equipment, the number of practical applications is immense. At every point in a radio system, or an intercommunication system, something can be done about designing the frequency characteristics in the system and the gain level of the system, in order to produce the best intelligibility. At the present time, there is little question that communication systems are not designed in terms of best intelligibility. Quite frequently, it is probable that an ideal design can never be achieved. If this ideal cannot be achieved, there is some best compromise in terms of intelligibility. Designs are frequently made in terms of an aesthetic quality when they should be made in terms of the practical application of the system. Intelligibility is more important than beauty. If we want to listen to music, many of these problems do not arise, because we do not want to distort music. We listen to music for its aesthetic qualities. But normally we listen to speech because we want to understand the words. In this case any radio or intercommunication system can be designed to serve that particular function best.

Hearing aids. One further application which we should mention because of its importance in very recent years is that of hearing-aid design. Considerable work has been done on the problem of the best way to design a hearing aid. We have not mentioned any of that work in this chapter, because most of the principles are the same as they are for any other communication device. Many times attempts have been made to adapt a particular frequency response of a hearing aid to a particular type of deafness. We saw in the last chapter, and to some extent in this chapter, that the frequency-response characteristic of the ear is very much dependent on the intensity of the sounds. If there is a masking noise in the background, the frequency-response characteristic is that determined by the intensity of the signal, not by the masking background. Deafness acts very much like a masking background. Realizing these facts, and the fundamental nature of the operation of the ear, we know that in most cases the best way to design a hearing aid is to have equal amplification for all frequencies. In other words no attempts should be made to compensate the frequency response of the hearing aid to the particular type of deafness of the individual. The frequency response of the ear is determined primarily by the intensity, not by the amount of hearing loss.

Hearing aids present a particularly ticklish problem, because the very small size involved produces many problems of acoustical design. It is hard to get a good frequency response with such a very small earphone. Likewise it is difficult to get good frequency-control characteristics with the size of amplifier used in most hearing aids. Even with these difficulties, however, there is a best design.

SELECTED REFERENCES

1. Davis, H. (Ed.). *Hearing and deafness: A guide for laymen.* New York: Murray Hill Books, 1947.
2. Egan, J. P. Articulation testing methods II. Psycho-Acoustic Laboratory, Harvard University, OSRD Report No. 3802, 1 November 1944. (Available through the Publications Board, U. S. Department of Commerce, Washington, D. C.)
3. Egan, J. P., and Wiener, F. M. On the intelligibility of bands of speech in noise. *J. Acoust. Soc. Amer.,* 1946, **18**, 435–441.
4. Fletcher, Harvey. *Speech and hearing.* New York: Van Nostrand, 1929.
5. French, N. R., and Steinberg, J. C. Factors governing the intelligibility of speech sounds. *J. Acoust. Soc. Amer.,* 1947, **19**, 90–119.
6. Kopp, G. A., and Green, H. C. Basic phonetic principles of visible speech. *J. Acoust. Soc. Amer.,* 1946, **18**, 74–89.
7. Kryter, K. D. Effects of ear protective devices on the intelligibility of speech in noise. *J. Acoust. Soc. Amer.,* 1946, **18**, 413–417.
8. Licklider, J. C. R. The effects of amplitude distortion upon the intelligibility of speech. Psycho-Acoustic Laboratory, Harvard University, OSRD Report No. 4217, 15 November 1944. (Available through the Publications Board, U. S. Department of Commerce, Washington, D. C.)
9. Licklider, J. C. R. Effects of amplitude distortion upon the intelligibility of speech. *J. Acoust. Soc. Amer.,* 1946, **18**, 429–434.
10. Miller, G. A. The masking of speech. *Psychol. Bull.,* 1947, **44**, 105–129.
11. National Defense Research Committee, Summary Technical Report, Div. 17, Vol. 3. *Combat instrumentation—II.* Washington, D. C., 1946.
12. Potter, R. K., Kopp, G. A., and Green, H. C. *Visible speech.* New York: Van Nostrand, 1946.

9. Tonal Signaling Systems

BECAUSE WE USE SPEECH SO MUCH, IT IS EASY TO FORGET THAT THERE ARE many other kinds of sounds that we can use to communicate with each other. Some of these sounds provide us a means of communication deliberately, and some accidentally. We whistle when we want to call our dog or occasionally when we want to let somebody else know of our arrival. We blow the horn of our automobile when we want somebody to get out of the way, or sometimes in simple protest. The factory whistle tells us when to go home, and the chime of the clock tells us how long we have to work before we can go home. The ring of the alarm clock tells us to get up in the morning, and so it goes. We produce many sounds other than speech to communicate with other people, and many sounds are produced mechanically or electronically to give us various kinds of information automatically.

USES OF TONAL SIGNALS

Occasionally, specially designed tonal signals are used to transmit information. The uses of tonal signals have not been fully exploited, and they could be used in many cases where they have not been tried. In this chapter we shall discuss some of the problems of existing tonal systems and some of the more general problems that would arise in the use of any tonal signaling system.

Symbolic nature of communication. Words are symbols or signs that represent objects or events, and language is the complete symbolic system. We use this symbolic system to short-cut the process of transmitting information. A single word can stand for an event, and a group of words can represent a very complicated idea.

The purpose of the symbolic system which we call language is to let us express any possible idea and refer to any possible object or event. In order to do this, the language has to get very complicated, and this complication has its disadvantages. There are many situations, however, where we want to transmit only a very limited amount or kind of information, and yet we have to use a language that was designed to handle much more complex situations.

Restricted communication. When the information to be transmitted is very restricted, it is sometimes worth our while to use a special type of signaling system—a system designed to handle only our special problem. Occasionally we need to transmit only yes–no-type information. Did an event happen or not? One noise or one tone is all we would need to transmit this information.

At other times we might want to know about the amount or degree of only one thing. For instance, is an airplane flying in the right direction; and if not, how much error is the pilot making? In this case, perhaps the intensity of a tone can indicate the size of an error, and the pilot could correct accordingly.

In more complicated situations, we might want yes–no information about several possible events, or an error indication of more than one thing at a time. The more complicated the situation, of course, the more complex we have to make the signaling system. The advantage of auditory signals is that the symbolic system provides no more information than we actually need. As a result, we can usually send more information about just one or two events because of the relative simplicity of the system.

Advantages of tonal signals. One of the advantages of a tonal signaling system, then, is that we can transmit more information in a short period of time because the total amount or kind of information is limited. In the radio range, for instance, practically continuous information is provided about just one kind of event—the course that the plane is flying. Likewise, if the communication time is limited, more accurate information can be provided.

Another reason for using tonal signaling systems, in many cases the really important reason, is that we do not need a man on the input side to provide speech. Very complex tonal signals can be produced automatically, but no really good means of producing speech automatically has ever been provided.

RADIO-RANGE SIGNALS

We have already pointed out that auditory signaling systems have not been fully exploited in practice. The need for them in the past has not been very great, and only recently has there been any real interest in their possible applications. The usefulness of such signaling systems has now been demonstrated. But at the same time many psychological problems have become more important.

Illustrations. We shall describe here two specific tonal signaling systems and use these two systems as illustrations of the kinds of problem we encounter. From these two cases we can deduce some general principles, and later in the chapter we shall discuss a few of the more general problems—problems involved in any tonal system that could be devised.

The first signaling system we shall discuss is the radio range, a type of signal that provides almost continuous indication about only one kind of information. It is, in a sense, a very simple type of signaling system and does not offer many complex problems. The other type of tonal signal we shall discuss is what has come to be known as "Flybar." This signaling system was developed quite recently and is relatively very complex. It provides simultaneous information about three different kinds of action for use by aircraft pilots.

What is a radio range? First, then, let us consider the radio-range signaling system.[2] For some 20 years the low-frequency radio range has been the most important single factor in making it possible for pilots to navigate in bad flying weather, when instruments must be used to fly at all. Even today, when there is a great deal of talk about such elaborate systems as ground-controlled approaches, the relatively simple radio range plays a very important role in our airways, both civilian and military.

Radio-range signals are commonly produced by using two directional radio beams at right angles to each other. One of these beams transmits in telegraphic code the letter A; the other beam transmits the letter N, also in telegraphic code. The code for the letter A is a dot and a dash; for N it is a dash and a dot. The two radio beams transmit the letters A and N in an interlocking fashion, so that the dot for the N goes between the dot and the dash of the A, and the dash of the N comes after the dash of the A, but before the A has started again. If the pilot flies just between the two crossed beams, the two signals will have the same intensity, and he will hear a steady tone. If he flies too close to the N side, however, he will hear a relatively strong dash–dot against a weaker continuous sound. He will hear a dot–dash, of course, if he flies too far to the A side.

The auditory discrimination. Although it is possible to present the A and the N signals to the pilot visually, it has been customary for the pilot to listen to the signals. The pilot's ability to fly along the correct path of a radio range, then, is determined by a human factor, namely, the ability of the pilot to discriminate between the A and the N signals. The pilot makes an intensity discrimination, and how well he can use the signaling device depends on his ability to make this discrimination correctly. Normally, the pilot flies where he hears a continuous tone. The more accurately he can make his discriminations, the more accurately will he be able to fly along a prescribed course. Any conditions that make his discrimination less accurate will increase the error he makes in flying this prescribed course. Let us have a systematic look, then, at those factors that affect the pilot's ability to discriminate between the A and the N signals.

INTENSITY

The most obvious factor that affects the pilot's ability to use the radio range effectively is the intensity of the signal. Here again we find that the absolute intensity of the signal is much less important

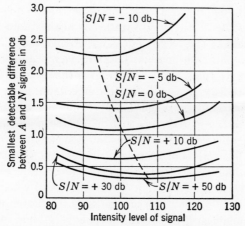

FIG. 112. This figure shows how different the intensities of the A and the N signals in a radio range must be for a listener to identify the A or the N. The abscissa indicates the intensity of the radio-range signal, and each curve is for a different signal-to-noise ratio. Notice that there is an optimum intensity for each S/N value, and that the optimum tends to increase with larger S/N values. (After Flynn *et al.*, 1945)

than the ratio of signal energy to noise energy, the S/N ratio, which we express in decibels.

Signal-to-noise ratio. Figure 112 shows us how the intensity discrimination for the radio-range signal varies with signal level and with the S/N ratio. We find that for every S/N ratio there is an optimal intensity—indicated by the dashed line in the figure. For very large S/N values, such as those shown at the bottom of the figure, the optimum is not very pronounced. But for very weak or unfavorable ratios, such as those shown at the top, the optimum is much more pronounced.

It is easy to see here that the signal-to-noise ratio itself has much more to do with how accurately the pilot can discriminate between the A and the N signals. When the S/N ratio is very unfavorable $(-10$ db), for example, the pilot may need as much as a $2\frac{1}{2}$ db difference between the A and the N signals in order to hear them as being different from a continuous tone. With a favorable S/N value, however, he may be able to hear a difference as small as half a decibel.

Noise in receiver. We probably should point out here again the meaning of these relations between signal intensity and the signal-to-noise ratio. We will recall from the discussion of speech that the best way to operate a radio receiver depends a great deal on where the masking noise is coming from. If the noise that is masking the tone (and producing the N of the S/N ratio) is in the radio receiver, then changing the gain of the receiver does not change the S/N ratio; when we turn up the gain, we increase both the signal and the noise. All we can do is to set the overall level to give the optimal intensity, and this optimal intensity is usually not the maximum gain.

Noise outside receiver. When, however, most of the noise is coming from outside the radio receiver, such as engine noise in an airplane, then we would always want to turn the gain up full to get the most signal for the fixed amount of noise. We cannot affect the intensity of the surrounding noise, but we can now affect the intensity of the signal to get the highest possible S/N ratio. And when we have obtained the best S/N ratio, we can get slightly better discrimination by the use of earplugs, if the overall level is very high. Earplugs have the effect of reducing the intensity of both signal and noise, so that we can get a more favorable overall intensity without affecting the S/N ratio.

FREQUENCY CHARACTERISTICS OF THE SYSTEM

The frequency characteristic of a radio range, as with speech communications, has a lot to do with the usefulness of the system. Would it be desirable in a case like this to filter out certain noise frequencies while at the same time not rejecting the tone frequencies? Would it actually increase the ability to detect differences in the tone? We must recognize that this is a slightly different problem from that involved in the masking of a tone or speech. Here we are concerned with the ability of the operator to discriminate between tones, both of which are against a background of noise.

Band-pass filters. Experiments have shown us that intensity discrimination can be improved by the use of narrow band-pass filters in the system. The frequency generally used with radio ranges is approximately 1,000 cycles, and in this particular system a band-pass

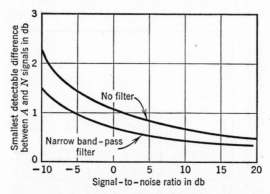

FIG. 113. Our ability to detect the *A* or the *N* signal in a radio range is improved when a narrow band-pass filter is put in the circuit. The filter used rejected all noise frequencies outside a band 200 cycles wide around the 1,000-cps signal. The intensity level of the signal was approximately 100 db, and at higher signal-to-noise ratios there would probably be little difference between the two curves. (After Flynn *et al.,* 1945)

filter was inserted that rejected all frequencies below 900 and above 1,100 cycles per second. Figure 113 clearly shows that the use of such a filter improves intensity discrimination between the *A* and *N* signals. This improvement is less at the higher *S/N* ratios, and probably at still higher values there would be no difference at all between the filtered and the unfiltered signals. Obviously if the signal level is so much greater than the noise that the noise has no effect at all, then we could not get any improvement with the band-pass filter, because the filter would be rejecting noise that has no effect anyway.

Design of earphones. Here we have an excellent case where we can predict something about the design of specific equipment from a fundamental relation. Phones differ greatly in the kind of response they have at different frequencies. Some earphones produce about the same acoustic intensity for a given electrical intensity at all frequencies. We say that such earphones have a "flat" frequency response. Other phones tend to produce much more acoustic energy at one range of frequencies than at others, and we call these phones "resonant," because they act like a resonator at one particular frequency or narrow band of frequencies.

We can choose flat phones or resonant phones for our radio-range listening, and if we choose the resonant phones the intensity of the signal will be somewhat higher, as long as the resonance of the phones corresponds to the frequency of the signal. Knowing that filtering

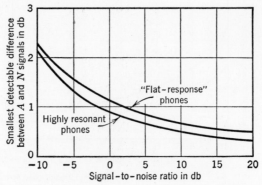

Fig. 114. Resonant earphones make it easier to hear differences between the *A* and *N* signals in a radio range. The resonant phones act like a filter, and this result would be predicted from the curves in Figure 113. Notice, however, that the resonant phones do not give quite so good results as the narrow band-pass filter. (After Flynn *et al.*, 1945)

improves intensity discrimination for this type of signal, we would predict that the use of resonant earphones would improve discrimination also, because the resonant phones act just like a filter. The flat phones would be poorer, unless we inserted a filter into the circuit somewhere.

These two kinds of earphones have actually been compared, and the results of that comparison are shown in Figure 114. The intensity discrimination is definitely better with the resonant phones than with the flat phones, which is exactly what we predicted. A comparison with Figure 113 shows that the resonant phones used in this experiment were not quite so good as the filter, but there was considerable improvement. If the flat and resonant phones are compared when a filter is also used, there is no difference in performance between the two kinds of earphones. For this particular job, then, resonant earphones are better than flat earphones. A narrow band-pass filter, however, produces better results than either of them without the filter.

SPECIAL DEVICES

There are a couple of special devices that can be used with the radio-range circuit. Some of these gadgets make the signal even better. Others might just as well be thrown away.

Expanders. One of these things is an expander—a device which amplifies large signals more than it does small signals. For instance, the expander would amplify an input of 1 volt to an output of 5 volts,

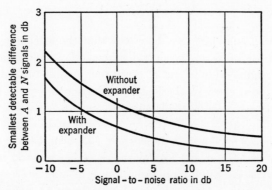

FIG. 115. Special devices like signal expanders can make it easier to hear differences between the *A* and *N* signals in the radio range. The expander tends to increase the difference between two signal intensities and thus increases the difference between the *A* and *N* signals if there is any difference at all. (After Flynn *et al.*, 1945)

but would increase a 2-volt signal to 15 volts. The general effect of this device is to make differences more pronounced. This is, actually, a form of nonlinear amplification, and in any system where it is not desirable it would be called distortion. The question quite naturally arose as to whether the use of an expander would appreciably improve the ability of an operator to distinguish between *A* and *N* signals. Figure 115 shows that it very definitely does. We see here that the ability to distinguish between the *A* and *N* signals is considerably improved when an expander is used in the system. The use of the expander, particularly with the more intense signals, has reduced the difference threshold to less than one-half its former value. The width of the area in which the plane will fly is cut approximately to one third of its former value—assuming the pilot can fly where his ears tell him to.

Pitch modulators. Another gadget that can be used to increase the discrimination between the *A* and *N* signals is a pitch modulator. This device translates the differences in intensity into differences in frequency, and it has been found that under limited circumstances we can hear the frequency differences better than the intensity differences. With very poor S/N ratios, however, the ear can detect differences in intensity better than differences in frequency, because the noise also changes the frequency at random. This random change in frequency makes it almost impossible to determine what is signal and what is noise.

SUMMARY

Now, in brief summary, we have seen that the efficiency of a radio-range system depends on the overall intensity of the signal, but even more on the signal-to-noise ratio. Filtering out all the noise frequencies except those close to the signal frequency improves discrimination, which leads us to predict that resonant earphones would be better than flat earphones, if the resonance is at the right frequency. This prediction was shown to be correct. Discrimination can also be improved by using such special devices as expanders and pitch modulators, although the pitch modulator is useful only at reasonably favorable S/N ratios. All in all, a great deal can be done to improve the efficiency of a radio-range signaling system and to see that it is operated under optimal conditions.

FLYING BY AUDITORY REFERENCE (FLYBAR)

Now we shall discuss another special type of auditory signaling system, one that has been developed in the past few years. This special type of signal has been called "Flybar," which means flying by auditory reference. Briefly, it consists of a combination of signals which a pilot may use to help him fly his plane. The signals may combine different sorts of information or indications up to as many as three at a time.

THE USES OF FLYBAR

You all know, or have heard, that blind flying, so-called, can be very hard on the eyes. The maze of instruments which a pilot must use can keep him very busy, and many a pilot who could fly contact all day and still have energy for vigorous social pursuits at night finds that blind flying for only a few hours tires him enough that he has a strong interest in just lying down.

Indications in blind flying. There are literally dozens of different instruments which a pilot must constantly check if he does not want to land in the nearest corn field. Many of these instruments are concerned with the safety and motor operation of the plane. As far as just flying the plane is concerned, the average pilot with instrument training soon comes to react almost automatically to three fundamental flying instruments which help him keep the plane level, right side up, and on a straight course. He needs some indication of tilt, altitude, or air speed, which are interrelated in flying; some indication of bank; and some indication of turn. Just the task of watching three instruments all the time is taxing, and, when we add all the other instruments to his task, his eyes can hardly keep up with their job. It would, therefore, be of rather obvious advantage if we could construct some kind of auditory signal which the pilot could use instead of, or along with, these various visual indications. It would take a great load off his eyes, to say the least, and it might make him better company when the day's flying is over.

The general problem. Although we are going to talk specifically about this problem of Flybar, we should keep in mind that there are many other places where auditory signals could be used to advantage. Many kinds of problems that have occurred with Flybar will also occur with other types of signal. The complex nature of the Flybar signals has brought to our attention some of the basic psychological problems involved in auditory signals.

DEVELOPMENT OF EXPERIMENTAL FLYBAR

But getting back to Flybar, let us relate part of the story of its development.[3] In attacking this problem of providing auditory signals for pilots, it was decided that the attempt would be limited to the three basic indications needed to keep the plane straight, right side up, and at the right altitude. In providing these indications, the pilot needed to know (1) when he is performing incorrectly, (2) the direction of any error, and (3) the amount of the error. Furthermore, he had to know all of this about all three indications. It is not enough to tell the pilot that he is wrong. In instrument flight, he has to make continual corrections for the sometimes inherent waywardness of his plane and for the vagaries of the elements. He cannot make these corrections with any efficiency at all unless he has good information about how much correction is needed and in what direction.

Auditory "realism." In the preliminary experiments in the Flybar problem the first thing that became obvious was that the auditory signal ought to sound as much as possible like what the plane is actually doing. If the plane is turning, the auditory signal should sound as though the plane is turning. Likewise, if the plane is going too fast, the auditory signal should sound like a plane going too fast. This, strange as it seems, makes the task very very difficult. It is extremely hard not only to provide sounds that imitate what the plane is doing but also to provide sounds sufficiently different that they can be accurately discriminated from each other.

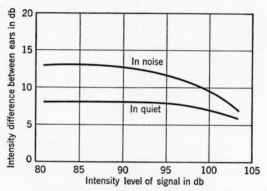

Fɪɢ. 116. These curves show how much difference in intensity there must be between the two ears in order for us to hear the difference. Notice that the rather large differences must be increased even more when there is noise in the listener's background. (After Forbes *et al.*, 1945)

As soon as the problem of Flybar was mentioned, it seemed that it would be the simplest thing in the world to indicate a change in direction. All we would have to do would be to give a different intensity to each of the two ears, and it would sound as though the plane were going in one direction or the other. And we could indicate not only direction but also amount very easily, because a greater intensity difference between the two ears would indicate a greater error.

Intensity as a signal. The first experiments, however, indicated that this was far from true. We see in Figure 116 that the difference in intensity between the two ears must be on the order of 6 to 8 db in order for the pilot to know, consistently, that he is not flying straight. This was rather surprising but nevertheless true. Thus we would need an intensity range of about 14 db—7 for each direction of turn—to indicate the null point; that is, to indicate the area in which the plane is flying correctly. This obviously was too much and the use of differences in intensity between the two ears had to be discarded almost immediately. More recently, we have also found that some individuals' ears do not agree with each other about how loud a tone is. This means that some pilots, flying by loudness cues, will fly in nothing but circles when they think they are going straight. Loudness in the two ears has very little to do with physical equality in the two ears. This again is unfortunate but true.

Three-tone signals. One set of signals was a three-tone combination. One tone was very low, one was very high, and an intermediate tone varied to indicate air speed. When this tone became high in comparison to the other two tones, it meant that the air speed was too great, and likewise, when this intermediate tone became too low, air speed was too low. When the middle tone approached either the high or the low tone, beats could be heard—indicating that the pilot had reached the limits of safety in variation of air speed. This same tone was heard in both ears. To indicate turn, the tones were interrupted in either one ear or the other, depending on the direction of turn. The rate of interruption indicated the amount of turn error. In order to indicate bank, three stepwise low tones were introduced into either one ear or the other, depending on which side was banked low, and the frequency of this tone indicated the amount of the bank. This signal was not very satisfactory, mostly because the pilot tended to listen to either one or the other of the signals when all three were presented simultaneously. When only one signal at a time was used, the system worked fairly well.

Two tones modulated. Another type of signal consisted of two tones heard in both ears when the plane was on course but in only one ear when the plane was off course. These two tones were frequency-modulated by a sawtooth modulation waveform; that is, the frequency would change steadily in one direction and then suddenly shoot back to its original position. The rate of this modulation indicated the rate of turn. The direction of the frequency change indicated the direction of the bank. Thus, if the pitch were going up in one ear and going down in the other ear, it meant that the wings were tilted in that direction. Air speed was indicated by means of a separate put-put which sounded very much like the motor of the airplane. The rate of this put-put indicated high or low air speed as compared to a standard rate, although the standard rate was not presented. As a result, air-speed errors were relatively high because of the pilot's inability to keep the "standard" rate in mind.

Sweeping-tone signal. A third type of signal which turned out to be fairly satisfactory consisted of a sweeping tone from one ear to the other. The tone changed in intensity, becoming louder in one ear as it became weaker in the other ear, giving an illusion of movement of the tone. The direction of this illusory movement indicated the direction of turn, and the rate of the movement indicated the rate of turn. At the same time this tone was being changed in intensity from one ear to the other, it was also being changed in frequency. Thus, if a tone started with a high frequency in one ear ending up in the other ear with a low frequency, that indicated that the side of the first ear was high in bank and the other side was low. The tone sounded as though it were sweeping across the horizon, starting high and ending low. That tone sounded exactly like what would be happening to the plane if it were turning in one direction with wings banked. If it were turning in the wrong direction with respect to the bank, then the frequency and intensity would be reversed. Air speed was still indicated by the use of a put-put, with the exception that now an alternating rate of put-put always provided a constant speed standard for the pilots. This provided a more accurate indication of the plane's rate.

Evaluation of Flybar

These several auditory signals were tried out and compared with a set of visual signals. The visual signals consisted of a spot on an oscilloscope and a meter. The controls which the subjects in the tests used were very much like the usual airplane controls. A foot rudder determined the meter position, and a joystick controlled the spot on the oscilloscope, when visual indications were used, although these same controls could be used with the auditory indications. The whole testing device was called an airplane pursuitmeter. An error score was produced electronically to indicate how successful the men had been in keeping all signals at the null point, that is, flying the "plane" straight and level.

Comparison of signals. Figure 117 shows the error scores on the pursuitmeter for both the auditory and the visual signals when one, two, and three controls were used simultaneously. In that figure, the signals labeled "1" are the three-tone signals, those labeled "3" are the two tones modulated, and those labeled "4B" are the sweeping-tone signals. The other signals were similar to those we have described but were tested less extensively. The visual signal offers very little advantage over the auditory signals when only one control is being used. The advantage of the visual over the auditory becomes greater, however, when two or three controls are used. Actually, this advantage consists in the auditory signals becoming somewhat worse, while the visual signals stay about the same. These tests did show, however, that there is a very good possibility of using at least one auditory signal and some possibility of using two or more signals. The task imposed on these operators was very severe, probably more severe than that imposed on pilots flying actual aircraft. Therefore,

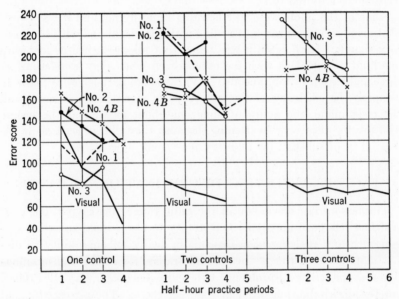

FIG. 117. This figure compares several auditory signals with visual signals when used on an airplane pursuitmeter. The abscissa shows successive practice periods, and the ordinate is an automatically recorded error score. Notice that the auditory signals become relatively poorer as more controls are added but that the 4B signal was less affected than the others. See text for further description of signals. (After Forbes *et al.*, 1945)

the best combination—the one entitled 4B here—was installed on a Link trainer.

The sweeping-tone signals were selected for further tests because they held up best when all three indications were used at once. These signals were not quite so good as some of the others when only one signal at a time was used. The advantage of the sweeping-tone signals, however, was that it was impossible to listen to one indication without hearing the others. All three indications were combined into one signal. In the other forms of signals, the pilots frequently lost track of one indication completely.

Link-trainer tests. When this best signal was installed on a Link trainer, tests were run comparing the use of the auditory signals with the use of visual ones. Most pilots were able to do as well with the auditory signals as with the visual signals, when the task was simply to fly a straight course. It is very doubtful that they could have done as well if they had had to make complicated maneuvers, and they were never required to.

Some of the pilots were just learning blind flying, and it was possible to compare their rate of learning with the visual and with the auditory signals. Here again it was found that pilots learned as fast with one kind of signal as with the other—even when they were using all three indications simultaneously. Various tabulations were made to compare the efficiency of the two types of signal, and, in nearly all the tests made, the auditory came out about as well as the visual. The results were very heartening, because they did at least show the feasibility of substituting auditory for visual indications.

FACTORS AFFECTING DISCRIMINATION OF TONES

Throughout our discussion of the radio range and Flybar, one general fact has been apparent: Our ability to use a tonal signaling system with any real precision depends basically on our ability to discriminate between tones. In the radio range, for example, discrimination was the only real problem. Other problems came up with Flybar, but the discrimination problem was still there. The air-speed signal which used one pure tone changing in pitch was unsatisfactory because the pilots could not tell what the pitch was until the tone approached the frequency of either the high or low reference tone. The tone in isolation had little meaning and made sense only when it could be compared with one of the other tones. The put-put air-speed indicator became usable only when a reference put rate was provided, because the pilots could not remember the standard rate unless it was constantly presented.

Of primary concern to us, then, are the problems of discrimination. If we know some of the fundamental facts about our ability to tell the difference between tones, we will be much better off when we want to design a set of tonal signals. If we do not know these facts, then we have to cut-and-try, as the previous signals were cut-and-tried. Since the radio range and Flybar were developed, we have learned some of the general factors that were affecting those signals.

DURATION

The duration of a tone or a pair of tones has a very serious effect on our ability to discriminate between tones and even on our ability to hear the tones. In most tonal signaling systems we would like to present successive pieces of information as rapidly as possible. The shorter each individual tone is, of course, the greater the number of tones we can present in a brief period of time. But, if the tones are

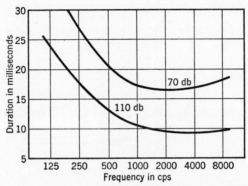

FIG. 118. These curves show the minimum durations necessary for a tone to sound like a tone. The frequency of the tone is shown on the abscissa and the minimum duration on the ordinate, for two different intensities. If the duration is shorter than that shown here, the tone will sound essentially like a click. The nature of the tone does not seriously change as the duration is made longer, however. (After Doughty and Garner, 1947)

so short that we are unable to tell the difference between them, then we might as well not have any signaling system at all.

Pitch versus click. One of the very first things we find out in this problem is that real short tones do not sound like tones at all; they sound like clicks.[1] Short tones are really made up of a wide variety of frequencies, and become in effect split-second noises instead of tones. There are many frequency components in a short tone, particularly when the tone first comes on, and when it goes off. These frequencies are known as transients, and they sound more like a click than a tone. If the tone is short enough, the transient frequencies at the beginning of the tone are still heard when the transients at the end start, and we never get a chance to hear the tone in between. All we hear is one brief click.

Figure 118 shows how long a tone must be if the ear is to recognize the fact that it is a tone and not just a click. We can see from these curves that even under the best conditions the tone must last almost 10 milliseconds for it to sound like a tone. Actually, of course, this is still a pretty short tone, and it is rather surprising that a tone can be this short and not sound like a click. At the lower frequencies the tone must be somewhat longer than at higher frequencies. This is reasonable, since the time of one complete cycle of the sine wave is longer. At 125 cycles per second, for example, the 24 milliseconds re-

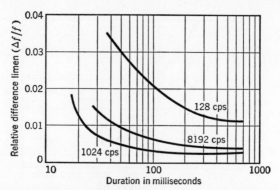

Fig. 119. The relative difference threshold for frequency increases as the duration of a tone becomes shorter, as shown in these curves. In these experiments, the first (standard) tone was always 500 milliseconds long, and the duration of the second (comparison) tone was varied, as indicated on the abscissa of the graph. All tones were 60 db above the threshold. Note that the effect is more serious at the lower frequency. (After Turnbull, 1944)

quired for tonal quality is only 3 complete cycles. The upper curve in this figure is for a lower intensity, and it indicates that the duration must be longer at lower intensities. The increase in duration is about the same for all frequencies.

Pitch discrimination. We might suspect, of course, that, if we cannot hear the pitch of a tone, we cannot very well discriminate between the pitches of two tones.[9] Figure 119 confirms this suspicion and adds the fact that pitch discrimination gets progressively worse as the duration is decreased. The ordinate scale in that figure is the relative difference limen, which simply means that it is the smallest discriminable difference in frequency, divided by the frequency of the standard or reference tone. The effect of the duration on the lowest frequency is much more severe than on the higher frequencies. This makes sense when we realize that the lower frequencies also have to be considerably longer in order for there to be any pitch at all.

The data plotted in Figure 119 were obtained by using a fairly long standard tone followed by a comparison tone of the duration shown on the abscissa. In other words, only one of the two tones was very short. At very short durations discrimination is a little better if both tones are of the same duration, because both tones then sound similar. It is very hard to judge the difference between a long tone and a very short one, but it is a little easier if both tones are short.

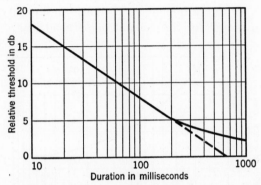

FIG. 120. As the duration of a tone is decreased, the threshold intensity of the tone increases. Below about 200 milliseconds, the increase in threshold is proportional to the decrease in duration, but there is relatively little change in threshold at durations greater than 500 milliseconds. This relation is approximately the same for all frequencies. Although the curve shown here was obtained by measuring the noise-masked threshold, we now know that the same relation is true at absolute threshold within wide limits of duration. (After Garner and Miller, 1947)

Intensity threshold. Another effect which occurs when the duration of a tone is decreased is that the threshold for the tone increases. The curve shown in Figure 120 was obtained by averaging data for four different frequencies, with noise-masked thresholds.[5] Other research, however, has shown that essentially the same relation is obtained over this range of durations even in the quiet.

Loudness. Not only the intensity threshold, but also the loudness of a tone changes as the duration is decreased, particularly at durations less than 200 milliseconds.[7] The loudness of a tone can be changed by an amount equivalent to an intensity of 20 db when the duration is decreased from 200 to 10 milliseconds. We could not, then, use changes in duration of tones as an indication of information if we wanted to use changes in loudness at the same time. The change in duration would cause a change in loudness, and the listener would not be able to tell whether the loudness had changed or whether just the duration had changed.

Intensity discrimination. Figure 121 shows, as an example, that, as the duration of a comparison tone is decreased, our ability to discriminate between the loudness of it and a standard becomes worse.[4] At very short durations, it is very difficult to distinguish two tones unless they differ quite a lot in intensity. As the duration of the comparison tone increases, we can hear smaller differences in intensity. Note that discrimination is best for tones about one second long.

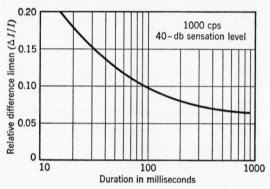

FIG. 121. Our ability to detect differences in the intensity of a tone becomes worse as the duration of the tone decreases. In this experiment, the listener heard a steady tone which increased in intensity every once in a while. The abscissa shows the duration of the increased intensity, and the ordinate shows the relative increase necessary for it to be heard. This same shaped function occurs with conditions other than those shown here, although the amount of the change may be greater under different listening conditions. (After Garner and Miller, 1944)

There are many ways of measuring the effect of duration on our ability to discriminate between tones, and the curve in Figure 121 illustrates the effect for just one type of measurement. In that experiment, the standard tone was on all the time, and every once in a while the intensity of the tone was increased for a brief period and then decreased to its former value. The measurement was the smallest increase in the intensity of the tone that the observer could detect. Under these conditions, maximum precision is obtained, and under other conditions the size of the difference threshold would be larger. If, for example, the standard tone were followed after a period of silence by another comparison tone, the difference limen would be considerably larger. But the general shape of the curve is the same, regardless of the type of discrimination problem.

Masking

We already know that masking affects the threshold for tones and that the amount of the effect is not the same for all frequencies. One additional factor should be mentioned: The intensity of a tone relative to the intensity of a masking noise (the signal-to-noise or S/N ratio) determines to a certain extent how well we can discriminate between tones.[6] This effect occurs for both intensity and frequency. If, for example, we have a 1,000-cycle-per-second tone which is just 5 db more intense than the masked threshold of the tone, the difference threshold for frequency is approximately twice as great as the difference threshold when the tone is 15 db more intense than the threshold intensity. Fortunately, once the tone is 15 to 20 db greater than the threshold value, the effect of the masking noise is negligible. In most cases, it can be disregarded except when the tone is just barely above threshold.

Distraction and Other Factors

We have already seen (Chapter 7) that the size of the difference threshold depends on both the frequency and intensity of the tones being discriminated. In general, the best discrimination occurs with frequencies in the middle range (500–2,000 cycles per second) and with intensities above 40–50-db intensity level. Relative discrimination is particularly poor at low frequencies and low intensities.

Any distraction invariably makes discrimination between tones less precise. A masking noise, for example, may have an effect on discrimination because of its masking effect, but it may also be a source of distraction. The most annoying noises, like interrupted high-frequency tones, will be the most distracting. Visual stimuli, or anything which attracts the attention, will distract an observer and decrease his precision. In fact, in most normal listening situations, the difference thresholds will be higher than those shown here, because the laboratory situation has the least possible amount of distraction.

FUTURE RESEARCH

There are many problems beside those involving simple discrimination of tones which are of concern in the design and use of auditory signaling systems. Many times the tonal signal should indicate the amount of error as well as its direction. We need much more information about the problems of indicating amount with the frequency and intensity of tones. These are essentially problems of scaling or establishing metric values for tones. How should a signal sound to indicate twice as much error, or half as much error?

We do not have these problems with visual indications, because we can put numbers right on the scale. With auditory signals we cannot say 1, 2, 3, 4, or 5 unless we actually do say them or use some kind of a counting system. Fortunately, these problems are not unanswerable, and considerable research is being done on them now, in several laboratories.

Illusions. One other problem which needs considerable study is auditory illusions. The Flybar signals worked best when the tones sounded like what is happening. There are undoubtedly other illusions than motion which can be used, and we need to know about them.

SUMMARY

In this chapter we have discussed the uses and some of the basic problems of special tonal signaling systems. Tonal signals can be useful when we have a limited kind of information, when we need speed or accuracy in the indications, and when the transmission of information must be automatic. Although tonal signals are not yet very common, there are many situations where they could be used to advantage.

In discussing some of the psychological problems in the use of the radio-range signal and Flybar, we saw that our ability to discriminate between tones is the basic problem with tonal signals. The duration of tones, masking, frequency, intensity, and distraction all affect our ability to tell one tone from another. These factors, then, will affect the usefulness of a tonal signaling system. For the more complicated tonal systems, we need to know about such things as the scale value of tones, and possible auditory illusions.

SELECTED REFERENCES

1. Doughty, J. M., and Garner, W. R. Pitch characteristics of short tones. I. Two kinds of pitch threshold. *J. Exp. Psychol.,* 1947, **37,** 351–365.
2. Flynn, J. P., Goffard, S. J., Truscott, I. P., and Forbes, T. W. Auditory factors in the discrimination of radio range signals: Collected informal reports. Psycho-Acoustic Laboratory, Harvard University, OSRD Report No. 6292, 31 December 1945. (Available through the Publications Board, U. S. Department of Commerce, Washington, D. C.)
3. Forbes, T. W., Garner, W. R., and Howard, J. G. Flying by auditory reference ("Flybar"). Psycho-Acoustic Laboratory, Harvard University, OSRD

Report No. 5123, 1 June 1945. (Available through the Publications Board, U. S. Department of Commerce, Washington, D. C.)

4. GARNER, W. R., and MILLER, G. A. Differential sensitivity to intensity as a function of the duration of the comparison tone. *J. Exp. Psychol.*, 1944, **34,** 450–463.

5. GARNER, W. R., and MILLER, G. A. The masked threshold of pure tones as a function of duration. *J. Exp. Psychol.*, 1947, **37,** 293–303.

6. HARRIS, J. D. Studies on pitch discrimination in masking. II. The effects of signal/noise differential. *J. Acoust. Soc. Amer.*, 1947, **19,** 816–819.

7. MUNSON, W. A. The growth of auditory sensation. *J. Acoust. Soc. Amer.*, 1947, **19,** 584–591.

8. STEVENS, S. S., and DAVIS, H. *Hearing: Its psychology and physiology.* New York: John Wiley, 1938.

9. TURNBULL, W. W. Pitch discrimination as a function of tonal duration. *J. Exp. Psychol.*, 1944, **34,** 302–316.

10. How We Make Movements

UNTIL NOW YOU HAVE BEEN READING ABOUT INDICATORS AND DISPLAYS —the input to the human machine which gives a man the information he needs to operate the machine. In this chapter and the next two chapters, we will discuss man's output—what he does to and with machines.

The problems. What is the most crankable crank? The most pushable pedal? When should we use a pedal, a switch, a lever, a stick or other kind of control? Where should controls be put? These questions and many more like them are what we want to answer. It would be nice if we could answer all of them. But we are not able to do that yet.

As we have said before, engineering psychology is a new field. Both the basic and applied research that we need to answer our questions have just begun. Most of it so far has dealt with aircraft controls. Even today the majority of engineering psychologists, working as hard as they can, are supported by the aircraft agencies in Government and industry. And there has been neither time nor money for the basic research that is so plainly needed for any kind of applications, whether in aircraft or in industrial production. So a lot of our story is just the statement of questions—the kinds of questions that must be answered before we have anything like a whole picture of the field.

Approaches. There are two rather different ways of thinking about men working with controls. One takes the point of view of the man: What kinds of movement does he make? How does he make them? How efficient is he in making these movements? And so on. The other approach starts with the machine: How can we classify controls? When should we use each type? How should they be constructed? Where should they be put? How should they be operated? Neither point of view is complete in itself. We need to know a lot about both of them to have a clear picture of how men can and should work with controls. In this chapter, we are going to study man's movements and how he makes them. In the chapter that follows, we look at the problem of controls.

Historical background. Before we go too far, we ought to take a glance at how people have been studying movements. There have been three different groups of people working with the problem. One very active group is the physiologists. They have done literally thousands of experiments on the processes that go on in muscles when they contract—for all movement is a matter of muscle contraction. They have measured the mechanical changes in muscles, the chemical reactions through which muscles store up and release energy, and the electrical changes which occur in movement. A second group are the time-and-motion engineers. They have made very practical analyses of man's movements in various production situations. We shall tell you more about their work in a later chapter. In between is a third group of psychologists, who have just begun to study the problem. They have fixed up all sorts of special tasks for people to do and have recorded the speed, accuracy, and form with which they perform the tasks. Most of what we say in this chapter, sketchy as it will be, will come from the work of the third group.

Action potentials. A few words are in order about electrical changes during movement, which some research workers have been especially interested in.[13] They have put electrodes on various muscles of the body while people are making various sorts of movements. If we put one electrode on the muscle we are interested in analyzing and the other electrode some place else, we usually will be able to pick up some pronounced electrical changes during movement. We can see them on all sorts of records: an ink-writing oscillograph, a photographic record of a galvanometer, or the face of a cathode-ray oscilloscope. Most such research has been done because people have been interested in what goes on in the muscles, not for any practical value. So these studies have little value at present for engineering psychology. The approach, however, needs to be exploited, and recently some psychologists have been using these electrical changes, called action potentials, as measures of efficiency in various sorts of tasks given to operators. In the future, we may expect some rather good research from this quarter.

Classification of movements. One interesting result has come out of the work with action potentials—a classification of movements. The classification, in fact, is a rather elaborate one. To save unnecessary complication, however, we will just mention the chief feature of the classification. This is a distinction between *fixed* movements and *ballistic* movements.[14] You probably know that we have antagonistic muscles in our arms and legs and in some other places too. For each muscle that pulls in one direction, there is another one, the antagonist, which pulls in the other direction. In many movements, we use both sets of muscles at once; the two groups are balanced against each other: for example, when we hold a pencil in our hand, or drive an automobile, or make any slow tense movement. Such a movement is a *fixed* movement. On the other hand, we sometimes just contract one set of muscles and then relax them suddenly. When we do that, a muscle literally throws our bones and other muscles around. When we throw a ball, for example, we suddenly contract and relax one group of muscles without the antagonists getting into play. That kind of a movement is *ballistic*.

This classification of movements has its uses. In general, the ballistic movements are the best, since we do not waste a lot of energy having antagonistic muscles work against each other but put our energy into one big heave. In learning to pitch a ball or to swing a golf club, the problem is to develop a nice free ballistic swing. If our movements are too *fixed*, we waste energy in our muscles instead of putting it into the ball—in fact, we have less chance of hitting the ball. In other things too, in writing, in conducting, and in driving, ballistic movements seem to be the best ones. Indeed, it looks as though people, when they learn all sorts of skills, gradually learn to reduce fixed movements to a minimum and develop good ballistic movement.

Such a classification, though useful, has its limitations. It cannot serve as an understanding of all movements we make, for few movements are either entirely fixed or entirely ballistic. For practical purposes, a different type of classification is necessary. At present we cannot be sure what is the best one, for engineering psychologists have just started studying it. Our main job is to explain what we know about making movements. To do that we have used a classification that is a mixture of others that have been proposed.

Here are the main classes of movement that you will find in the following pages: (1) static reactions, which are not really movements at all but rather consist of all instances in which an operator must keep his fingers, hands, arms, or feet in a fixed position—in short, holding operations; (2) positioning reactions, in which an operator moves his arms or legs—usually his arms—from one position in space to another; (3) tapping reactions, consisting of repeated banging or tapping; (4) cranking and winding movements; and (5) tracking and steering movements. As the discussion proceeds, some of these classes will be broken down into smaller subclasses.

STATIC REACTIONS

Static reactions have been defined by the Wright Field psychologists [4] as including "all of the instances where a bodily member is held for a time in a fixed position in space, the maintenance of that position being the central task imposed on the individual concerned." As far as we can tell now, static reactions are not particularly important in equipment design, for we seldom ask anybody to take hold of a control and hold it in a fixed position—if we do, it is not a particularly hard job for him. Even so, we do need some basic data about static reactions, how efficient people are in making them, what differences there are between people in static reactions, and how their ability in this area correlates with other movement abilities.

Measures of static reactions. We can measure two things about static reactions. There is muscle tremor, the fairly rapid trembling which we see when somebody holds his hand or arm in a fixed position. A second aspect of static reactions is drift, the gradual movement of the limb when it is held in one position for a while. Drift, as you might imagine, does not occur when there is some clear way of seeing where the hand is. If a dial moves when the hand drifts or if the finger points toward a target, there will be no drift. A man can move his hand back where it belongs as long as an indicator tells him when his hand moves. Thus, in practice, drift in static reactions is not especially important.

Methods of studying tremor. We know something about tremor, because we have laboratory methods of studying it. One method is to use the Whipple Steadiness Tester.[15] This gadget has a metal plate with a hole in it. An operator holds a metal stylus in the hole and tries to keep the stylus from touching the side of the plate. The plate and stylus are wired up so that a counter clicks any time they touch. By counting the number of clicks in some standard test interval, we can get a measure of hand tremor.

Another way to study tremor makes use of threads and riders (Edwards [6]). Three threads are attached to a man's finger. Each thread is attached to a rider, one for each dimension, so that any movement in any dimension causes some rider to move. The positions of the riders, after some standard period of measurement, gives the sum of the movement in each dimension. Another method (Fossler [9]) recently devised uses a movable coil in a magnetic field. The movements of the person holding the coil show up on an oscilloscope and can be photographed, giving a very detailed record of the person's tremor.

Characteristics of tremor. Here are some of the things we know about tremor in static reactions: The amount of tremor we will find varies considerably from one individual to another and from time to time. In fact, it is a question whether a score for a particular person means very much. If he is measured one day and then again another day, the two scores do not correspond very well ($r = 0.73$). The score can be used, however, along with other scores on motor coordination to help characterize an individual. There are other studies of tremor in children as compared with adults and of differences between men and women, but the results are neither very great nor very significant for any practical purpose.

There are a few practical points about tremor. Some you would expect; others perhaps not. If a person has some friction to work against, his tremor goes down. In other words, tremor is decreased by having something to lean on or to grasp solidly. Also, the harder a person tries not to tremble, the more he does. As you might expect, fatigue increases tremor. As a person gets more and more tired, his tremor gets worse: the frequency of it, the size of the movements, and the jerkiness. We do not know what exercise has to do with tremor; sometimes it seems to make it worse and sometimes it seems to have no effect.

How a subject is standing and how he is holding his arm has something to do with tremor. In general, the better anchored the body and the arm, the less tremor. Most people have less tremor in a fine finger coordination when they are seated than when they are standing. And, if the hand is anchored at the palm, with the palm on the table, there is less tremor than when the hand is pivoted at the wrist or the elbow. The amount of tremor is generally greatest in the up–down, less in the front–back, and least in the right–left direction.

All this does not have wide practical consequences. If, however, there is any possibility that hand tremor might affect the way you hold a control in place, the best things to do are: (1) Make sure, if possible, that the control has some friction, (2) have the operator sit down rather than stand up, and (3) arrange the table or work surface so that his arm and hand have as much support as possible. All these precautions cannot hurt, and they are likely to reduce any errors in holding a control in place.

BLIND-POSITIONING REACTIONS

In the classification of movements we are following here, a positioning reaction is a movement of the arm or leg from a fixed resting place to some other point in space. There are two ways to make positioning reactions—with and without seeing what we are doing. If a person can and does see the spot that he is moving to, there usually is little problem regarding the accuracy of the movement. He moves his hand until it takes hold of the control he is looking at. Sooner or later, in such *visual-positioning movements,* he gets to his target accurately. The main problem in such movements is the rate and time of the movement.

In *blind-positioning movements,* however, accuracy of movement is the chief problem. The operator cannot see where he is moving his arms or legs. He may have seen it at one time or another, but, for one reason or another—because his eyes are busy elsewhere or because the spot is not visible at the moment—he cannot see it when he makes the movement. Obviously, it is rather hard to be accurate under these circumstances, and so accuracy becomes our chief concern in considering blind-positioning movements.

We shall take up these two types of positioning movements in turn, first blind-positioning movements and then visual-positioning movements.

Types of blind-positioning reactions. Blind-positioning reactions are important in everyday life. In almost all machine operations, there are some things the operator does without looking. Even in handling materials in a carpenter or machine shop, many blind-positioning movements are made with the hands—using the buzz saw and the drill press, operating the controls on a lathe. We cannot see everything at once, so we usually watch the operation while our hands are busy somewhere else. In the operation of aircraft, the pilot keeps his eyes on his instruments or on points outside the plane, while his hands grope around for the appropriate controls.

So it makes sense to ask questions about blind-positioning reactions. How well can people tell where they are reaching? How well can they tell just how *far* they are reaching? Those are the two principal questions, but there are many more detailed questions as well. To make it a little easier to answer these questions, we ought to make a distinction between two types of blind-positioning reactions: (1) restricted positioning reactions, in which a person moves a lever or knob along a more or less straight line, toward the body or away from the body, up and down or in and out; and (2) free-positioning reactions, in which the subject moves his hand from one position out in space to another, side to front, front to side or side to side. The research which we have to talk about falls conveniently into these two types of blind-positioning reactions.

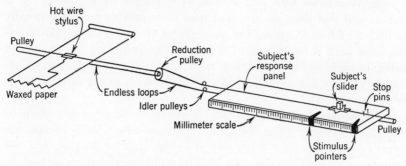

Fɪɢ. 122. A rough sketch of the apparatus for studying restricted positioning reactions. The stimulus pointers tell the subject the extent of the movement to be made. After the subject closes his eyes, he moves the slider to the appropriate position. The slider is attached to a wax-paper recorder which shows exactly how the subject made the movement and how quickly. (After Brown, Knauft, and Rosenbaum, 1947)

Rᴇsᴛʀɪᴄᴛᴇᴅ Pᴏsɪᴛɪᴏɴɪɴɢ Rᴇᴀᴄᴛɪᴏɴs

Psychologists have studied these reactions in a very simple way.[5] They put a knob on a slider frame sitting in front of a person (see Figure 122). They arrange two pointers along the slide to tell the operator what positioning movement he is supposed to make. Then they turn a light on for a moment so that the operator can see where he is supposed to move. Then they turn off the light and ask the subject to make the movement as accurately as possible. They can then score how accurately the operator makes the positioning reaction and how quickly he makes it. They can vary the experiment from time to time to see whether people are better at making this kind of positioning reaction when they are moving away from the body or toward the body, moving in a vertical position or in a horizontal position, and moving for very short distances or long ones.

Distance. What we find out about the accuracy of positioning movements is interesting. Consider first the question of distance. We might expect that the error of positioning movements depends somewhat on the distance or extent of the positioning movement (see Figure 123).* It does. In general, people overestimate small distances and undershoot the mark at greater distances. By short distances we mean 1 to 4 inches; by greater distances we mean positioning movements of 4 to 15 inches. The only time this is not true is when the person makes a vertical positioning movement toward his own body (data not shown in Figure 123). Such a movement has gravity work-

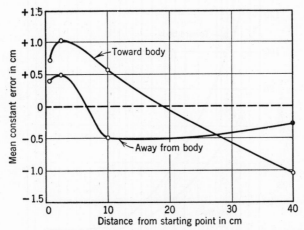

Fig. 123. The error of blind restricted positioning movements for different distances and directions of movement. We see that subjects tend to overestimate short distances and underestimate long distances. Notice that the curves are different for moving toward the body and away from the body. (After Brown, Knauft, and Rosenbaum, 1947)

ing against it, and it is no wonder, therefore, that *all* positioning movements of this sort tend to fall short of the goal. It is interesting to know, incidentally, that this overestimation of short distances and underestimation of longer distances is something that turns up very frequently in other parts of psychology, such as estimating the position of dots between range rings on a map and so on.

But returning to positioning reactions, it is interesting to see how large the positioning error is for different distances. As we have seen before, there are several ways of computing error, but for this purpose it is probably easiest to think about relative average error. This is the average amount by which the operator misses the mark in making a positioning reaction divided by the distance he has to go. In a word,

* The coordinates in Figure 123 are in centimeters, the scale of distance ordinarily employed in scientific measurement. To help the reader who feels more at home with inches, the discussion in the text is in terms of inches.

it is percent error. The facts are shown in Figure 124. There you can
see that percent error is greatest for very short distances and that the
percent gets smaller when the distance is reasonably great. Beyond
10 centimeters (about 4 inches) percent error does not change very
much.

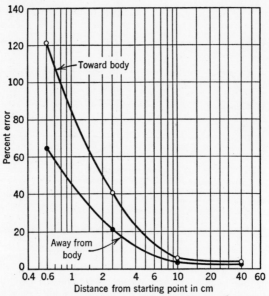

Fig. 124. Relative error for different distances and directions of movement. The
percent error (error of movement divided by distance to go) is much less for
large movements than for small ones. It is also less for movements away from
the body than for those toward the body. (After Brown, Knauft, and Rosenbaum,
1947)

Direction. There is another interesting point in Figure 124. It is
that positioning reactions are more accurate away from the body than
toward the body. The experimenters who did this study analyzed
their data in several different ways—more than we have time to take
up here—but, no matter how they did it, they always came out with
the conclusion that percent error, or relative average error, was less
when positioning movements were made away from the body.

This statement, however, needs some qualification if we talk about
relative variability, rather than percent constant error. Variability (σ)
concerns the uniformity of positioning reactions around the mark,
rather than how far off, on the average, they are from the mark. Figure 125 gives variability, that is, the standard deviation of position-

ing reactions, for different distances of reaction. There you can see that the variable error, in absolute terms, gets larger as the distance increases, just as the constant error does. Yet, if you take percent variability and divide the standard deviation by the distance, you will find that percent (or relative) variability decreases with increas-

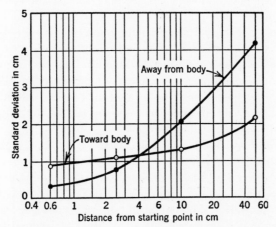

FIG. 125. The standard deviation of restricted positioning reactions. Variability increases with increasing distance, but more so for movements away from the body than for those toward the body. If we divide the standard deviation by the distance, we will see, however, that *percent* variability decreases with increasing distance. (After Brown, Knauft, and Rosenbaum, 1947)

ing distance, just as it does in the case of constant error. Percent error is not shown in Figure 125, but you can estimate it easily with a little arithmetic. Note, too, in Figure 125, how variability depends on direction of movement, whether toward or away from the body.

Summary. So much for the experiment on restricted blind-positioning reactions. There ought to be more research on this point before we can be sure of any rules and regulations we might want to deduce. As matters stand, however, there are a few practical consequences of the experiments. (1) If we are setting up controls to be operated by positional movements, the smallest relative error and variability will result if distances of the order of 4 to 15 inches are used. (2) If percent error is the important thing, then it would be best to emphasize movements away from the body. (3) If the absolute variability of the positioning movement is important, it is better to arrange the control setup to emphasize movement toward the body.

FREE-POSITIONING MOVEMENTS

We are indebted to the Wright Field psychologists for another study of positioning movements.[7] They are concerned primarily with pilots in airplanes and the ease and accuracy with which pilots can operate controls. They interviewed a large number of pilots, looked over records of accidents and their causes, and came to the conclusion that accidents, both serious and minor, were often due to pilots not being able to make the correct free positioning movements. Pilots ordinarily have plenty to do with their eyes, and many controls must be located and operated without the pilot looking at them. Thus positioning movements are of immense practical importance in the airplane. Moreover, since controls may be located in front of, below, to one side or another, and even sometimes more or less behind the pilot, the problem is one of free-positioning movements.

Experimental setup. To get some basic data of people's ability to make this kind of positioning reaction, the Wright Field psychologists [8] made an experimental enclosure which contained a number of target squares placed in a regular order around it (Figure 126). One row of squares was placed at shoulder height in an incomplete circle around the pilot, beginning far to the left and ending far around to the right. Another row was placed just below these at the level of the pilot's seat. Another row was put above his head. The target squares were so arranged that each of them was just 30 inches from a reference point between the pilot's shoulders. This distance was selected because more than 95 percent of pilots can reach it. That had been determined by anthropologists beforehand.

Procedure. Pilots were put in this kind of setup. Then, they were given a letter code for each of the 20 targets in the array around them. The particular target they were supposed to reach for was called out to them, and they immediately put their hand around to the point where they thought the target was. All this time pilots could not see the targets. To make the situation realistic, however, the pilots were provided with red goggles and asked to keep their eyes on a red light directly ahead of them, much as they would do if they were flying in a plane and reaching for controls while looking out of their windshield. With the red goggles on, however, the pilots could see nothing but the red lights. They always had a pencil in hand, so that every time they reached for a target, they marked the spot they had touched.

To score the results was a simple matter. Each target had a bull's-eye on it surrounded by a number of target rings. When a series of

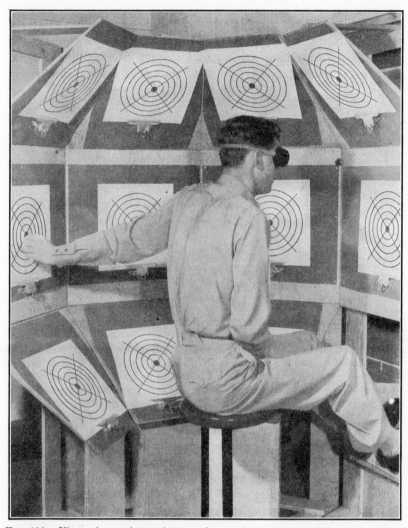

Fɪɢ. 126. View of experimental setup for studying blind-positioning reactions. The subject wears red goggles which allow him to look at a light straight ahead but not to see any of the target cards. When he reaches for a target card, he makes a mark which lets the experimenter tell how far off the bull's-eye he is. (After Fitts, 1947)

experiments was over with, the research psychologists simply took the cards and counted the number of marks in each part of the card.

It is a little difficult to explain how the study came out. The accompanying illustration (Figure 127) is the best way of summarizing the results and making them evident at a glance. There you will see 20 large circles, each standing for one of the target cards in the experi-

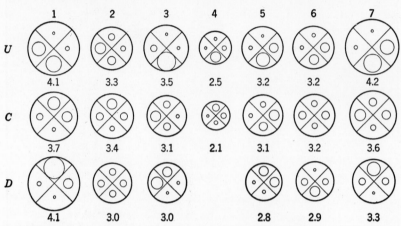

Fig. 127. Summary of results on free positioning movements. Each circle stands for a target square in the experiment. The upper row represents the seven targets above the shoulders of the operator, the middle row is the center row of squares in the experiment, and the row marked *D* is the group that were "down under." The size of each circle depicts the probable error of judgments for the corresponding square—the smaller the circle, the better the accuracy—and the number under the circle is the probable error. The little circles in the quadrants of the large circles show the relative number of errors in each quadrant. (After Fitts, 1947)

ment. The seven in the top row represent the row of targets above the pilot's head; the seven in the middle row stand for those at shoulder height; and the six on the bottom are those which were placed above the level of the pilot's seat. The blank space is the place where the pilot had his feet during the experiment. These 20 circles, divided into quadrants with little circles in each quadrant, tell the whole story.

Accuracy scores. The size of each of the large circles represents the accuracy scores in positioning reactions. Large circles mean that the pilots made large errors. When these circles are smaller, it means that the average error was smaller. You can see that the accuracy of positioning reactions is best directly in front of the pilot. The average error is only 2.1 inches. In front and above is almost as good; the average error is only 2.5 inches here. At the other extreme, the positions around to the side and slightly behind are the hardest to reach accurately. At these extreme positions the error is about 4 inches. All this means that controls can be placed nearer together when they are directly in front of the operator than when they are at the back and side. To derive a practical rule from an average error we must remember that the average error includes only a little more than 50 percent of the cases. To set the range that covers all cases of error, we must multiply by 3 to 4 (see p. 44). Completing this arithmetic, we can see that controls should be separated about 6 to 8 inches in the preferred areas in front of the pilot or operator and about 12 to 16 inches in the nonpreferred areas at the back and side. With these separations, the pilot can nearly always hit the right control.

Note, too, that accuracy of positioning movements is somewhat better for controls below the pilot's shoulder level than for those at shoulder level or above it. There is only one outstanding exception to this rule, and it occurs in one of the most unfavorable positions (1D in Figure 127).

Direction. Another kind of result is summarized in Figure 127. It is the direction in which positioning reactions are characteristically in error. The representative circles have been divided into quadrants on the target card. The research workers counted the number of marks falling in each quadrant and then drew a small circle in each quadrant proportional in size to the number of marks. By noting the size of these small circles in comparison to each other, we can get an idea whether the operators overshot or undershot and whether they reached too high or too low on the average. One thing that is rather clear is that positioning reactions in the upper area tend to undershoot; they are too low. That is quite consistent in the upper row of circles. There is a similar tendency to estimate the lower target positions too high, but this is by no means consistent. This undershooting of upper positions is most prominent near the center (but not right in the center) and around at the extremes of left and right. The overshooting of lower positions is greatest at the extreme left and right.

Obviously other experiments will have to be done with different populations of subjects before we can draw up specifications for the placement of controls to be operated by positioning reactions. We have described this experiment in detail, however, because it is a good experiment, and it is the only thorough experiment of its kind that has been done so far. It certainly gives us a rough idea of a person's positioning reactions, and the data can be used as a general guide in various kinds of practical situations.

VISUAL-POSITIONING MOVEMENTS

Let us now discuss the next class of movements: visual-positioning movements.* The main difference between this type of movement and the blind-positioning movement is that the operator can keep his eye on the mark as he makes the movement. Because he can see what he is doing, he gets it right sooner or later. Thus, there is no problem of accuracy, but time and pattern of the movement become matters of concern.

Examples of visual-positioning movements are plentiful in military, industrial, and everyday life. When a gunner is suddenly directed to a target in a new sector, he has to move his handlebars or gun controls from one position to another in a hurry. Many industrial production processes, including many types of assembly, require rapid movements from one position to another. Many of the transport movements— to use the language of motion-and-time economy—are visual-positioning movements. The quick turn of the wheel by the automobile driver to make a turn or avoid a collision is a positioning movement aided by vision. This class of movements, therefore, is of some importance in practical situations.

MOVEMENT BETWEEN STOPS

There are a few studies of visual-positioning movements in the literature of psychology and of motion-and-time engineering that bring out some interesting points. One of them (see Barnes) tells us about the time taken and the rate of movement of the hand motions back and forth between two stops. Careful measurements were made of the time required to get the hand started, the time during which it picks up speed, the time during which it is moving at maximum speed, the time of slowing down in speed, and the time stopped. These measurements were made for three different distances of movement: 5 inches, 10 inches, and 15 inches. You find the results in Figure 128.

Notice what happens. It takes practically as long to move your hand 5 inches and back as it does to move it 15 inches. Instead of picking up speed in a constant time after starting, you simply move

---

* The Wright Field psychologists (Brown and Jenkins) have called this class of movements "discrete movements." This term is a good one for some purposes, but for this particular summary we prefer to use "visual-positioning movement" because the principal difference between "blind-positioning movements" and "discrete movements" is that the latter permit the operator to use vision while making the movement.

faster for a longer distance. If the distance is small, the hand accelerates more slowly than if the distance is great.

The next result is that very little time is saved by shortening the distance of the movement. Notice, too, how much of the time is spent in changing direction. The top of the curves represents the hand finishing one discrete movement and getting ready to make the second one back to the original starting point.

It takes quite a while to stop one discrete movement and start the

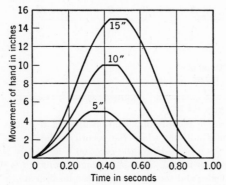

FIG. 128. The form of visual-positioning reactions at different distances. The curves show a movement to points 5, 10, and 15 inches, respectively, from the starting point and back again. Notice that the form remains about the same for different distances and particularly that it takes just about as long to make a 15-inch movement as a 5-inch movement. (After Barnes, 1940)

next; it represents about 15 to 24 percent of the entire time. Moreover, it is about the same, regardless of the distance of the discrete movement.

MOVEMENTS BETWEEN MARKERS

Another recent report from Iowa [12] gives us more data about visual-positioning movements. In this case, the psychologists fixed up a knob for the operator to push along a slide. The slide was arranged in front of him so he could make discrete movements either to the right or left. Three different distances of movement were studied: 2.5 centimeters (about 1 inch), 10 centimeters (about 4 inches) and 40 centimeters (about 15 inches). When the operator got a signal, he made his movement as rapidly as possible from the starting position to the aimed-for mark. The knob pushed by the operator was attached to a stylus on a moving tape so that a complete record of the time and form of the movement was made for later analysis.

Components of movement. The experimenters broke down the results into three kinds of measures: (*a*) reaction time, or the·time elaps-
ing between the signal to start and the beginning of the movement;
(*b*) primary-movement time, or the time from the beginning of movement to get the hand near the mark; and (*c*) secondary-movement
time, or the time of making minor corrective movements to get right
on the mark. You can see these three parts in some sample records
shown in Figure 129. The flat top of the record is the time the sub-

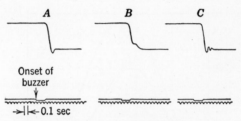

Fɪɢ. 129. Three sample records of visual-positioning reactions. In each record,
the operator is doing nothing while the record is flat at the top. When the
buzzer sounds, there is a brief delay, the reaction time, before the operator moves
and sends the record downward. The big change downward is the primary movement time. The wiggles and small changes at the bottom are the secondary movements made in the vicinity of the marker. When the record flattens out at the
bottom, all three phases of the movement have been completed. (After Slater-
Hammel and Brown, 1947)

ject is making no movement and the latter part of it, after the buzzer
sounds, is the reaction time; the big movement downward is the primary-movement time; and the minor movements before the record
flattens out on the bottom make up the secondary movement.

Time versus distance. Now we can see what happens to these different time measures when different distances of movement are used and
movement is made in different directions (see Figure 130). As we
might expect, the reaction time is about 0.25 second, and it is the same,
regardless of the distance to be moved or the direction of the movement. The reaction time is a constant. Primary-movement time gets
larger as the distance is increased: for 2.5 centimeters, it is about 0.20
second; for 10 centimeters, about 0.33 second; and for 40 centimeters,
about 0.56 second. But though the time increases, it does not increase
proportionately to the distance. For a 16-fold increase in distance,
there is less than a three-fold increase in time.

A similar but not identical thing happens in secondary corrective
movements. For 2.5 centimeters, these average 0.10 second; for 10 cen-

timeters, 0.18 second; and for 40 centimeters, 0.18 second. In other words, the time for corrective movements increases between 1 and 4 inches but after that seems to remain about constant. A more elaborate statistical analysis made by the authors ties in nicely with this conclusion.

Summary. Now, finally, let us look at the whole picture given by this study. Reaction time is a constant. The time of primary move-

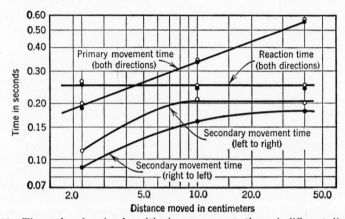

Fig. 130. Time taken for visual-positioning movements through different distances. Reaction time stays practically constant, regardless of the distance. Primary-movement time increases slightly with distance but not in proportion to distance. Neither do secondary-movement times. In fact, they are almost constant for distances greater than 10 centimeters (2½ inches). (After Slater-Hammel and Brown, 1947)

ments increases with distance, but not nearly in proportion to the distance. Secondary movements up to 4 inches take increasingly a little more time but not longer than 4 inches. All in all, there seems to be a basic mechanism in human visual positioning which makes the movement adjust fairly well to the distance. The greater the distance, the faster we move, so that time is roughly the same for many different distances.

We have described this Iowa study in detail because it is recent and thorough. There have been several other experiments on the same subject, however. They all point in the same direction: It does not take much more time to make big positioning movements than to make small discrete movements. The musical conductor, waving his baton, takes just about as long to make a big down stroke as a short one. It takes just about the same time to write in your own hand with large

letters as with small ones. And in movements made by gunners swinging onto targets, it again is practically as costly in time for a short
swing as a long one. The story is always the same. It has some practical applications which it would be a little better to take up later
when we talk about problems of arranging our work.

OTHER VARIABLES

So far we have talked only about positioning movements of the
hands and only about the importance of distance to be traversed.
There are a number of other questions one can ask—and answer—
about visual-positioning movements.

Direction of movements. First, does the direction of a movement
make any difference? The Iowa study has covered that problem, and
so have some others. In general, there is no startling difference. In
Figure 130, we see that direction makes no difference for reaction time
or primary adjustive movements. It does seem to make a little difference in secondary movement times, but this difference, shown in the
graph, is not highly significant. In some other experiments, there has
been a suggestion that right-to-left movements with the right hand
are slightly faster, and, in some, that left-to-right movements are
faster. In none of the cases, are these tendencies significant in a
statistical sense, and we might as well forget them. For hand movements, therefore, we can say that left–right direction of discrete movements is of no great significance.

We cannot be too sure, but there is some indication that discrete
movements with the left arm (or nonpreferred arm) may be a little
faster than those with the right arm. Also it looks as though flexing
the arm (bending movement) is somewhat slower than extension
(straightening movement). More experiments ought to be done on
these questions, but if we had to make a choice on the basis of our
present information we should assume that these small differences are
correct.

Control sticks. Another practical question about visual-positioning
movements is what happens when an operator is using a control stick
of the type commonly employed in aircraft. One thing we know is
that the rate of movement of the control stick is greater for push than
for pull. This ties in with extension movements being faster than
flexion movements. We know, too, that the rate of stick movement
is greater for greater displacements of the stick. The finding is like
the other one we discussed: Rate of movement is faster when the distance of the discrete movement is greater so that it does not take much

longer to make a big movement than a small one. Finally, it would appear that, under the best of operating conditions, the maximum rate of push that can be expected in discrete stick movements is about 250 inches per second, whereas that for pull stick movement is about 140 inches per second. Another experimenter, checking the same point, comes out with somewhat lower values of rate for pull and push—we know that the value will depend on the individual and the conditions —so these figures ought to be taken simply as indicating the general order of rates that might be expected.

Friction and load. In studying stick movements and other movements of the hands and feet, people have tried to find out what effect there is of putting a resistive load on the stick or control when it is moved to a new position. As we might expect, a load cuts down the rate of movement. In some cases, it looks as though there is simple proportionality between load and rate, in which the rate of movement goes down as resistive load is increased. In the future, we hope there will be a lot more data on this question. Most kinds of movements which operators perform in practical situations involve some load, and it would be good to know how much the speed of the reaction is cut down for different amounts of load.

There are some other items of information concerning positioning movements, but they will fit in best if they are put in a later section on the design and use of controls.

REPETITIVE MOVEMENTS

The name repetitive movement, as we want to use it here, means just about what it sounds like. It refers to any movement that is done over and over again. If we simply take one cycle, many repetitive movements might break down into other kinds of movement discussed previously. As we shall see, however, the fact that a movement is repeated gives it some special characteristics which are somewhat different than if the movement were made singly and only occasionally.

There is quite a bit of literature on repetitive movements (see Brown and Jenkins). In fact, as studies of movement go, one could say that the greatest percentage of them concerned repetitive movement. Unfortunately, most of the information has relatively little direct bearing on problems of instrument design and operation. It does, however, constitute some of the basic subject matter of engineering psychology.

The two kinds of repetitive reactions that have been studied most

frequently either in the laboratory or elsewhere are tapping movements
and cranking movements. Tapping movements are very easy to study
—all one needs is a board, something to tap, some kind of stylus, and
a system of counting—and they have caught the fancy of a number
of experimenters. We therefore have a lot of data on tapping.

TAPPING

Individual differences. As we might expect, there are wide individual differences in people's ability to tap. If we ask people to tap as
fast as possible, some can only get up to a maximum rate of 8 per
second; some can manage to do as well as 13 per second. This difference between people has been used as one of many possible tests of
mechanical ability, and some agencies concerned mainly with vocational counseling have used tests of rate of tapping to advise people
about their vocational abilities. It is questionable, however, whether
tapping ability has anything to do with anything except tapping. Put
another way, it is questionable whether one can predict from a person's tapping score whether he is efficient or not at other types of
movement.

Preferred tapping rate. A little more realistic than maximum tapping rate is the preferred tapping rate, that is, the rate a person will
tap if you tell him to go at a comfortable speed for a long period of
time. Preferred tapping rates for different people run between 1.5 and
5.0 taps per second. This rate, however, is not particularly stable.
You can change it by a number of conditions. If you force a person
to tap at some prescribed rhythm, paced, say, by the sound of a metro-
nome, then tell him later to tap at his preferred rate, you will find
that the preferred rate has changed—in the direction of the rate at
which he was forced to work for a while.

Tapping amplitude. One point of interest is the matter of the
amount of excursion in tapping. This is like the distance of a discrete
movement, and the answer is about the same. It does not make much
difference in tapping rate whether the excursion is very small, say, 1
millimeter, or relatively large, say, 40 millimeters (nearly 2 inches).
Extremely small or extremely large tapping motions are a little hard
for an operator to make, and it turns out that there is some advantage to a tapping rate of making an excursion of about 20 millimeters
(a little less than an inch). Most of the time in tapping, however, is
taken in starting, stopping, and changing direction, so tapping rate is
relatively constant, regardless of excursion.

How to tap. People have paid some attention to how we should tap, whether with the fingers, wrist, elbow, or the whole arm. In general their experiments agree that the highest rate is gotten when most of the arm is used, either completely freely or at least with the whole arm from the elbow. You cannot tap as fast when you use only wrist motions as you can with your whole arm, and your tapping speed is even worse if you try to use only your fingers and keep your hand still.

There are a few factors in tapping movements which are easily converted into practical applications. We will mention just one here—the question of the position of the hand in tapping, whether tapping up and down or sideways. Contrary to what we might expect on first thought, most people can tap somewhat faster sideways than up and down—like drumming the fingers on the table. Also we can continue tapping longer if we tap sideways. This fact has been translated into practice in the redesign of telegraph keys to be manipulated by sidewise motion rather than up-and-down motion. Such keys have found their way into practice in some quarters.

CRANKING MOVEMENTS

There is another kind of repetitive movement we are beginning to learn something about. In scientific language we would call it manual rotatory performance, but you will understand, no doubt, what we mean when we speak simply of cranking.

We could ask a good many questions about cranking. Some of them, if answered correctly, might make many cranks that we have to contend with a lot more crankable. First of all, how fast can we crank, and under what conditions? Do we crank better if we make big circular movements than if we make small ones? Do we crank better if we have a load to work against than if we do not? Can we crank better in one plane than another or at one distance than another? We know the answers to some of these questions, but we will need more research before we can find all the answers.

Cranking radius. The easiest way to talk about the size of our cranking movements, whether in big circles or in small ones, is to speak of the radius of a crank. For when we are cranking, it is the radius of the crank that determines how large our movements are. In Figure 131 are some curves showing how fast one subject in an experiment was able to crank with different radii. For the moment, look only at the top curve, and forget the others. Though this curve is for one subject, a lot of other curves like this one have been measured,

and they all look much the same. The curve tells us for one thing
that we can crank about 275 revolutions per minute. It also shows
that the rate of cranking goes down when the radius of the crank is
very large. But notice, too, that, when we increase the radius by a
factor of ten times, say, from 2.4 to 24 centimeters, the cranking rate
is cut less than half. In other words, how fast we can crank is not

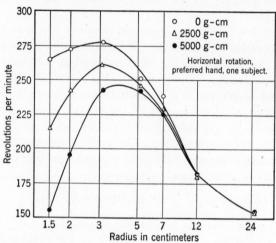

Fig. 131. Fastest cranking rates for different radii and different drags on the
crank. The upper curve is for a crank with hardly any friction, and the lower
two curves have increased friction (or load). Notice that cranking rate goes
down as the radius is increased, but not so much as we might expect. Notice too
that putting on a load affects the shorter radii much more than the larger ones
and shifts the radius for optimum performance slightly to the right. (After Reed,
1948)

directly proportional to the size of our cranking movements—far from
it. This is like some of the other things we have noticed. It does not
take 10 times as long to move 10 times the distance either. So, in
cranking, as in other kinds of movements, the movements tend to compensate for the distance and to be more nearly constant than proportional to the distance to go.

Force and resistance. Now look again at Figure 131, and observe
the lower two curves. These answer the question about load or resistance in making cranking movements. First of all, there is an optimum point in all of these curves—a value of radius about 3 centimeters which gives the best cranking rate. And, second, in the region
of the optimum, any load or drag imposed on the crank cuts down our

ability to crank. At high radii, where cranking is rather poor anyway, the load does not make much difference. Notice, too, that the optimum shifts upward a little as the load is increased; the peak of the curves goes from about 3 to 4 centimeters. This is a general rule which may be applied to a lot of things about cranking that we do not have time to go into: Any factor that tends to impair motor coordination or make the task harder shifts optimum performance to higher radii.

There are other things we know about cranking and other things to be learned through more research, but we shall let this brief summary do for the present. It demonstrates that in cranking, as well as in other kinds of movement, some principles are fairly useful. When applied, they can make a good deal of difference in the efficiency with which we can crank a crank.

CONTINUOUS ADJUSTIVE MOVEMENTS

Our classification of movements is not perfect, and we are not too satisfied about what gets called continuous movement, repetitive movement, or positioning movement. We must nevertheless have some classification, and we shall keep the present one until a better one comes along. In talking about continuous movements, we mean that a man must continuously do something, like adjusting a wheel, turning a wheel, pushing a rudder, or adjusting a lever to compensate for the changes in the outside world. Steering a car is a continuous movement, for the man must continuously make adjustments for the curve of the road or obstacles in his path. Driving almost any vehicle, whether it be a tank, automobile, or airplane, requires continuous control movements. Tracking a moving target with a gunsight involves continuous movements.

What do we know about continuous movement? Unfortunately, not so much as we would like to. What information we have comes from experiments concerned with aircraft or military applications, and more is needed for industrial purposes. This is what we know so far:

ANALYSIS OF HANDWHEEL TRACKING

First we want to know what goes on in continuous adjustive movements. Recently there were some exploratory experiments in this field conducted at the University of Indiana [10] under the sponsorship of Wright Field. A large handwheel was chosen for continuous adjust-

ment, and the operator was presented with two pointers. One pointer
moved left or right on a predetermined course not known to the operator. The other pointer was moved by the adjustive movements of
the operator. His problem was to keep the two pointers lined up
by moving the wheel as much as was necessary.

Measures of movement. The subjects were first thoroughly trained
in the problem until they got to be rather good at it. Then very careful measurements were made on a recording device of just what movements were made by the operator in keeping the two pointers matched

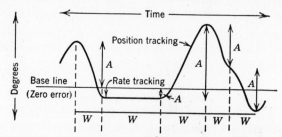

FIG. 132. A sample record of tracking movements. The dotted lines show different
wavelength (actually half-waves) components of the record *W*. The arrows show
the amplitude of the wavelength component *A*. The two kinds of tracking waves,
position tracking and rate tracking, are indicated. (After Hill, Gray, and Ellson,
1947)

up. In Figure 132, you can see the kind of record the Indiana psychologists got. This is not an actual record, but one showing the kinds
of movements that are recorded. As you can see, the record is "wavy";
it looks as though an analysis of the records could be made in terms
of the size and types of waves that make them up. That is what the
psychologists tried.

They made three types of measurements on all of their records:
They measured (*a*) the wavelength of each wave, (*b*) the amplitude
or excursion of each wave, and (*c*) the initial error of each wave. Put
another way, they used each corrective movement as their unit for
analysis and determined how long it took to make the movement
(wavelength), how far off the operator was when he started to make it
(initial error), and how far off he was when he finished the movement
(amplitude of the movement). This apparently is a good way to approach the problem, and it gives some interesting results.

Types of movement. For one thing, it became clear that there are
two kinds of adjustive movements: The first is *rate-tracking* movements in which the operator makes a continuous adjustment at just

about the same speed as the target pointer is moving. This kind of movement has a small initial error, for the operator stays fairly close to the true course. It has relatively small amplitude, for the operator is attempting to make his correction continuously at the same rate as the target pointers. And it has a relatively long wavelength, for the operator maintains the continuous corrective adjustment for relatively long periods of time. The second type of movement is a *position-tracking* movement in which the operator gets some distance off course

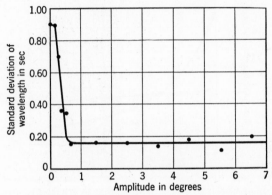

Fig. 133. The variability of wavelength of adjustive movements for different amplitudes of movement. We see that variability is very high for amplitudes less than ½ degree, but constant for larger amplitudes. For this reason, ½ degree was taken as the dividing line for rate-tracking and position-tracking movements. (After Hill, Gray, and Ellson, 1947)

and makes a quick adjustment to get back on course. Movements of this type have high initial errors, they have high amplitudes, and the wavelength, that is, the time taken to complete one adjustment, is relatively short.

This division of movements into corrective movements and rate-tracking movements is an experimental fact which shows up in all sorts of ways of analyzing the data.

Wavelength versus amplitude. Consider first, the problem of wavelength of movements versus the amplitude of the movements. In Figure 133, you see the standard deviation of wavelengths, that is, the variability of time taken to make a movement, plotted against the amplitude of the movement. There is great variability when the amplitude of the movement is less than ½ degree (error was measured in degrees); the standard deviation of wavelength for small amplitudes is very high. On the other hand, with amplitudes of adjustment greater than ½ degree, the time taken for a movement is much more constant, and, it does not matter how great the movement is, the variability in time to make the movement is just about the same. Thus it looks as though two different things were going on below and above ½ degree. Accordingly, ½ degree of movement was taken as the line for dividing rate-tracking movements from position-tracking movements.

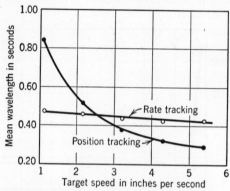

Fɪɢ. 134. The average time (wavelength) for rate-tracking and position-tracking movements at different target speeds. Notice that the time of rate-tracking movements is practically constant for all target speeds, but, on the other hand, the time for a position-tracking movement steadily decreases with increasing speed until it becomes a constant at about 5 inches per second. (After Hill, Gray, and Ellson, 1947)

Wavelength versus pointer speed. You can see the difference between the two kinds of movements again in the plot of wavelength versus target speed (Figure 134). In the experiments, there were five different target speeds which can be specified either in terms of inches of movement of the pointer or in terms of the equivalent rotary motion of the handwheel. If we plot the wavelengths of corrective movements of amplitude greater than ½ degree, we see that there is very little relation to target speed. The curve is almost flat. The mean wavelength (time) to make a corrective adjustment gets a little faster when the target speed goes up—but not much. The rate-tracking movements, on the other hand, are of much shorter wavelength when the target speed is high. The decrease in wavelength of these tracking movements is almost directly proportional to the increase in target speed, though not quite so.

Types of movement and target speed. There are other facts from this study which fit into the picture. The percentage of rate-tracking movements goes down as target speed goes up, and the percentage of corrective movements goes up as target speed goes up. Moreover, a further breakdown of the data shows that (a) the total number of movements of any sort tends to decrease as the target speed goes up, (b) the number of corrective movements remains almost constant, though increasing slightly, and (c) the number of rate-tracking movements decreases tremendously with increases in speed.

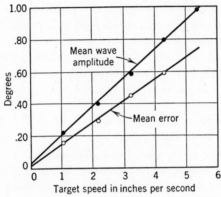

Fɪɢ. 135. The average amplitude of waves and the average error for different target speeds. We see that both simply increase proportionally with target speed. This means that the relative error is about constant for different target speeds. (After Hill, Gray, and Ellson, 1947)

Error and target speed. Perhaps before we leave this subject we should explain what consequence all this has in terms of error of the continuous movements. The graph in Figure 135, which disregards the difference in the two types of movement, tells what the average error is, in degrees, for the movement problem at different target speeds. We see that the average error increases with target speed in a uniform fashion. Also in Figure 135 and showing roughly the same thing is a plot of average wave amplitude for increasing target speeds. Wave amplitude is simply the average size of adjustment by the operator. This, too, increases with speed.

The interesting thing, however, is that the increase with speed is just what we would expect if the size of the adjustment were proportional to the target speed. Put another way, it is what we would expect if percentage (relative) error stayed constant. By actual computation, relative error increases from 3.08 percent at the slow speed to 3.51 percent at the highest speed. Thus it is practically constant.

Time error as a measure. There is another way of measuring the effectiveness of continuous movements. It seems a little strange at first, but it makes sense. The measure is time error. This is not to be confused with a special phenomenon of time error frequently described by psychologists. Here, it is simply the error of an operator put in terms of the amount by which he is behind or ahead of his target at the rate the target is moving. Thus, by measuring the number of inches of error or the degrees of handwheel movement and dividing it by the speed of the target, we can convert any error measurement into time. The nice thing about this measure is that it is completely independent of a lot of variables we might have in an experiment, such as scale factor, handwheel size, gear ratios—any factor, except the speed of the target. Any time error for a particular speed, however, can always be corrected for the speed of the target by multiplying by the appropriate factor.

Handwheel speed and adjustive movements. This kind of measure has been used in some experiments done during the war on continuous movements (Helson [1, 2]). One thing Helson did, which the Indiana psychologists did not do, was to measure the effect of handwheel speed on tracking performance. In the Indiana experiments, the amount of turn of the wheel to make a movement of the pointer was kept constant at 4.77 degrees of wheel turning to 1 inch of pointer movement. Changing target speed required a higher rate of turning the handwheel to keep up with the target. In Helson's experiments, however, he kept his target at constant speed and changed the amount of turning required to keep up with the target. The correct handwheel speed could then be specified in terms of revolutions per minute. He could study, then, the effect of error of different handwheel speeds on tracking performance as measured by time error.

His results are shown in Figure 136. They are quite clear. Up to about 200 revolutions per minute the greater the handwheel speed the less the error. He did not go above 200 revolutions per minute, but we may expect that, at some speed above that, error would get worse, because a person can only turn a handwheel so fast and still have it under control. After that, he might spin the wheel and make it coast, but he would lose control of the rate at which he could make it move. It is interesting, however, that increasing handwheel speed is a means of making continuous movements more accurate. This ought to be true regardless of target speed, for target speed can change only the relative error, not the absolute error. Helson has, in fact, shown that faster handwheel speeds are better than slower ones, no matter what conditions are used, whether of inertia of handwheel, friction, diameter of handwheel, course magnification, course difficulty, or duration. He found that the optimal speed, that is, the speed of lowest error before the "breaking" of the operator varied a little with the various conditions (140 to 200 revolutions per minute), but the highest possible handwheel speed before the operator breaks was, in all his experiments, the best for getting the lowest error.

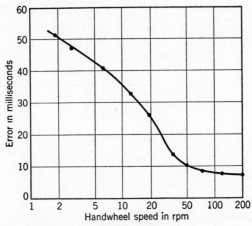

Fig. 136. Error in handwheel tracking at different speeds. The time error corresponds to the distance the operator is ahead of or behind the moving target. We see that error is high for slow handwheel speeds and becomes smaller with increasing speed. Error is least at relatively high speeds of 100 to 200 rpm. (Anonymous source, 1943)

Characteristics of the handwheel. There are some other factors in continuous tracking that Helson has studied quantitatively.[2] These are "weight" or "heaviness" of the handwheel, the "inertia" of the hand, the friction against which the handwheel must be moved, and the size of the handwheel. All these factors are of some importance in performance, but they interact with each other in a fairly complicated fashion. The results are summarized in the series of graphs in Figure 137.

You can see there that inertia is a good thing. It decreases error at slow handwheel speeds but not so much at high speeds. Thus it is a good idea to make a handwheel heavy. If it is not possible to have a high handwheel speed, then it is also a good idea to provide additional inertia if that is possible. The size of the handwheel in diameter is not so important, but it does help a little to have it bigger if the handwheel is light in weight and if handwheel speeds are low. You can see that friction is a bad thing. It reduces accuracy somewhat under almost all conditions, but it is particularly bad for light handwheels and for low handwheel speeds.

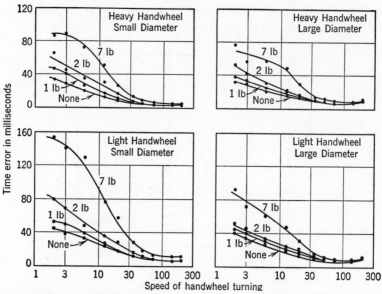

FIG. 137. Error in handwheel tracking for handwheels of different size, of different diameter and with different amounts of friction. We can see that friction is always harmful, but especially at low handwheel speeds. A large diameter is usually better than small diameter particularly for light handwheels. A heavy handwheel is better than a light one. (Anonymous source, 1943)

SUMMARY

In this chapter, we have reviewed some of the things we know about the ways people make movements. There is much to be learned through future research, and our present knowledge raises more questions than it answers. There are, however, a few things that stand out rather clearly.

First, it is possible to classify movements, even if crudely, to help us think more clearly about them. And we can measure them in several ways: by action potentials taken from contracting muscles, by measuring the speed of the movements, and by measuring the accuracy of movements. There are a good many things that affect these measures of movement: whether we can see what we are doing or not; which direction we move in, whether up or down, or toward or away from the body; the distance of the movement; the friction and inertia impeding the movement; and the speed of the thing we are trying to follow when we track. It is very worth while, too, to make measurements of movements under these various conditions, for we often discover certain conditions which are most favorable and most efficient for the kinds of movements we want to make.

This chapter, however, does not end our study of movements. In those that follow, we shall discuss some more specific problems of moving and using controls and of arranging our work most effectively.

SELECTED REFERENCES

1. ANONYMOUS. Handwheel speed and accuracy of tracking. Office of Scientific Research and Development, Report No. 3453, 1943. Publication Board No. PB–40615, Office of Technical Services, U. S. Department of Commerce, Washington, D. C.
2. ANONYMOUS. Inertia, friction and diameter in handwheel tracking. Office of Scientific Research and Development, Report No. 3454, 1943. Publication Board No. PB–40614, Office of Technical Services, U. S. Department of Commerce, Washington, D. C.
3. BARNES, R. M. *Motion and time study* (3d Ed.). New York: John Wiley, 1949.
4. BROWN, J. S., and JENKINS, W. O. An analysis of human motor abilities related to the design of equipment and a suggested program of research. In FITTS, P. M. (Ed.). *Psychological research on equipment design.* U. S. Government Printing Office, 1947, 35–63.
5. BROWN, J. S., KNAUFT, E. B., and ROSENBAUM, G. The accuracy of positioning reactions as a function of their direction and extent. *Amer. J. Psychol.,* 1948, **61**, 167–182.
6. EDWARDS, A. S. The finger tromometer. *Amer. J. Psychol.,* 1946, **59**, 273–283.
7. FITTS, P. M. Analysis of factors contributing to 460 "pilot-error" experiences in operating aircraft controls. Engineering Division, Air Materiel Command, Dayton, Ohio, Report No. TSEAA–694–12, 1 July 1947.
8. FITTS, P. M. A study of location discrimination ability. In FITTS, P. M. (Ed.). *Psychological research on equipment design.* U. S. Government Printing Office, 1947, 207–217.
9. FOSSLER, H. R. Range and distribution of tremor frequencies. *J. Gen. Psychol.,* 1931, **5**, 410–414.
10. HILL, H., GRAY, F., and ELLSON, D. G. Wave length and amplitude characteristics of tracking error curves. Engineering Division, Air Materiel Command, Dayton, Ohio, Report No. TSEAA–694–2D, 22 April 1947.
11. REED, J. D. Factors influencing rotary performance. The Johns Hopkins University, Ph.D. Dissertation, 1948.
12. SLATER-HAMMEL, A. T., and BROWN, J. S. Discrete movements in the horizontal plane as a function of their length and direction. Office of Naval Research, Special Devices Center, Report No. 57–II–2, 1947.

13. STETSON, R. H., and BOUMAN, H. D. The action current as a measure of muscle contraction. *Science,* 1933, **77,** 219–221.
14. STETSON, R. H., and McDILL, J. A. Mechanism of the different types of movement. *Psychol. Monogr.,* 1923, **32,** 18–40.
15. WHIPPLE, G. M. *Manual of mental and physical tests. Part I: Simpler processes.* Baltimore: Warwick and York, 1924.

11. Controls for Human Use

THE LAST CHAPTER TOLD BRIEFLY ABOUT MAN'S WAYS OF MAKING MOVE-
ments. In this chapter, let us take a step closer to the engineer's problems of designing controls which human operators must use. Let us
see what can and should be done to make controls more usable.

Tools versus controls. Most of this chapter will deal with controls,
but some of it will apply also to tools. The distinction, for our purposes, is a minor one. A control is something attached to a panel or a
machine; it is anchored to something that keeps one from walking away
with it. That fact creates a lot of special problems of placement of
controls, shape of controls, size, direction of movement, and the like.
It is such problems that will be of most concern to us here. A tool, on
the other hand, from the human point of view, is something like a
screwdriver, hammer, or saw that a man can pick up and move about
as he likes. There are some things to be said about tools, such as their
proper shape, weight, and kind of use. These are not so important as
the problems of controls, but we will say something about them, too. In
the broad sense of the term, of course, a tool is anything, including a
very elaborate machine, that is used to make something with. But in
this discussion we can forget machine tools and worry only about the
tools and controls that are manipulated directly by human operators.

Hands and feet. Cats in puzzle boxes sometimes operate latches by
hitting them with their tails or bumping them with their heads. Some
monkeys do pretty well at picking things up with their tails. Man,
however, is not quite so versatile. In theory, he might operate some
controls with his teeth or his head, but, in practice, he has to do just
about everything with his hands and feet. All the controls, therefore,
that we shall discuss in this chapter are those that people work with
their arms and hands or with their legs and feet.

Industrial engineers now usually accept the maxim that "the hands
should be relieved of all duties that can be taken over by the legs and
feet." Because we are best with our hands, we get in the habit of

having our hands do all of the work—just as we tend to have our eyes do all the perceiving because they are so good at it. There is, however, hardly a machine used in everyday life or in industry where we do not have to do several things at once. And, although the hands are good, they cannot do everything at once. The feet can do some things, and the answer to this problem is to shift some control functions to the feet. Driving an automobile, for example, is a pretty simple job, but even that requires three or four movements close together in time. The automobile designers, therefore, have been putting more and more controls on the floor to be operated by the feet. The same is true of other modern machines. So throughout this chapter we shall take up problems of foot controls as well as those of hand controls.

The importance of controls. One of the important problems in engineering is to tell how much to expect of a machine and how much to expect of the operator. The engineer frequently designs the best machine he knows how to build, and, then if something goes wrong with it, he lays the blame at the door of maintenance or of the operator who runs it. He may not have realized that he designed the controls of the machine so that no one but a genius with a lot of time on his hands could possibly run it. But, of course, this miscalculation is not the fault of the engineer either, for someone should have told him just what to expect of the operator.

Unfortunately, there are very few studies analyzing the operator's side of running a machine. There ought to be many more of them. One good example of such a study comes from the aviation psychologists. The cockpit of a plane is a serious problem in the operation of controls. We will discuss it briefly as an illustration of what can be done and as a way of introducing the main problems and facts of this chapter.

CONTROLS AND PILOT ERRORS

The aviation psychologists at Wright Field [3] were given the task of doing something about controls in the airplane cockpit. People have known for a long time that many aircraft accidents were ascribed to "pilot errors," not to failure of the plane. Pilot errors frequently become a life-and-death matter, not only for the pilot but also for all who are riding with him. Thus it was important to find out how many of these so-called pilot errors might have something to do with the design and use of controls in the aircraft. The Wright Field psychologists, therefore, started to track down all cases of aircraft accidents in which the pilot lived to tell the tale. The pilots were located and extensively interviewed. Every "error" which they made personally or observed was carefully recorded. Altogether 460 pilot errors were studied. The data were then analyzed to determine the sources of error.

Confusion of controls. By far the largest source of pilot error was in the confusion of controls—mistakenly operating one control when another was the correct one. And one of the most frequent confusions was operating the wrong control in the throttle control quadrant. In other words, the pilot would pull the throttle when he intended to pull the propeller control or change the gasoline mixture when he meant to pull the throttle. A look at the design of different planes made it pretty clear why this type of error happened frequently. The different but related controls were arranged in a different sequence on every different plane the pilot had to fly. The throttle was on the left in the B-25 and in the center in the C-47 and C-82. The propeller control was in the center in the B-25, on the left in the C-47, and on the right in the C-82. And similarly, the gas-mixture control was on the right in the B-25 and C-47 but on the left in the C-82. It is no wonder that a pilot makes mistakes when he finds the same control in a different place in every machine he flies.

Crowding of controls. Another trouble occurs because controls that are placed together have very different uses. These three controls we just talked about were located close together. Also, on many planes, the control for the wing flap and the landing gear were side by side—though to land a plane you must put one up and the other down; to take off you do just the opposite. Serious accidents could be traced to confusing these two controls. Later designs of airplanes usually avoid making this mistake nowadays.

There were several other sources of confusion in operating controls, such as operating the control for the wrong engine or identifying the wrong switches for landing lights. But these two examples are enough to illustrate the point.

Control adjustment errors. The Wright Field psychologists found another type of error in operating controls to be quite common: adjustment errors. Sometimes pilots would select the wrong fuel tank, sometimes follow the improper sequence of controls in lowering wheels, or fail to adjust their wing flaps at the correct rate. Most of these mistakes happened because the job was too complicated—there were just too many adjustments to make for the proper setting. The cure that was suggested was to make some of the adjustments automatic and to simplify the sequence of motions for the pilot.

Forgetting errors. In addition to these two classes of errors, which were large percentagewise, there were four other general categories of errors. One was of simple forgetting errors. But even these could be eliminated by engineering devices. Forgetting errors seemed to appear in long and involved check-off procedures, such as a pilot goes through in getting ready to take off. Any little distraction can make him forget where he is in the sequence. The Wright Field psychologists suggest that controls should be made to remain locked until all previous adjustments in a sequence have been made.

Reversal errors. A fourth class of errors they called *reversal errors.* The pilot moved the control in the direction opposite to what he intended or to what he should have done to produce the correct result. You might think this would be the pilot's fault—but not necessarily. Some of these reversals are due to the "unnaturalness" of the movement required by the control. If the pilot is supposed to move a control to the right, when he wants to go left, or if he is supposed to push a control inward while he is pulling another control outward or pulling his whole body back to go into a climb, there may be some excuse for making an error. Psychologically, certain directions of movement are natural. At least they go along with other things we are doing. To avoid errors, the controls should be designed to take account of such natural bents on the part of operators.

Unintentional errors. A fifth class of errors, described by the Wright Field psychologists, involves accidentally moving a control. This happens when controls are too close together and the operator knocks one control in attempting to operate another one. Or his arm can brush a control located too close to his body when he is reaching out for another control. Such unintentional errors are certainly an engineering fault, for they can happen only when controls have been crowded too close together or have been placed so that the operator cannot move freely without knocking them.

Reaching errors. Finally, an error that may not seem reasonable— but nevertheless happens in airplanes, and in other machines as well— is a reaching error. The pilot just cannot reach the control that he wants. This happens sometimes because the instrument panel containing the control is too far away from him, and no provision has been made for the adjustment of his seat—if he is a short man—to get him closer to it. Or, occasionally, the operator must be operating one control close to his body, say, the control stick, and cannot at the same time reach another control. Such reaching errors are plainly a fault of engineering design and may be remedied by insuring that controls are located so that any two may be reached at the same time—at least any two that must be used together.

We wish that there were more and better studies of how errors or losses in efficiency in the operation of machines depended on the design and arrangement of controls. The story of the pilot errors, however, will give an example—one that can concern life and death—of how such studies can be conducted and the results they will give. With it, too, we are introduced to the kinds of problems with which we deal in the engineering psychology of controls.

THE SELECTION OF CONTROLS

If we were given the task of designing some controls for the best human use, we would want some logical way to go about the problem. We would have a whole series of questions to answer. The rest of this chapter will take up those questions, one by one.

The first question would be what kind of control to select for a particular task. This is not easy to answer. There are an infinite variety of controls. Their names and their physical types defy good classification. We have pedals, pushbuttons, toggle switches, selector switches, joysticks, levers, throttles, and so on through a long list. Some day we may have a little handbook giving a complete list of physical types of controls together with recommendations for how they can be used. It is a little too early to attempt that now.

Types of controls. At present, there are two things we can do: (1) think through very carefully what kind of control would be most helpful to the operator; and (2) run controlled experimental tests of the merits of different types of controls. The first task requires only some common sense—but good sense nevertheless. If the operator needs only to turn something on and off, he should be given a simple *contact control*—a control that merely turns things on and off with a relatively effortless motion. If the operator must choose one of several conditions, he should be given a *selector control* which allows selection of one of several positions. Finally, whenever the operator must make continuous adjustments, he should be given an *adjustment control* which allows him to make any desired setting. Such a crude classification of controls according to their use is a matter of common sense. Sometimes, however, engineers forget to consider the operator and pick a control that may be logical from the standpoint of the machine's design but neglects the job the operator has to do.

Experimental selection of controls. Though common sense is something we should never be without, there are many questions concerning the selection of controls that cannot be answered by just using our heads. Some questions need scientific measurements of human performance with different kinds of controls before we can decide which kind of control to choose. Such experimental measurements are extremely

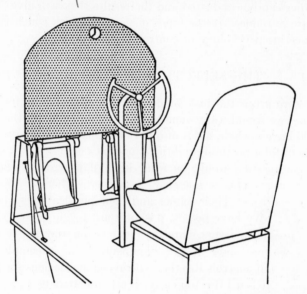

Fig. 138. Apparatus for comparing effectiveness of different flight controls. The operator sits and watches the small clock-type indicator at the top of the panel. This indicator has two pointers which are moved by some automatic machinery to simulate changes occurring in flight. The operator can use the different controls to keep these pointers on their correct marks. (After Grether, 1947)

rare—so rare that all we can do now is give one example of how such experiments can be done. There are several experiments of this kind going on today, and in a few years from now there may be some extensive information on the selection of controls.

The example again comes from the Wright Field psychologists.[5] They selected for study the question of what types of flying controls should be provided for a pilot. They compared rudder movements of the feet, stick movements of the hands, and wheel movements of the hands. The operator of the controls had to keep an indicator in front of him centered at all times (see Figure 138). An automatic device kept pushing this indicator a little off the mark, just as the drift of the plane and air currents would if the plane were in flight. The operator's job was to use the control to compensate for the drifting movements of the indicator. The psychologists measured the percent of the time the operators managed to keep on the target with each control.

Actually the experiment was done in several different ways, but the variations need not concern us here. Here are the main things they discovered from the experiments: The arm controls—the stick and wheel—were consistently better than the leg control—the rudder. So, any time precise adjustment is needed, we should use arm controls. Leg controls can be used for coarse adjustments.

Second, they discovered that pilots are just as accurate with a stick as with a wheel. Of course, the wheel takes two hands to operate, and the stick only one. Thus, if there is any important reason for freeing one hand, the stick control should be selected. No harm would be done because performance would be just as good as with the wheel control.

This is just an example. The important point about it is that we can select controls scientifically. The matter need not be left to guess nor to personal opinion. We can design scientific experiments that will tell you which of several possible controls is the best and how much so. Experiments of this sort would do much to improve design by selecting proper controls for human use.

REALISM IN CONTROLS

Selecting the proper type of control is merely the first of many problems in the engineering psychology of controls. A second problem is how to design the control so that it is most "natural" or "realistic" for the operator. The use of realism has become an important principle in the selection and design of controls.

There are many different ways in which the principle may be applied—each depends on the particular engineering problem involved. In some cases, there will have to be research studies to find out what is natural or realistic to the operator. In many other situations, a little common sense will do. If a control in an airplane is supposed to make the airplane go down, then it would be a good idea if the control had to be pushed down to accomplish this result. If we want to make a lathe go clockwise, then the control should go clockwise. If we want to produce a movement to the left, the control should move to the left. This principle is not always applied in the design of controls. We are not sure how much it costs not to use this principle, but we hope that the research men will do something on the problem in the near future.

Natural direction of control and indicator movement. One research from Wright Field [11] is a good example of how to find out what is natural or realistic for an operator. Five different panels were set up as shown in Figure 139. Each panel had a circular control knob and a

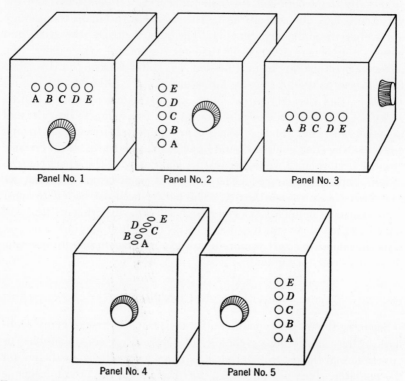

FIG. 139. Five panels with different relationships between control and indicator movement. Operators were tested on each panel to see what direction of control movement was natural or realistic to the operators. (After Warrick, 1947)

row of five lights. In each case, a light was presented off center, and movement of the knob in either direction would bring the light back to the center position of the five lights. The problem presented to pilots was to find out which way they naturally turned the knob to bring the light back to center.

You see in Figure 139, however, that the arrangement of lights and knobs on each panel was different. On one, the lights were arranged horizontally above the knob. On another, they were placed vertically to the left of the knob, and on another in a vertical position to the right of the knob. On the other two panels, the lights and knob were on different sides of the panel box. The question for study was: What directions of rotation for the different setups seem natural or realistic?

On three of these panels, there were clear-cut results. These were the three in which the knob and the lights were mounted on the same panel face. On panel 1, subjects turned the knob clockwise to move the lights from *A* or *B* toward *C* and turned it counterclockwise to turn the lights from *D* or *E* back toward *C*. Similar results were obtained on panels 2 and 5. On panel 2, the operators turned the dial clockwise to move the lights from *A* or *B* to *C*, and counterclockwise to move them from *D* or *E* to *C*. And on panel 5, which differed only from panel 2 in that the lights were on the left rather than the right of the knob, exactly the reverse results were obtained. All these choices occurred between 70 and 95 percent of the time and represented strong and significant tendencies. All the results follow a simple rule: An operator naturally turns a knob clockwise to get clockwise movement of the signal controlled, and he naturally turns it counterclockwise to get counterclockwise movement. We have experimentally confirmed the commonsense rule stated previously that a control should move in the same direction as the thing controlled.

As you might guess, panels 3 and 4 showed equivocal results. The lights were not mounted in the same plane as the knob. With this situation, there did not seem to be any particularly natural way to turn the knob. Anxious to find out whether there was any significant difference, the experimenters carried the experiment a step further. They revised the two panels to make 11 lights rather than just 5 (see Figure 140). Then they deliberately had operators turn the knobs in one direction or the other to see how quickly and how accurately they could adjust the light to the center position with the two different directions of rotation. With these measures of performance, rather than simple preferences for direction of movement, some differences could be found. The reactions were faster and somewhat more accurate when the clockwise movement of the indicator moved the indicator lights to the left. And in the revised panel 4, errors were fewer, and speed somewhat greater, when clockwise motion of the knob moved the indicator lights away from the operator. The differences obtained, however, were rather small. It was concluded in this type of setup that, if other engineering considerations are important, it does not matter too much what the direction of control and indicator movements are.

Control plane and display plane. There is still a third study [1] in this series about realism or naturalness in controls. The purpose of

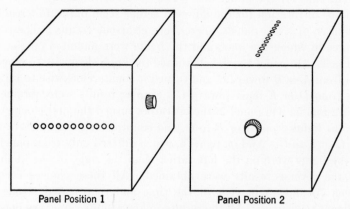

Panel Position 1   Panel Position 2

FIG. 140. Two control-indicator arrangements studied for "realism." These are similar to the two arrangements in Figure 139 which gave equivocal results, but they have 11 lights rather than 5 lights. For the results, see text. (After Warrick, 1947)

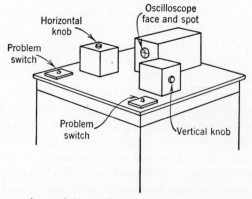

FIG. 141. Apparatus for studying realism in control movement. The spot on the oscilloscope can be moved in two dimensions, up and down and side to side. The horizontal and vertical control knobs can be so connected to the oscilloscope that either one moves the spot in either direction. The problem switches are used to time the ending of each adjustment of the respective controls. (After Carter and Murray, 1947)

this study was to see what *plane* the control should move in to give the best results with an indicator moving in a given plane. You can see the apparatus for the study in Figure 141. It consisted of one rotary control with its shaft in the perpendicular plane, another rotary control with its shaft in the horizontal plane parallel to the face of the display, and a display tube consisting of a cathode-ray tube with a spot on it. The operator's problem in the experiment was to control a spot on the tube face which initially was always off center and to bring the spot back to the center of the hair lines by rotating one or the other of the

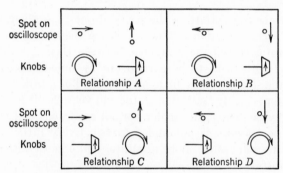

FIG. 142. The relationships between movements of knobs and movement of spot on oscilloscope. The diagram represents the relationships in the apparatus and experiment shown in Figure 141. These four relationships and their opposites were studied experimentally to see which ones were most natural for the operator.

controls. One control always affected one dimension of movement of the spot, and the other control always moved the spot in the other dimension.

If you stop and think a minute, you will see that there are eight different combinations of control movement and display movement. Four combinations are exactly the reverse of the others in direction of movement, and so let us consider only four combinations. These are shown in Figure 142. In two of these conditions, the axis of the control is perpendicular to the plane of movement of the display, or, put another way, the plane of rotation of the control is parallel to the plane of display movement. In two of these conditions the plane is reversed.

The results of this study may be considered in two parts: plane of movement, and direction of rotation. Clearest of all was the superiority of relationships *A* and *B* over relationships *C* and *D*. In other words, the relationships depicted in the top part of Figure 142 were better than those in the bottom part. The time taken to solve the problem—get the spot back on the cross-hairs—was smaller, and the number of false starts (moving spot in wrong direction) was smaller. The results on direction of movement were also conclusive. They showed that the direction of rotation of the left control should be clockwise for horizontal-display movement, and for the right control it should be clockwise for vertical movement of the displays. In other words, the combination shown in the upper left-hand corner of Figure 142 is the best one.

DISTINGUISHABILITY OF CONTROLS

Now we come to the third of the series of questions about the design of controls. This question is how we design them to make it easiest for the operator to tell the difference between them.

In dealing with tasks to be carried out by human operators, it is well to use the slogan "every little bit helps." For a task may be relatively easy for a highly trained operator and yet difficult for the novice. The task may be done easily under normal conditions and yet may be difficult if the operator is put under stress. Every little facility can help make the job faster, more accurate, and free of infrequent but important mistakes.

One of the minor things, which is nevertheless an important principle, is to do everything possible to make controls distinguishable. There are four general ways of doing that: (1) make controls obviously different in location, even when the operator is not looking at them, (2) make the controls different in color, (3) make them different in size, and (4) make them different in shape. All these are psychological problems for which we need data about the capacities of human operators before we can incorporate features of distinguishability into engineering design. We have some of the data; the rest must come from future research.

Coding for location. Some of the facts already exist for coding controls according to location. They were presented in the last chapter under "positioning reactions." There we saw how well an operator could put his hand to the right location without looking. We discovered that ability to distinguish locations, all at arm's reach, varied somewhat from one region to another, that about 6 to 8 inches separation was necessary for the best areas and about twice this amount in the poorer regions.

Color coding. Painting different controls in different colors is another obvious way of making controls more distinguishable. If a control used for some particular function always has the same color, then it does not matter so much whether all machines have this control in the same place. An operator could step up to a strange machine, or one of different design, and know pretty much what each control was for without any instruction or without reading the labels on the controls. This statement is particularly true in such machines as airplanes which have a large number of controls and which must vary somewhat in design from one plane to another. Moreover, painting controls in different colors not only would make controls more distinguishable but also might make them a little more pleasing to the eye.

Despite the fact that color coding would be an obvious advantage, there is relatively little research on the problem, and relatively little use has been made of color coding of controls. One experiment [12] by engineering psychologists in the Air Forces showed clearly that color coding of controls helps operators learn a new set of controls more easily and operate controls correctly even when they are considerably changed in position. Other practical applications to controls of industrial machines could be tried and their effects on performance measured. Moreover, it would be very helpful, if we knew how many different colors most people can tell apart, and how many different colors can be used without making the job too complicated. It is conceivable, for example, that four or five basic colors would be the optimal number of colors for color coding and that such a large number as 10 or 12 colors would be too many for most operators to keep in mind and use effectively. Only systematic research on this problem, however, can tell us how to use color coding of controls most effectively.

Size coding. We could also, of course, make controls distinguishable by using different sizes. If the size of a control were different for different control functions, the operator could tell the controls apart visually as well as by their feel. At the present time, there are no standard rules for coding controls according to size, and a deliberate size coding has not been introduced in most control-design problems. We have, however, recently acquired the basic data from which we might proceed to use size coding of controls. They are presented in Figures 143 and 144.

In the first of these illustrations, we see a Weber fraction $\Delta I/I$ (see p. 316) for size discrimination. The curves for two experiments are put on the same graph. In one of them, subjects had two vertical plates which could be adjusted for separation, and they changed the distance until they thought it matched another set of standard plates. By getting a lot of judgments at a lot of different distances of separation, it was easy for the experimenter to work out percentage error

$\Delta D/D$ for different distances. Notice, too, in this experiment that two different ways of grasping the knobs were studied: One way was the natural grasp using all fingers, and the other used just the thumb and middle finger in making the judgments. The second experiment used a lot of knobs of different sizes. One knob was the standard, and the subject judged whether another knob was the same or different than the standard. The data for the two experiments are in Figure 143.

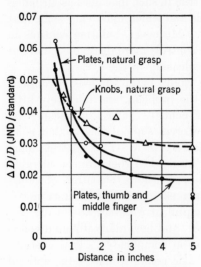

Fig. 143. Discriminability of knobs and plates. In plate discrimination, subjects adjusted the distance of two plates until they seemed to be the same distance apart as two other plates. In the knob experiments, subjects were given two knobs and asked whether they were same or different. You can see that the results of the two different experiments are about the same and also that the kind of grasp makes some difference in the discrimination. The aberrant point at 2.5 inches for knob discrimination remains unexplained. (After Williams, unpublished)

Those are the basic data for discrimination of size. The next step is to translate them into values for coding knobs or distances, according to size. To do that, we should first make a distinction between two possible ways of coding according to size. One is in terms of *relative size*. The operator in handling controls feels first one control and then another, making a relative judgment of the size of the controls. The other possible way of coding is in terms of *absolute size*. In this case, the operator would reach for what he thought was the right control, but if it were the wrong size he would know immediately. In other words, he would be able to tell just by feeling one knob whether or not it was the right one. Obviously, absolute judgment is more difficult than relative judgment. So far we have not done the experiments necessary to give the answers for absolute judgment, and we will simply have to pass that by until we have the data.

The relative discrimination data,[18] however, given in Figure 143, are adequate for prescribing size coding wherever the operator makes a comparison of two or more knobs before deciding which one is the right one. There are several different ways of making the prescription. One simple way is shown in Figure 144 (derived from Figure 143) where a graph is given for the separation or difference for knobs of various sizes to be discriminated 99 percent of the time. If, for example, one knob is 1 inch in diameter, a second knob must be 0.22 inch larger in order to be discriminated. As another example, a knob must be about 5.75 inches in order to be discriminated from a knob 5 inches in di-

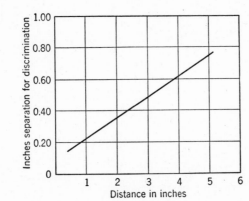

Fig. 144. The separation between knobs that we would use to have discrimination 99 out of 100 times. The curve is derived from the data in Figure 143 for knobs. The curve tells you the number of inches difference in knob size that we should have to tell the difference 99 percent of the time. (After Williams, unpublished)

ameter. The figure, 99 percent, of course, is arbitrary. Figure 143 will let us work out curves for any level of confidence. If we wanted to be sure of 100 percent discrimination, we would want to make all differences in Figure 144 somewhat larger than they are represented there.

Shape coding. The fourth way in which controls may be coded to give them greater distinguishability is to make them different in shape. But the question is how many shapes and what kinds of shapes are distinguishable. Fortunately, we have a rather good answer to that.[8]

Look at Figure 145. There you see 22 different shapes—about all that anyone could dream up without getting into very peculiar and complicated shapes. These 22 different shapes were put on a circular board that could be swung around on its center to bring any shape of control knob in front of the operator. The operator was blindfolded and given one of the shapes to feel for 1 second. This was the correct shape. Then the turntable was swung around so that the operator would not know where the correct one was, and he was told to find it.

He went along feeling one knob and then another until he said he had found the correct knob. This general procedure was used with 80 pilots of the Army Air Force—people who have a lot of experience with controls.

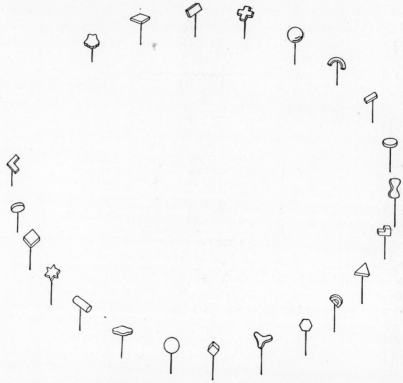

Fᴵɢ. 145.   Twenty-two different shapes of knobs for shape coding of controls. These were the shapes that operators were asked to distinguish by touch to see which shapes are best for shape coding. (After Jenkins, 1947)

In Figure 146 you see the results. The table shows what shapes were confused with other shapes, and how many times the confusions occurred. In the upper left-hand corner, you see eight shapes that were never confused with each other. They are what the experiment was looking for, the knob shapes that are never mistaken for one another, even when the operator is not looking and even when the controls are not where he expects them.

After these eight knobs had been selected—these were "Army knobs" —some designers in the Navy submitted three more knobs [8] that they thought might be good ones to use (see Figure 147). So a follow-up study was made using the eight Army knobs and the three Navy knobs together. Two knobs were presented in succession to the operators to see whether they would be confused or not. Every knob was paired

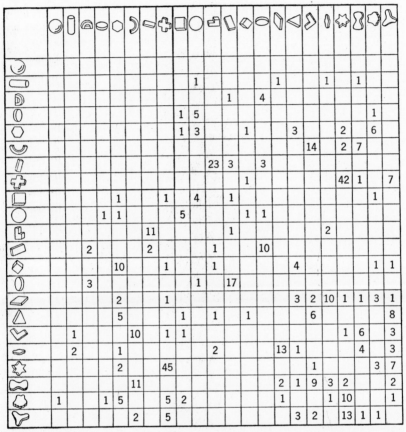

Fig. 146. Confusions among the 22 knob shapes. Each block gives the number of mistakes made between the particular pair of shapes. Notice that there are eight shapes in the upper left-hand corner that were never confused with each other. (After Jenkins, 1947)

with every other knob at some time in the experiment. In 1,980 comparisons, a total of nine errors were made, eight of them with the three new "Navy" knobs. It looked as though the 3 new knobs were not quite so good as the other 8, but the number of errors was so small that all 11 of them could be considered rather good for coding controls according to shape.

Color plus shape coding. Now we ought to mention another experiment on the value of shape coding of control knobs.[12] This experiment was so complicated that it would take several pages to explain exactly what was done. But here is the idea: The operator had in front of him a gadget developed at the School of Aviation Medicine for measuring accuracy and reaction time to complex signals. The gadget had

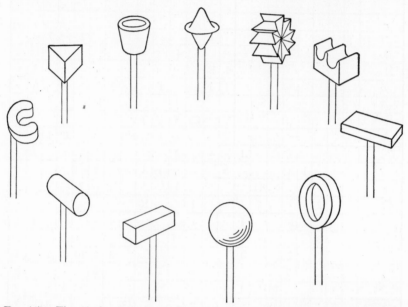

Fig. 147. The 11 shapes that are best for shape coding of controls. Eight of these come from the Army Air Force study with 22 shapes, and 3 come from a similar study by naval personnel and were later compared with the 8 "Air Force knobs." (After Jenkins, 1947)

on it four lights, arranged in a square (see Figure 148). A pair of lights on one side of the array would be flashed on—there were four different pairs, up, down, left, and right—and the particular pair could be made to go off by pulling the correct control. There were four controls, one for each pair. The operator could be scored on whether or not he pulled the right control and how long it took him to do it. In the different experiments, changes were made in the controls. Sometimes they were coded according to color, sometimes according to shape, and sometimes the position of the controls in the control box was moved from one place to another in the course of the experiment.

To make a long story short, it proved to be a very good idea to code the controls in both shape and color. With such coding, the operators made fewer errors by using the wrong control and, in general, were considerably faster. Moreover, when the coded controls were moved in relative position, the operators could go right on making accurate, correct responses. Without the coding, they had to learn all over again which control was the correct one for the correct pair of lights. This was a laboratory experiment, but it was a very realistic one. It dem-

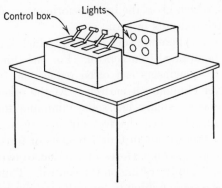

FIG. 148. Apparatus used to study value of coding controls by shape and color. The lights come on in pairs. For each of four pairs of lights, there is a control which will turn them off. The position of the control can be changed; so can the shapes and colors of the controls. (After Weitz, 1947)

onstrates that operators are aided materially by coding of controls, and moreover, it makes their using the correct controls easy even if these controls are put in very different positions from one machine or cockpit to another.

CONTROL FORCES

We have talked so far about the selection of controls, realism in the operation of controls, and the distinguishability of controls. Now we come to a fourth question which faces the engineering psychologist when he tries to design controls for human use. What shall the control forces be? Or, put another way, how much effort must the operator exert to operate the control? This, too, is a psychological question. To answer it for every type of control and for every purpose is more than we can do at present, because we do not have all the research necessary. There are, however, some general principles which come out of what we already know, and there are some examples of how to find out about control forces.

In dealing with the question of control forces, there are usually three different values we would like to know for a particular control. One is the *maximum control force,* the greatest force that an operator can exert under any and all conditions of using the control. On the other end of the scale, we are interested in *minimum control force.* This is not a matter of physical exertion but rather of psychophysical discrimination, as we shall see in a minute. Then, thirdly, there usually is an *optimum control force,* some value in between the minimum and maximum forces, which gives the best performance. We shall take up each of these three concepts in turn.

Minimum forces. There are several things which limit the minimum force that must be applied to a control. For one thing, every control has some friction. Engineers can often reduce the friction considerably but can never eliminate it entirely. At the other extreme is the fact that an operator usually has some minimum force that can be applied. For example, when the feet are just resting on the rudder bar in an aircraft there is about 6 or 7 pounds of force exerted. Controls must have enough counterforce or friction to overcome the force of the foot or hand simply resting on the control. Third, in many controls, there must be some minimum force to give the control "feel"—as the aviators say. If small movements of the control are necessary to make the proper adjustments of the control, some force must be overcome; otherwise the operator has no "feel" of how far he is moving it. He cannot tell by feel whether he has moved it the right amount.

This matter of feel is always important. It is particularly important in flying aircraft, for it is part of the ability of a pilot to "fly by the seat of his pants." Being able to tell by "feel" how far he has moved his control is a matter of the operator's discrimination of pressure, his ability to judge how much movement he has made. Such pressure-discrimination ability is like other abilities to discriminate, such as visual and auditory discrimination.

There is a general function which psychologists have found to be rather universal in all such discriminations. They call it the Weber function after the early psychophysicist who first studied such things. A graph of this function always shows the relative difference threshold on the ordinate and the intensity I of stimulation on the abscissa. The relative difference threshold $\Delta I/I$ is the smallest noticeable difference in stimulation divided by the intensity. A typical Weber function is seen in Figure 149. As we can see, the amount that can be discriminated in relative terms $\Delta I/I$ is fairly constant when the intensity of stimulation is great, but, when the intensity is small, the relative discrimination is very poor—$\Delta I/I$ is large. That is a general principle of all discrimination, and it applies as well to the forces we should have in our controls.

Actually Figure 149 is the result of an experiment [7] with control forces in the stick of a (mock-up) airplane. The force on the stick was experimentally varied from very large values to very small ones. The operators pulled the stick out to some particular pressure, say 20

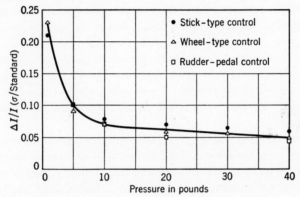

Fɪɢ. 149. The Weber fraction for control forces in airplane controls. The standard deviation of the errors in making settings of controls is divided by the standard force to get the fraction. The fraction tells us the relative, or percentage, error of discrimination. Notice that this relative error is high for small values of the standard and gradually decreases as the control forces are increased. This shape of function is typical of all Weber fractions for human sensory discrimination. Notice how nearly alike are the three different types of controls: the rudder-pedal, the stick-type, and the wheel-type controls. (After Jenkins, 1947)

pounds and were told that that was the correct pressure. They were then asked to reproduce it. When they thought they had done so, they were told how far off they were and allowed to try again. By this method, the ability of the operators to reproduce any desired pressure could be measured. How far off they were could be measured for several different pressures. The error was put in terms of standard deviations (see Chapter 2) and plotted as we see it.

The function is fairly flat above 10 pounds; in general, the standard deviation is about 8 percent of the standard pressure. With forces below 10 pounds, however, the relative standard deviation goes up toward a value of 25 to 35 percent. Translated into practical terms, this means that with forces below 10 pounds ability to adjust a control is poorer than with forces of more than 10 pounds.

Understand, of course, that these data apply to only one type of control—the stick that is used in an airplane. The function we get, in fact, depends on how far the stick is away from the body, the height of the seat from the floor, and such other variables as affect the force that a man exerts or can exert. Weber functions for the use of a wheel-type control and of the rudder-type control are very similar to that for stick controls. For these conditions, in fact, the same curve could be used for all three. But we need such curves for other types of controls: throttle-type, levers of various sorts, accelerator-type, and hand-wheel controls. With them we would know the minimum forces we can use.

There are, of course, other criteria for minimum control forces. Some types of controls must be used continuously at high speed, such as cranks and some handwheels. These raise the question of speed of performance. For example, when an operator must crank as fast as he can, how is his speed affected by the control force? To that specific question we have an answer. In the study of cranking, cited in the previous chapter, the effect of load (force to be overcome) on maximum cranking rate was measured. As one might imagine, almost any drag at all prevents a maximum cranking rate. But a little load does not retard it very much. As the force to be overcome is increased, it has a more and more serious effect on maximum performance. The whole matter is summarized in Figure 131 in Chapter 10 (p. 286).

Maximum control forces. The problem of the maximum forces that must be overcome is different from that of minimum forces. Here the limiting factor is the greatest force that can be exerted by the weakest person likely to operate a control. To find out how large a control force we can use, we need population studies of large numbers of individuals. Then we can find out what values will be within the limits of a large percentage of the population. There is the difficult problem, too, that maximum control force depends on such factors as: what kind of control one is talking about; what part of the body, whether hands, arms, or legs, is being used to operate the control; what position that part is in when operating the control; what the general posture of the body is, whether it is supported by back rests and so on.

Putting together these two aspects of the problem, we come to the conclusion that we need population studies using large numbers of people to determine the maximum force they can exert with different members of their bodies in different positions. We could then get a very large number of curves showing the percentage of the population that can exert a particular force in each situation.

Such population data are available only for a few cases of control forces. One of these is the force that is exerted in a handgrip control.[2] The measures were made on a dynamometer in which the individual squeezed two bars just as hard as he could with one hand. The result is seen in Figure 150. There you see that 90 percent of the population (young men) can exert less than 158 pounds in their right hand grip, and 10 percent can exert less than 113 pounds. The left

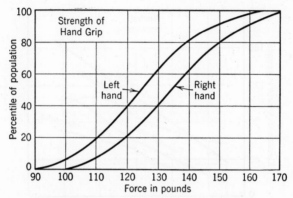

FIG. 150. The forces people can exert in hand grip. The curves are accumulative incidence curves. They tell us what percentage of the population can exert less force than any particular number of pounds. They show too that, on the average, the left hand is about 10 pounds weaker than the right hand. This graph is an example of the kind of population data needed for other sorts of control forces.
(After Clarke, 1945)

hand, in general, runs about 10 pounds weaker. The maximum force that could be required in a hand-grip control, therefore, and would accommodate 90 percent of the population would be 113 pounds. One hundred pounds would be better, for it would include about 95 percent of the population.

That is about all we have in population studies of maximum force that can be exerted on different controls. There are several studies using one or a few subjects—who may or may not be representative of the general population. In fact, the control-force measurements used by the Civil Aeronautics Board as the basis for specifications of control forces in planes are based on studies of two pilots. We do not know how well they represent the population of pilots. But let us see what kind of data they present.[4]

Take stick control forces. The stick is moved forward and backward in a plane to move the elevators. These are the major means of controlling climb or descent of the plane. Thus, the forward and backward stick forces are called elevator control forces. The stick is moved from one side to another to operate the ailerons, which in turn effect the turn of the plane. Thus we speak of aileron control forces.

Both sets of forces vary considerably with the position of the stick. Using the weaker of the two pilots employed in the CAB study, we can

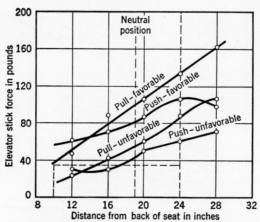

FIG. 151. Maximum exertable elevator forces for the weaker of two pilots. Elevator forces are push–pull forces exerted backward or forward on the pilot's stick. The two upper curves are for the favorable positions of the stick—one for pull and the other for push—and the lower two curves are for the most unfavorable lateral positions of the stick. (After Orlanski, 1948, based on data of Gough and Beard, 1936)

see what the maximum forces are for elevator control. In Figure 151 you see that the force that can be exerted varies from about 30 to over 160 pounds. The greatest force is for pull rather than push—which you might guess. The forces are greatest when the stick is far from the body and least when it is close to the body. Although Figure 151 does not show it, the maximum exertable force also depends on whether the stick is in a center position or lateral to the left or right. The center position gives the highest control force, the right position (for the right hand) gives the poorest amount, and the left position gives a value in between.

Again, using data from the weaker of two pilots, we can see the picture for left–right control forces in using the airplane stick—in brief, the aileron forces. Figure 152 shows that these forces vary from about 30 to 60 pounds. The amount of force that can be exerted varies with the position of the stick. There is a position a little toward the left where the exertable force is maximum. In general, too, the maximum exertable force is greatest when the stick is fairly close to the body.

Since the data are available, we can briefly consider the maximum exertable forces on rudder controls. The situation is the same here. We do not have population data but only those for a couple of pilots. The results are shown in Figure 153. You can see that the maximum rudder control force varies between about 160 and over 400 pounds. It is greatest in the central position with the cross bars parallel to the operator. It depends considerably, too, as has been found in many studies, on the height of the rudder bar. If the bar is too low, the maximum force drops considerably; the highest values for maximum exertable force are found when the rudder bar is at a reasonable height, about 6 inches below the height of the seat.

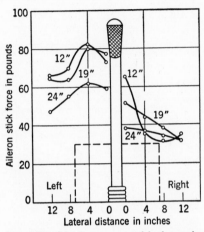

Fig. 152. Maximum exertable forces in the lateral direction for the weaker of two pilots. The three curves show maximum force exerted laterally with the stick at three different distances from the back of the seat. The dotted area represents present NACA specifications for the limit of force that may be required and the limit of lateral distance that the stick may be moved. (After Orlanski, 1948, based on data of Gough and Beard, 1936)

Optimum control forces. Obviously, whenever the control forces exceed the amount an operator can exert, the effect is bad. Also in many situations, to have no control force at all is bad, for it gives the operator nothing to "feel," nothing to use as a clue to how he is operating the control. Thus, for most controls, there must be some optimum control force. There is practically no research on any type of control that tells us what the optimum control forces are.

In the case of the airplane stick, an attempt has been made to work out the "control-force curve" for the airplane stick. The recommended optimum stick-force displacement curve is shown in Figure 154. The first leg of the curve *A* represents a relatively large increase in force for a small displacement of the stick. This is intended to provide a neutral point for the stick, some point that has practically no force to keep it in a neutral position. But this shape of leg also takes account of the fact that ability to discriminate forces is very poor at relatively low force values, and the steep slope tends to compensate for the operator's relatively poor discrimination. Leg *B* has less slope—the increase in force with stick displacement is small. This is the part of the curve (see Figure 149) where force discrimination

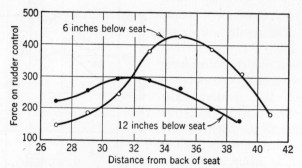

Fɪɢ. 153. Maximum control forces (pounds) on rudder control for the weaker of two pilots. Notice that the force depends both on the distance of the rudder from the back of the seat (inches) and on the height of the rudder with respect to the seat. The best condition is at 35 inches from back of the seat when the rudder is about 6 inches below the seat. More data of this type on a larger population of operators would be very desirable. (After Gough and Beard, 1936)

on the part of the operator is maximal. Thus, the amount of displacement for a given change in force can be small. The third leg, the one which means another considerable increase in force for stick displacement is the "danger" region. It is the region where the operator is reaching his maximum exertable force, and also it is the point where the forces on the plane are reaching a serious proportion. The great increase in force for extreme displacements warns the operator, therefore, that both his own limit and the limit of the plane are approaching.

This is an example of how some basic data on control forces can be used to work out recommendations for the design of control forces. While we are on this subject, let us recall the experiments on cranking which we discussed in Chapter 10 (pp. 285–287). In those experiments, one point studied was the drag or force to be overcome in cranking. The conclusion reached was that any load put on the crank would keep one from cranking at one's best speed. It is particularly harmful when the radius of the crank is small. If you have forgotten the experiment, turn back to Figure 131, where the results are summarized.

CONTROL RATIOS

By this time we have dealt with four aspects of the engineering psychology of controls: the selection of controls, realism and naturalness in controls, distinguishability of controls, and control forces. What we have said ought to make it clear that the design of controls has its psychological problems, even if there are many questions we cannot answer yet.

There is another general aspect of the design of controls which also has its psychological angles. That is control ratio, the ratio between the dimensions of movement of the control and those of the thing controlled, say, an indicator. What we are saying is that even the gear ratios which are selected to go with a control ought to be determined from the human point of view.

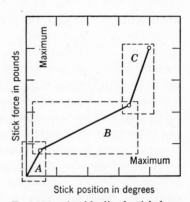

Fig. 154. An idealized stick-force diagram. Zone A is the region in which discrimination is poorest but is important for self-centering of the stick. Zone B is the region in which discrimination is best and is used in maneuvering plane. Zone C is also an area of good discrimination but a region of danger to plane and pilot—thus the increased force for warning the pilot. Numerical values are not given for the coordinates because they vary with a number of conditions—this is an idealized diagram. (After Orlanski, 1948)

Actually there is much more to the problem of control ratios than the gear ratio alone. The gear movement determines how much of the movement of the control is translated into movement of the indicator or the machine—or whatever is controlled. But gear ratio is only one factor in control ratio. Another is the size of the control. If we are talking about a rotary control, say, a knob which is rotated, then the size of the knob enters into the problem. If the knob is big, more movement of the circumference of the knob is required for a given number of degrees of rotation of the shaft than if the knob is small. So the size of the knob, quite aside from the question of coding the control for distinguishability, which we discussed earlier in the chapter, is something to consider. If the control were a joystick, as in an aircraft, the length of the joystick would determine the control ratio, as well as any other gears that might translate the joystick movement into action. Or in steering a car or tracking with a hand-wheel the size of the wheel is part of the system relating the operator's movement to the final movement that results. In addition to size of control, there are, as we shall see, other factors that determine the efficiency of a control ratio from the operator's point of view.

Gear ratio. There are many psychological experiments on control ratios that can be done and need to be done. Several are planned or are in progress in different laboratories in the United States. So far, however, there is only one extensive experiment which deserves very much attention here. This experiment has been done recently by the Lehigh University psychologists. Some of the results are fairly dramatic and illustrate very well how such experiments can help us design controls.[6]

The experiment used a laboratory-built apparatus which would permit systematic change of a number of factors. The operator had in front of him an indicator in which the pointer moved back and forth and could be brought to rest in line with a target line above the pointer. He had a knob which he could turn to move the pointer. The gear ratio of knob movement to pointer movement could be varied over a wide range from about 0.1 to 33 inches of pointer movement per revolution of the knob. The diameter of the control knob could be varied from ½ to 4 inches. The criterion of accuracy could be changed from 0.002 to 0.020 inch tolerance. In any particular experiment, the operator was given an indicator setting that was off the mark and a signal to start, after which he turned the control to get the indicator on the mark. When he achieved the accuracy of setting desired he got a signal telling him so. A recording system measured the operator's movements and the time required to make them.

The records for this sort of task are like those in some of the other experiments we described earlier. There was an initial lag after the starting signal before the operator began moving the control. This time is the reaction time or *starting time*—either name will do. Next, there was a large movement of the control to bring the pointer near the target mark. This is the primary movement time or travel time; both names will do, but the Lehigh psychologists called the time for this big movement the *travel time*. Finally, there was a series of small adjusting movements to line the pointer up with the target mark.

This is comparable to the secondary movement in tracking and positional-movement studies. The time required to make these movements is called the *adjusting time*.

Now we can proceed to the actual experimental results. First, consider the question of gear ratio. In Figure 155, we see a sample set of results. They cannot be taken as gospel truth, for they are not based on a large number of observers, but they do show the kind of results that have been obtained repeatedly with different operators.

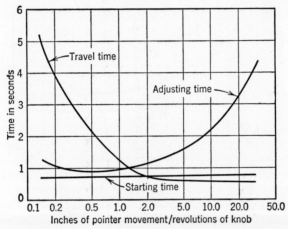

Fig. 155. The time for setting indicators with different control ratios. Times are divided into three parts: the reaction time or starting time, the time of travel to get the pointer in the vicinity of the target, and the time for adjusting pointer accurately on the start. Note that there is an optimum at 1 to 2 inches of pointer movement for each revolution of the knob. (After Jenkins and Connor, 1948)

Note that the *starting time* (reaction time) remains relatively constant, regardless of the gear ratio. That is just as we would expect. Notice, too, that *travel time* is very slow when a very small ratio is employed—the operator has to make many turns of the knob to get the desired movement of the pointer—but decreases rapidly as the ratio is increased. From this curve, you can see that a ratio greater than 2 gives relatively constant minimum *travel time*. On the other hand, see what happens to the *adjusting time* as the ratio is increased. As the ratio goes up and there is more and more movement of the pointer for a turn of the control knob, the time taken to reach a given criterion increases very rapidly. In a word, then, increasing the ratio is good for cutting down travel time, but it greatly increases adjusting time, and vice versa. Now put the two factors together, and it is clear that there is an optimum at about a ratio of 1.2. At this value the travel time is practically minimum, and so also is the adjusting time. At this value, it takes far less time to control the indicator than with any larger or smaller value.

Control size. The size of the control is also a factor in control ratio determining the relationship between the movement of the control and the movement of the indicator. In Figure 156, you see that control

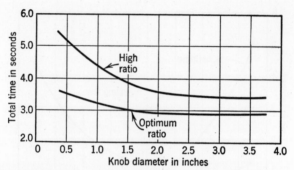

Fig. 156. Knob size and time for making settings when optimum and high control ratios are used. We see that performance gets somewhat better with increasing knob diameter up to about 2 or 2.5 inches. (After Jenkins and Connor, 1948)

size makes a difference too in the efficiency of the control task. In these experiments, measurements of different gear ratios are lumped into two groups. One group includes ratios of 1 to 2 inches of pointer movement per revolution of control. This ratio is labeled the optimum ratio. The other includes ratios of 3 to 6 inches of movement per revolution. This is called the high ratio in Figure 156. If we use a small size of control, it takes longer to get the pointer on the mark than if we use a larger one. The difference is much more marked for the high ratios than for the optimum ratios. In either case, it is a good idea to use a control knob with a diameter of about 2 inches or more.

Tolerances. There are some more points to be brought out by these experiments. One concerns the tolerance allowed an operator in controlling the position of an indicator. As you might expect, the travel time to get the pointer in the vicinity of the target mark is not particularly affected, and we have not shown it in the graph of Figure 157. On the other hand, the adjusting time is of considerable importance. If the tolerance is very small, the adjusting time becomes very long, but, above a certain point—in this experiment, about 0.01 inch—the tolerance allowed makes no difference in adjusting time, if the optimum control ratio is used. Of course, the particular curves that we get in an experiment of this sort depend on a lot of things, including the size of the pointer and the distance of the observer from the indicator. The results therefore cannot be applied generally to other

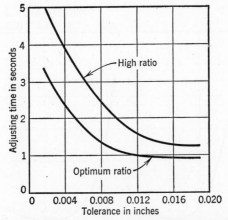

Fig. 157. The influence of tolerance of adjustment on speed of adjusting pointer. There is no effect on starting time or travel time. We see that tolerance makes quite a difference—more for high ratios than for optimum ratios. (After Jenkins and Connor, 1948)

situations, but they do show that it is worth making such measurements to find out what the optimum and allowable tolerances are.

Muscle action potentials. In the beginning of this chapter, we said that there had been a lot of research using electrical methods of recording the movement of muscles. In that sort of work, the electrical changes coming from the muscles are recorded on a meter and correlated with other aspects of the movement in which we may be interested. Sometimes the potential changes correlate very well with other ways of measuring the performance of the operator. In these experiments on control ratios, such potential measurements have been made and give about the same results as measuring the amount of time taken to get on target.

As an example of the kind of agreement that we can get, you see in Figure 158 two curves for various control ratios. One curve on the

left is of the total time taken to make complete the task. This shows
the optimum point about 2 which was shown in the earlier illustrations.
On the right is a curve of potential measurements on the same operator for the same set of tasks. The absolute values of the curve are
of no importance because the meter can always be calibrated in any
way desired. The shape of the curves, however, is important. And
you see that the shape of the potential curve is just about the same

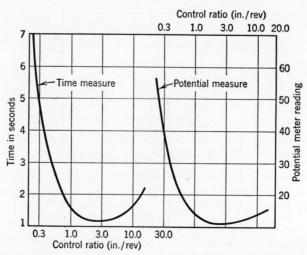

Fig. 158. An example of agreement of two different measures of the effect of
control ratios. The curves are for one subject and are not necessarily representative of the general population. In general, however, the size of muscle action
potentials corresponds with the time (start to finish) for setting an indicator on
the proper scale position. (After Jenkins and Connor, 1948)

as that in the time-measure curves. Thus, in this type of experiment,
it would not make much difference whether one used a measurement
of time or of muscle potentials. The general results would be about
the same.

SUMMARY

Now, a look backward at this chapter will be helpful in getting an
overall picture of controls for human use.

People do make errors in using controls. They may not make them
often, but, when they do, the results can be serious. We have seen
some of the kinds of errors that pilots make and some of the things
that can be done to eliminate errors.

There are many things we can do, not only to eliminate errors, but also to reduce time and inefficiency in using controls. We can make sure to select the type of control appropriate to the task. We can make the type of control and its operation psychologically realistic by running the appropriate tests and experiments. Then, too, controls can be coded by position, size, shape, or color to make them much more distinguishable. Even control forces are important, for they should be adjusted, not only to the force that people can exert, but also for the values at which people are best in discriminating forces. And, finally, remarkable increases in efficiency can come from getting the right ratios between control movement and indicator movement.

These are just the high lights of the subject of controls for human use. There are many factors that enter into particular practical problems. Further research will certainly tell us a lot more than we know now.

SELECTED REFERENCES

1. CARTER, L. F., and MURRAY, N. L. A study of the most effective relationships between selected control and indicator movements. In FITTS, P. M. (Ed.). *Psychological research on equipment design.* U. S. Government Printing Office, 1947, 147–157.
2. CLARKE, H. H. Analysis of physical fitness index test scores of air crew students at the close of a physical conditioning program. *Research Quart.,* 1945, **16**, 192–195.
3. FITTS, P. M., and JONES, R. E. Analysis of factors contributing to 460 "pilot-error" experiences in operating aircraft controls. Engineering Division, Air Materiel Command, Dayton, Ohio, Report No. TSEAA–694–12, 1 July 1947.
4. GOUGH, M. N., and BEARD, A. P. Limitations of the pilot in applying forces to airplane controls. Washington: National Advisory Committee on Aeronautics, Technical Note No. 550, 1936.
5. GRETHER, W. F. Efficiency of several types of control movements in the performance of a simple compensatory pursuit task. In FITTS, P. M. (Ed.). *Psychological research on equipment design.* U. S. Government Printing Office, 1947, 227–239.
6. JENKINS, W. L., and CONNOR, M. B. Optimal design factors for making settings on a linear scale. Unpublished manuscript, Lehigh University, 1948.
7. JENKINS, W. O. A psychophysical investigation of ability to reproduce pressures. In FITTS, P. M. (Ed.). *Psychological research on equipment design.* U. S. Government Printing Office, 1947, 171–186.
8. JENKINS, W. O. The tactual discrimination of shapes for coding aircraft-type controls. In FITTS, P. M. (Ed.). *Psychological research on equipment design.* U. S. Government Printing Office, 1947, 199–205.
9. McFARLAND, R. A. *Human factors in air transport design.* New York: McGraw-Hill, 1946.

10. ORLANSKI, JESSE. The human factor in the design of stick and rudder controls for aircraft. Office of Naval Research, Special Devices Center, 3 February 1948.

11. WARRICK, M. J. Direction of movement in the use of control knobs to position visual indicators. In FITTS, P. M. (Ed.). *Psychological research on equipment design.* U. S. Government Printing Office, 1947, 137–146.

12. WEITZ, JOSEPH. The coding of airplane control knobs. In FITTS, P. M. (Ed.). *Psychological research on equipment design.* U. S. Government Printing Office, 1947, 187–198.

13. WILLIAMS, S. B. On the manual estimation of size. (In preparation.)

12. The Arrangement
of Work

IN THE LAST CHAPTER WE TALKED ABOUT INDIVIDUAL CONTROLS—HOW
to select them, how to distinguish them, how to turn them, how much
force to apply to them, and how to pick out good control ratios. There
is more to say about controls in this chapter, but our approach is
different. Here the main theme is how to make our work more effective. This includes such topics as how to group controls and how to
work out sequences of operation for controls. But it also includes a
lot of other things like posture, comfort, seats, heights of work tables,
and so on. So we are going to start the chapter off on a different note.
We shall begin with the problem of how to carry a load, proceed to
the question of comfortable seats, and then to the areas in which controls should be placed, and consider at the end some general problems
of arranging complicated operations involving several men and several machines cooperating together.

A general word of caution and apology is necessary before we begin.
Most but not all of the points made in this chapter come from common sense and industrial experience rather than from controlled scientific experiment. This is particularly true of the motion-and-time
principles which we discuss. They have grown up through industrial
experience and have not in most cases been tested for their validity
by specific experiments. These practical principles nevertheless are
the best we have at the present time, and we shall therefore talk about
them.

SOME PRINCIPLES OF WORK

As something of a teaching device, we shall talk about principles.
The principles to be described come from all sorts of places. Some
have been the result of the efforts of motion-and-time engineers, some
come from psychological experimenting, some from anthropological
studies of human build, and some are just plain common sense. We

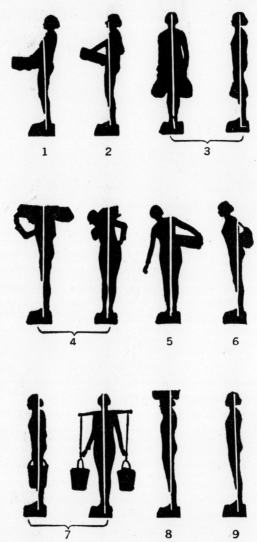

FIG. 159. Eight different ways to carry a load, and erect posture without a load. These ways were compared for efficiency in an experiment to determine the best way of carrying a load. The white line in each figure, whether front view or side view, is the perpendicular line by which we can tell how erect or contorted the body is. Look in Figure 160 to see which ways are the best. (Reproduced by permission of the Controller of His Britannic Majesty's Stationery Office from E. M. Bedale, Comparison of the energy expenditure of a woman carrying loads in eight different positions, *Industr. Fat. Res. Bd.*, 1924, No. 29, p. 27)

shall state the principles in each case and wherever possible show how to apply them.

THE PRINCIPLE OF ERECTNESS

About the simplest and yet the most burdensome work a man can do is to carry a load from one place to another. But simple or hard,

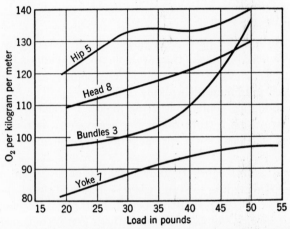

FIG. 160. The efficiency of different ways of carrying a load measured by the amount of oxygen consumed. Each curve shows the amount of oxygen consumed for each unit of work for loads of different weight. The numbers following each label refer to the silhouettes in Figure 159. Note that the yoke method is definitely the best. The hip method is the poorest. The curves not shown for some of the methods lie between the curves for the hip method and the bundles method. (After Bedale, 1924)

quite a bit of such work goes on all the time, and even for this weak-mind–strong-back sort of job there is a best way to work. This was established in a very exhaustive study [3] of the physiological work done in carrying loads in many different positions (see Figure 159)— in front with the hands, in front with shoulder straps, on the side with handles, on the head with the hands to steady the load, on one shoulder, on one hip, in packs strapped to the back, in packs suspended down the back from a yoke worn on the shoulders. Of all these possible ways, the primitive yoke method is by far the best. It costs much less in energy expenditure and may be maintained for longer periods of time (see Figure 160).

It will help us to understand why the yoke method is the best method if we note that it is the only method that lets the man keep a perfectly erect posture while carrying the load. And it is also the method that distributes the load over a relatively large area. (The head method permits erect posture but puts undue strain on the neck muscles.) This posture principle is important, as we shall see, in all sorts of tasks performed by human beings, whether sitting or standing. That method is the best method, other things being equal, that permits a man to keep a perfectly erect posture from head to hips.

PRINCIPLES OF POSTURE

Now let us consider posture in tasks that do not require lifting of loads or even walking, tasks that are done by individuals in one place, either sitting or standing. Most modern machines have been designed to reduce to a minimum all walking and carrying. The individual, in most cases, handles controls with or makes movements only of his hands or feet. This getting rid of the heavy work is nice—and it is efficient—but it creates some special problems in sitting, standing, and change of posture.

Operator's option. This we know: We can make a man more comfortable by allowing him to stand when he wants to stand and sit when he wants to sit. Prolonged sitting becomes tiresome. If you need evidence, just read this chapter through without getting out of your chair, and then consider introspectively the sensations emanating from your sitting equipment. Standing also gets tiresome, as you also know if you ever defied one of those signs reading "standing room only" and bought a ticket anyhow.

By allowing the operator to work the machine just as easily one way as the other, sitting or standing at his option, we add materially to his comfort, allay fatigue, and increase productivity. To accomplish this purpose, of course, the machine must be designed at a greater height than is usually the case, and a high chair must be provided. The worker's head, arms, and body should be at the same height with respect to the machine whether he is sitting or standing. We do not have experiments to prove this point, but common sense and industrial observation support it.

Variations in human build. It may occur to you at this point that these fine principles may be easier to state than to put into practice. After all, some people are tall and some are short; some who are tall have short legs and vice versa. How do we arrange things so that people can stand or sit at will and yet always be at the right height with respect to their work? That problem is a bit difficult, but the anthropologist is the man we need to solve it. If he will tell us how the population is built, we can take the appropriate steps to adapt this principle to our problem. Fortunately, he has given us some good data to use for this purpose. We do not have all the data we would like, but we have some.

First, how tall are people? On that question we have two different studies, summarized in Figure 161. One gives us the heights of a fairly representative sample of the general population (people selected

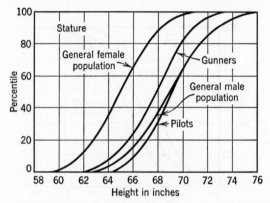

FIG. 161. How people vary in height. The curves are accumulative incidence curves. They tell what percentage of the population is as short as or shorter than any particular height. The general female and male populations are about 4,000 adults selected at random in railroad stations. The gunners and pilots are about 4,000 Army Air Force personnel. (Based on data of Hooton, 1945, and Randall *et al.*, 1946)

at random in Boston and Chicago railroad stations)—about 2,000 men and 2,000 women—ranging in age from young adults to aged. These are labeled "general female" and "general male" populations in Figure 161. The other study [9] is based on about 4,000 Army air-crew personnel, divided into two categories, pilots and gunners. Gunners, as we can see, tended to be somewhat shorter than the pilots. On the average there was about 1 inch difference in the heights of gunners and pilots. The two groups together, however, match the general population fairly well. These data for height are useful in a number of connections, and we shall see some of the other uses later.

THE DESIGN OF SEATS

Now let us consider the problem of people sitting. When people are sitting they should be comfortable. It is hard to say how much production can be increased by providing comfortable seats because that is hard to measure directly. But there is good reason to believe that efficiency in work and amount of work output may be raised significantly simply by providing good comfortable seats. To make seats comfortable requires several things, which are not always easy to achieve.

Seat height. First, if possible, seats should be of adjustable height, because everybody's sitting height is not the same distance from the ground. Measurements have been made of the seat heights of about

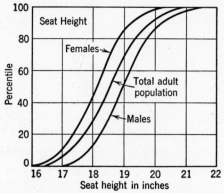

Fig. 162. How people vary in seat height. Seat height is the distance from the seat to the ground when a person is seated with feet planted on the ground and the knees at right angles. This is a percentile graph like Figure 161. It shows the percentage of people who have seat heights equal to or less than any given height. (Based on data of Hooton, 1945)

4,000 people representative of the general population.[5] The results are given in Figure 162. These measurements were made by having people sit in chairs of adjustable height and put their feet flat on the floor at right angles to the seat. As you see, the seat height of males varies from about 17 to 21.5 inches, and the seat height of females varies from about 16 to 20 inches. Altogether the variation of the combined population is about 16 to 21.5 inches—a range of 5.5 inches. Good chairs should be adjustable for this amount. Moreover, if sitting height and standing height are to be the same, a special foot rest, taking the place of the floor, should be provided under machines so that it is 16 to 21.5 inches below the seat.

Seat length. Second, comfortable seats should be of the right length to fit the human fundament. The seat length is defined as the distance from the back of the seat (buttocks), when the individual is sitting erect in a chair, to the back of the leg just below the knee, when the legs are placed squarely on the floor. A distribution of these measurements is shown in Figure 163. There you can see that seat length varies from about 16 inches in short women to 21 inches in tall ones and from about 17 inches in short men to 22 inches in tall ones. Altogether the variation of the entire population is about 16 to 22 inches.

This variation creates some problems of establishing a standard seat length. If we select a short seat length, then the long-legged in-

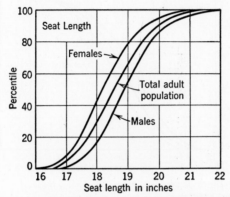

Fig. 163. How people vary in seat length. The measurement is from the back of the buttocks to the back of the leg underneath the knee. The graphs tell what percentage of people have a seat length equal to or less than any particular length. (Based on data of Hooton, 1945)

dividual has 3 or 4 inches of his thighs hanging out over the edge of the seat and is uncomfortable. On the other hand, if a long seat is selected, the short person must slump down in the chair with his or her buttocks out 2 or 3 inches from the back rest. Otherwise he cannot get his legs to hang down from the chair.

People who have considered this problem at some length make the following recommendations: If the seat one is planning is a passenger seat, say, in a railroad car or airplane; if the comfort of the sitter is the main consideration; and if there is no objection to people slumping a bit in their seats, then a seat length of 20 inches is about right. This accommodates about 90 percent of people, including 85 percent of the men and 95 percent of the women. At least such a seat will put no uncomfortable pressure on the thighs, though the people may have to slump a little to let their legs hang freely. If, on the other hand, one is concerned primarily with working situations in which operators should sit erect in order to do their work, then a shorter seat length is better. A seat of about 18.5 to 19.0 inches is adaptable to a little more than 50 percent of the population. The remainder of the people may have some discomfort from under-thigh pressure, but, on the whole, the seat will be about as comfortable as possible—in regard to seat length—and at the same time erect posture will be possible. So much for seat length.

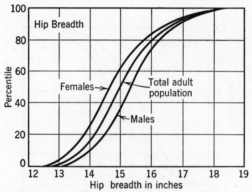

Fig. 164. How people differ in the width of their hips and seats. Hip breadth and seat width are about the same, and, if chairs have arms on them, it is hip breadth we are interested in. Again the graphs tell what percentage of the population have hip breadths equal to or less than any particular value. (After Hooton, 1945)

Seat width. The final consideration is seat width. The measurements available are for hip breadth, rather than seat width, because the man who made them had in mind chairs with arms. However, hip breadth and seat width on the average are practically identical. Moreover, for chairs with arms, the distance between the arms is equivalent to seat width, and so hip-breadth measurements are satisfactory. These are given in Figure 164, and they vary from about 12.5 to more than 18 inches. There is little harm in having a wide seat, and so it is recommended that seats be made 17.5 to 18 inches wide. This is adaptable to practically 100 per cent of the population.

Worth mentioning in passing is the back rest. Whether this is important or not depends on the nature of the work. For people who must sit and remain reasonably erect while they work, back rests should be provided to support the lower trunk in the hollow of the back. Perhaps you have seen some peculiar looking secretarial chairs, of steel frame with wide but shallow seats and with backs that are only a few inches high but fit nicely into the low hollow of the back. They are good not only for secretaries but also for the often-more-masculine backlines of all sorts of machine operators (see Figure 165). Again we should say that specific experiments have not checked this conclusion, but experience indicates that it is probably valid.

THE PRINCIPLES OF WORKING AREAS

No matter how much experience you have had in a boarding house, you can reach only so far. This is a simple point, but one, nevertheless, that is consistently neglected. In the last chapter, for example, we pointed out that some pilots' errors in flying aircraft had been traced to the simple fact that they could not reach the proper control. And it is not uncommon in industrial life to observe controls that are practically out of reach of the operator. These mistakes in design occur sometimes because engineers either do not know how far people can reach or do not stop to think about it. This business of reach is even more complicated and more important than appears on the surface. Let us digress a moment to explain how and why.

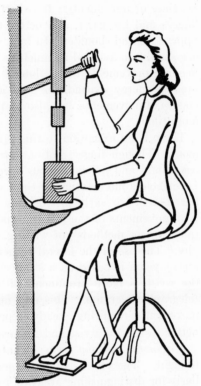

FIG. 165. A well-designed and properly adjusted back rest which may be used for many kinds of chairs, including secretarial chairs and the chair of a drill-press operator shown here. (After Barnes, 1949)

Least effort. First let us note that any work done with the hands *can* involve five different parts of the arm: (1) the shoulder, (2) the upper arm, (3) the forearm, (4) the wrist, and (5) the fingers. Work done by the hands can be classified according to how many of these parts of the arm it requires. Note that the more classes that are involved the more energy is expended, or, conversely, the fewer the classes involved in the work the less effort is required. The lowest and most economical class of movements simply requires the fingers, the next class involves the wrist, the next the forearm, and so on.

From this kind of thinking, industrial engineers have evolved the principle that work should, so far as possible, be restricted to the lowest class of movements. It is better to use the fingers alone than the fingers and the wrist, and better to use the forearm than to use the upper arm and shoulder. In fact, any movements involving the shoulder should be avoided as much as possible. This general principle of keeping movements to the lowest class is supported not only by the greater energy expenditure and discomfort produced by the higher classes of movements, but also by the fact that they usually take much more time.

There is an exception to this principle which is worth a short comment. Though finger motions are faster and should be used where occasional and noncontinuous speed is the important thing, they are nevertheless more fatiguing than wrist or forearm motions. Remember that in our early instructions in writing we were taught that the free movements of the forearm and wrist are easier and less fatiguing than "finger methods" of writing. A similar point holds for telegraphy. The use of the lateral rather than the vertical telegraph key in recent years is based on a study showing that the loose movement of the wrist is more prominent with the lateral key and helps avoid telegrapher's cramp. This and much other evidence shows that, for movements requiring steady repetition over periods of time, it is better to use the wrist and forearm than the fingers alone.

Maximum working areas. That brings us back to our main line of thought. The classes of movement that we have described are the basis for distinguishing areas of reach in which work should be done. Shoulder and trunk movements should be avoided as much as possible. Thus the area that can be reached without contortion of the shoulder, head, and trunk is regarded as the *maximum working area*. And, because movements of the forearm and wrist are much to be preferred, the areas that may be reached with these movements alone have been called the *normal working areas*.

A diagram of the maximum and normal working areas on a horizontal surface is shown in Figure 166. There you can see that neither is a straight flat area, but each has the shape of a semicircle. The solid semicircles are the limits of the maximum working area; the dotted semicircles are the limits of normal working areas. Notice that there are two sets of semicircles, one for each arm. The shaded areas in which the semicircles for the two arms overlap represent the places that can be reached or used normally with either or both hands.

The diagram in Figure 166 is for a horizontal working surface. There are also maximum and normal working areas on vertical surfaces. In both cases, the actual dimensions of these areas depend on a number of factors: the build of the particular person who is working, the height of the working surface with respect to the person's shoulders and arms, and the distance of the surface away from the body.

To show how these various factors can be mastered in any given

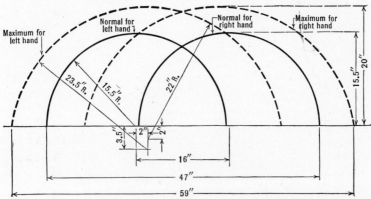

Fig. 166. Normal and maximum working areas on a horizontal surface. The measurements given are fairly conservative and should accommodate about 95 percent of the adult population. (Reproduced by permission from *Work methods manual* by R. M. Barnes, published by John Wiley & Sons, 1944)

situation, we will cite one study of maximum reach on a vertical surface. Just a few subjects were used. A viewing distance of 20 inches was chosen. Measurements were then made of the maximum limits of reach on the surface with subjects seated with their head and shoulders in a fixed position. After all measurements were taken, they were corrected for the reach of the general population by comparing the reach of the particular subjects used with the measurements of a large population of pilots.

The final result [6] is shown in Figure 167. There you see three pairs of overlapping circles. The center of each circle is the point on the vertical surface exactly representing shoulder level and position of the man. One circle of each pair is for the right arm, the other for the left arm. The smallest pair of circles is very conservative, for it represents the very small man (only 5 percent of the population are smaller). The largest pair of circles is for the very long-armed man (only 5 percent are longer). And the middle pair is for the typical or average man. If we wanted to apply these findings to the general population, we would want to take the smaller conservative circles

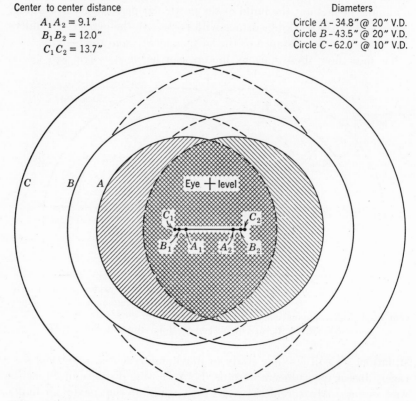

Center to center distance

$A_1 A_2 = 9.1''$

$B_1 B_2 = 12.0''$

$C_1 C_2 = 13.7''$

Diameters

Circle A - 34.8" @ 20" V.D.

Circle B - 43.5" @ 20" V.D.

Circle C - 62.0" @ 10" V.D.

Fig. 167. Maximum reach on a vertical working surface. The centers of the circles correspond to the left and right shoulders, respectively. Circles A and B are at a viewing distance of 20 inches, and circle C is at a distance of 10 inches. The smallest circle A is the area that the short-armed man can reach; the middle pair B of circles is the reach of the average man; and the largest pair C show the reachable area of the long-armed man. (After Lipschultz and Sandberg, 1947)

in order to stay within the maximum reach of 95 percent of the population.

We cannot discuss every possible problem of reach that may be encountered in practice. Anthropometric data of body build exist for arm reach, elbow length, shoulder height, and other dimensions of build. With these data and a little geometry, we can figure out the best dimensions for any particular problem of working areas.

In closing this section, let us simply present a general picture of the maximum and normal working areas in three dimensions. In Figure 168, note the complex surfaces which describe the three-dimensional working areas. One surface is for maximum reach and another sur-

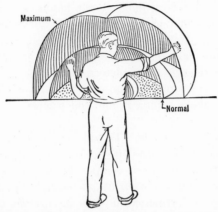

Fig. 168. A three-dimensional sketch of the maximum and normal working areas of an operator. (Reproduced by permission from *Work methods manual* by R. M. Barnes, published by John Wiley & Sons, 1944)

face for normal reach. This kind of picture should always be kept in mind in designing the layout for tools and controls.

MOTION-AND-TIME STUDY

The principles we have reviewed so far are not based on any unusual or highly evolved methods. They developed through common sense and the experience of industrial engineers. In order to apply some of them, we have used the measurements of body build supplied by the anthropologists. In a moment, however, we shall come to some facts and principles based on the particular methods of the motion-and-time engineer. For those who have had no special training in time or motion study, it is necessary to give a brief review of its methods and concepts.

The best way to work. Time-and-motion engineers stake their professional lives on the idea that there is always a better way to do a job. They cannot always be sure that they have found the best way, but at least they very frequently find better ways. To succeed in their efforts, they usually must first find out what the job actually is and then find out how it is being done at present. Often they can analyze the job simply by observing it carefully, timing the various parts of it with a stop watch, and thinking of better ways to do it. Usually, however, the problem takes somewhat more sophisticated techniques.

Time-and-motion photography. When you are watching a magician you know very well that "the hand is quicker than the eye." But this is true for all sorts of work done by the hands and feet. Time-and-motion engineers decided a long time ago that they missed a good deal when they tried to study a job with the naked eye. So they used the motion picture camera to photograph the jobs they wanted to improve. Having gotten a complete moving picture record of a job, they could run the picture over and over again, watching for each element of the work cycle, timing it, and constructing a detailed analysis of the job.

Elements of the work cycle. To aid in such reconstructions, they long ago developed some "units" or fundamental elements of the work cycle. The "elements" are basic components of the movement pattern —sometimes they are not movements at all, but rather lack of movement, but they are nevertheless the steps in carrying out any particular job. The engineers call these elements *"therbligs."* This strange sounding term is "Gilbreth" spelled backward but with the "th" unreversed. It was Mr. and Mrs. Gilbreth who many years ago pioneered this approach to motion economy.

The therblig is a so-called element of the motion cycle. It is not an absolute quantity, for human movements do not lend themselves to notions of absolute units. In some ways, the therblig is just a convenience. At any rate, it is the aspect of work that is significant for the operation being studied. There are, of course, an indefinite number of particular movements or elements, depending on the operation, but for most practical purposes industrial engineers have found that 18 basic therbligs will do.

In Figure 169, you find a list of these 18 therbligs. As you see, they begin with the time that an operator is searching for a tool or control. The next therbligs refer to such steps as finding the control, grasping it, turning it or transporting it, and so on. There is no need to repeat all of them. If you study the list in the illustration, you will see that it makes good sense and can apply—at least in part—to almost any sort of work or operation of controls.

One significant thing about this list of therbligs is that it has been standardized. The therbligs now have a generally accepted set of initials and hieroglyphics which mean the same thing to all those trained in the field. Indeed, when time-and-motion engineers want to communicate with each other, they use a standard set of colors

Name of Symbol	Therblig Symbol		Explanation-suggested by	Color	Color Symbol	Dixon Pencil Number	Eagle Pencil Number
Search	Sh	⌒⊃	Eye turned as if searching	Black		331	747
Select	St	→	Reaching for object	Gray, light		399	734½
Grasp	G	∩	Hand open for grasping object	Lake red		369	744
Transport empty	TE	⌣	Empty hand	Olive green		391	739½
Transport loaded	TL	⌣̮	A hand with something in it	Green		375	738
Hold	H	⌓	Magnet holding iron bar	Gold ochre		388	736½
Release load	RL	⌒	Dropping content out of hand	Carmine red		370	745
Position	P	9	Object being placed by hand	Blue		376	741
Pre-position	PP	⌀	A nine-pin which is set up in a bowling alley	Sky-blue		394	740½
Inspect	I	0	Magnifying lens	Burnt ochre		398	745½
Assemble	A	#	Several things put together	Violet, heavy		377	742
Disassemble	DA	++	One part of an assembly removed	Violet, light		377	742
Use	U	U	Word "Use"	Purple		396	742½
Unavoidable delay	UD	⌒o	Man bumping his nose, unintentionally	Yellow ochre		373	736
Avoidable delay	AD	⌐o	Man lying down on job voluntarily	Lemon yellow		374	735
Plan	Pn	℘	Man with his fingers at his brow thinking	Brown		378	746
Rest for overcoming fatigue	R	℮	Man seated as if resting	Orange		372	737

Fig. 169. The therbligs and their symbols. The therbligs are component parts of a motion cycle. Note their names, the abbreviations, the shorthand codes, and the color codes which motion-and-time engineers use in analyzing working operations. (Reproduced by permission from *Motion and time study*, 3d ed., by R. M. Barnes, published by John Wiley & Sons, 1949)

which can represent these therbligs graphically. And, to avoid any confusion between the colors and color symbols, they even specify the manufacturer's numbers of the commercial pencils. We can see the colors and color symbols and pencil numbers in Figure 169.

The analysis sheet. With the 18 therbligs and symbols for representing them, any time-and-motion engineer may take a motion picture of a particular sequence of operations, play the picture back slowly and repeatedly, and finally reduce the whole sequence to a scheme on an analysis sheet. In Figure 170, we see a sample of an

MICROMOTION STUDY
ANALYSIS SHEET

PART   Bolt and washer assembly ~ Old Method   DEPARTMENT   AY16   FILM NO. B21

OPERATION   Assemble 3 washers on bolt   OP. NO. A32

OPERATOR   M. Smith 1C634   DATE 1-26-48   ANALYSED BY M.E.R.   SHEET NO. 1 OF 1

CLOCK READING	SUBTRACTED TIME	THERBLIG SYMBOL	DESCRIPTION LEFT HAND	CLOCK READING	SUBTRACTED TIME	THERBLIG SYMBOL	DESCRIPTION RIGHT HAND
595	7	TL	Carries assembly to bin	595	26	TE	Reaches for lock washer
602	2	RL	Releases assembly	621	6	St+G	Selects and grasps washer
604	4	TE	Reaches for bolt	627	7	TL	Carries washer to bolt
608	2	St+G	Selects and grasps bolt	634	6	P	Positions washer
610	17	TL	Carries bolt to working position	640	12	A+RL	Assembles washer onto bolt and releases
627	5	P	Positions bolt	652	8	TE	Reaches for steel washer
632	104	H	Holds bolt	660	8	St+G	Selects and grasps washer
736	7	TL	Carries assembly to bin	668	9	TL	Carries washer to bolt
743	2	RL	Releases assembly	677	3	P	Positions washer
745				680	10	A+RL	Assembles steel washer and releases
				690	6	TE	Reaches for rubber washer
				696	10	St+G	Selects and grasps rubber washer
				706	9	TL	Carries washer to bolt
				715	5	P	Positions washer
				720	16	A+RL	Assembles washer and releases
				736			
			Time in 2000ths of a minute				

FIG. 170. An analysis sheet used to record the therbligs and the time they take for a job being studied by the motion-and-time engineer. (Reproduced by permission from *Motion and time study*, 3d ed., by R. M. Barnes, published by John Wiley & Sons, 1949)

analysis sheet, which describes in time-and-motion symbols the therbligs involved in assembling bolts and washers. Because the motion pictures are taken either with clock readings in the picture or by highly standardized speed of photographing and playing back, it is possible to record the time, down to the hundredth of a second, required for each therblig of the motion sequence. That too goes into the analysis sheet.

From such a sheet, the time-and-motion engineer can get ideas for eliminating useless motions or for redistributing the work among the hands and feet. The engineer may develop several alternative ways of performing the operation, set them up experimentally for an operator to carry out, photograph and reanalyze the changed operation, and determine which of the several possible ways is the best way to do it. To guide him in his thinking about better ways of working, the time-and-motion engineer follows some of the principles, developed from long industrial practice, that are described in the following paragraphs.

THE PRINCIPLE OF DISTRIBUTION

Because our eyes are so efficient, we give them too much to do. And because man is so adept with his hands, we usually put too much responsibility on them. In fact, because we are usually more facile with our right hand than our left, it is very common to give the right hand a lot to do and the left hand only a little. Recognizing that fact leads to an important principle of arranging our work most effectively. *Distribute the work as well as possible between both hands and both feet.*

The feet and hands. Those occasional individuals who were unfortunate enough to be born without arms or to lose them can manage to do amazing things with their feet and toes. Many, in fact, can use eating utensils, "thumb" the pages of a book, button their clothes, and do almost anything that people normally do with their hands. Most people, fortunately, have not had to train themselves to such lengths. But the feet ought to be more than something an operator brings in, puts under his chair, and forgets. There are many simple operations such as switching, or raising and lowering a fixture, that can be done very easily with the feet. When the hands are thus relieved, they are given more time to do the remaining work, and the result is that the work is speeded up and much time is saved without any appreciable increase in effort.

Another aspect of this principle of distribution is the sharing of work between the two hands. To design a job so that both hands can be used to their fullest extent usually saves 50 to 80 percent of the time for a particular sequence of operations. Thus this principle has become important in industrial situations and accounts for some rather dramatic increases in the production of certain items. The principle, in modified form, has also found its way into modern basketball. Players are taught to use the left hand for those layup shots where the use of the right hand would demand considerable awkwardness and contortion.

Simultaneous motion. An extension of the idea of using both hands in work is to use them both at once. The two hands should never be idle at the same moment—except during rest. One example of the application of this principle can be seen in the task of coating terminal blocks with solder to which wires are later to be fastened. An analysis of the original method, practiced before application of this principle, is diagrammed in Figure 171. There you can see that the right hand does practically all the work. All the left hand does is pick up the block from the supply pan and move it to a central position, whence the right hand moves the block to the flux pot, to the solder pot, to the knock-off plate, and finally to the finished stock.

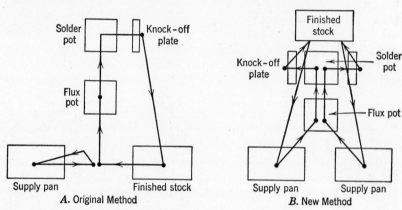

FIG. 171. Improving work efficiency by using the hands simultaneously. On the left is the diagram of how a soldering operation was originally performed—practically all with the right hand. On the right is a sketch of the same job redesigned so that both hands are working symmetrically and simultaneously—with a considerable increase in efficiency. (By permission from *Common sense applied to motion and time study*, by A. H. Mogensen, copyright 1932, McGraw-Hill Book Co.)

A revised layout, however, designed to distribute the work equally between the hands is diagrammed on the right of Figure 171. There both hands carry out the same pattern simultaneously and do two units at once, rather than one at a time as before. Of course, the time per unit is not cut in half by this method because two hands cannot work twice as fast as one, but the total increase in production is about 85 percent—a factor not to be sneezed at either in production or in machine operation.

The Simo chart. So important is this notion of both hands working together that motion-and-time engineers have a special chart—the Simo chart—which they use to analyze simultaneously the motions of the two hands. What each hand is doing moment by moment is recorded in this chart (see Figure 172). A study of it will show, almost

MICROMOTION STUDY
SIMO CHART

| PART Bolt and washer assembly–Old Method | DEPARTMENT AY16 | FILM NO. B21 |

| OPERATION Assemble 3 washers on bolt | OP. NO. A32 |

| OPERATOR M.Smith 1C634 | DATE 1-27-37 | MADE BY S.R.M. | SHEET NO. 1 OF 1 |

DESCRIPTION LEFT HAND	THERBLIG SYMBOL	TIME	TIME IN 2000THS OF A MIN.	TIME	THERBLIG SYMBOL	DESCRIPTION RIGHT HAND
Carries assembly to bin	TL	7				
Releases assembly	RL	2				
Reaches for bolt	TE	4				
Selects and grasps bolt	St G	2		26	TE	Reaches for lock washer
Carries bolt to working position	TL	17		6	St G	Selects and grasps washer
Positions bolt	P	5		7	TL	Carries washer to bolt
				6	P	Positions washer
				12	A RL	Assembles washer and releases
				8	TE	Reaches for steel washer
				8	St G	Selects and grasps washer
				9	TL	Carries washer to bolt
Holds bolt	H	104		3	P	Positions washer
				10	A RL	Assembles steel washer and releases
				6	TE	Reaches for rubber washer
				10	St G	Selects and grasps rubber washer
				9	TL	Carries washer to bolt
				5	P	Positions washer
				16	A RL	Assembles washer and releases
Carries assembly to bin	TL	7				
Releases assembly	RL	2				

FIG. 172. The Simo chart, an example. The chart shows what each hand is doing for each moment of the motion cycle. A glance at it tells us whether one hand is idle too much of the time when the other one is busy. Close study gives us ideas for improving the motion cycle to get simultaneous use of the hands. (Reproduced by permission from *Motion and time study*, 3d ed., by R. M. Barnes, published by John Wiley & Sons, 1949)

at a glance, how much time is being wasted by unequal balance of work between the two hands.

Symmetry. Still another principle is illustrated by the diagram of the soldering operation you saw in Figure 171: that motions of the two arms should be in opposite and symmetrical directions, instead of in the same direction, and their moves should be made simultaneously. This principle is upheld, not only by many motion-and-time studies, but also by the basic physiological design of the human organism. Areas of the cerebral cortex, pathways in the central nervous system, the pattern of nerves to the muscles, and the structure of the muscles themselves—all these are laid out in duplicate mirror images of each other. Activity in one side of the body tends to be mirrored on the other side. As a consequence, it is very difficult to do two different things at the same time with the two hands, but it is very easy and efficient to do the same thing in symmetrical patterns at the same time. A good demonstration of this point is to try rubbing your stomach circularly with one hand while patting your head with the other. It is much easier to rub both or to pat both. Application of this principle to the design of tasks and machines often can increase output by a good many percent.

The operation of controls. Before we end this review of motion economy, let us present an example of a different type of application, not to the assembly or production line, but to the handling of controls of complex machinery. The particularly complex machine in this case is the airplane—an airplane, in fact, that is now fairly common in military and commercial flying. It goes under several different names and numbers, but you will probably recognize it as the DC-4.

We have already discussed at length the tremendously complicated task of the pilot. This study [4] was aimed at making life a little simpler for him without changing anything except the sequence of his operating controls. The first step was a careful study of every aspect of the pilot manipulating his controls: before take-off, during take-off, in normal contact flight, in instrument flight, and in landing operations. Moving pictures were taken of typical operations in many flights in order to record every detail of his operation of controls. All the data were analyzed much in the way we have been describing. Then diagrams were constructed of the sequence of movements made in different aspects of flying.

Here let us simply consider take-off and all the things a pilot has to do to get his plane checked out and ready for take-off. To understand all control operations of the pilot, the motion-and-time engineer had to make a rough classification of the areas in which the pilot operated controls. Seven different areas were picked out and diagrammed. There is no need to delineate their names or functions. They are pictured diagrammatically in Figure 173. Also in that figure you will see what the pilot was doing. Just follow the arrows to see where the pilot was moving his hands and adjusting or checking controls. You can see at a glance that this is not a very efficient way to work. The hands of the pilot traveled back and forth from one control area to another, repeating movements and taking the long way around.

With all the facts in hand, it was a pretty simple matter to work out another better sequence of control movements. Of course, certain controls must be moved or checked in a certain order, but, even respecting that limitation, a simpler sequence was possible. The improved procedure coming out of the motion-and-time study is shown in Figure 173. The simplification illustrated in the diagram resulted from two basic changes: (1) Instead of the hands going back and forth repeatedly between different areas, they were used to do all of the jobs in one area at one time; and (2) instead of the hands moving from one area to another far distant from it, the procedure was arranged to have

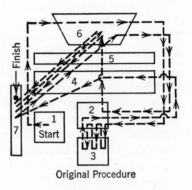

Original Procedure

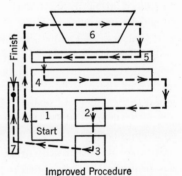

Improved Procedure

Fig. 173. Improving the check-off procedure in preparing a plane for take-off. In the top part of the figure we see a diagram of the sequence of the pilot as revealed by time-and-motion analysis. In the lower part you see the procedure recommended after the analysis was complete. There is no question but that the procedure saves time and eliminates possible mistakes. (After Channell, 1947)

the hands move on to an adjacent area. We do not know what the final figures are for saving in time and mistakes, but we would guess that they ought to be rather substantial.

THE ARRANGEMENT OF WORK

That concludes our review of some of the more important general principles of the design of tasks. They have come mainly from the efforts of motion-and-time engineers, but they belong in any psychological treatment of problems of human efficiency. There are many other principles and subprinciples, but, since this is not intended to take the place of a textbook in motion economy, we will not go into them. Before we proceed, however, with some other problems of the arrangement of controls, it would be well to list quickly certain other principles of motion economy which are particularly applicable to industrial problems of assembly. These principles stress the proper design and arrangement of tools and materials rather than of controls.

The list runs something like this: (1) All tools and materials should be placed at permanent and fixed stations. (2) Tools and materials should be arranged in front of and as close as possible to the worker. (3) Gravity-feed bins should be used wherever possible to deliver material as close to the worker and point of assembly as possible. (4) Tools and materials should be arranged so as to permit the best sequence of therblig movements. (5) The work place should be illuminated to permit good vision. These principles, as well as many others, are well illustrated in the standard reference works on motion-and-time engineering.

Now let us turn to the arrangement of controls. This can be a serious problem because controls get built into machines. Once the machine has been designed and the controls have been placed, it is usually too late to go back and change the machine according to the shortcomings that are found in it after an operator has been using it for a while. If and when such changes are made, they are usually expensive, and everybody concerned wishes he had known how to arrange the controls correctly in the first place.

It is easy to state some general principles about the arrangement of controls. Just recall some of the things we have been saying in this and the previous chapter.

Maximum reach. Obviously, no control should be out of reach of the operator, unless this is absolutely unavoidable. If a control must be placed out of reach, it should be a control which is never used in the ordinary course of operating a machine, but only at odd times either before beginning work or after finishing a sequence of work on the machine. Controls that are used for calibration, adjustment, or maintenance of the machine may be in this category—out of reach. Second, and closely related, all controls normally used by the operator should lie within the maximum reach of the operator. We have already shown how it is possible to determine what is the maximum reach—even for the short man.

Normal reach. Controls that are used occasionally but not frequently may be placed outside the normal working area but within the maximum working area of the hands. Controls that must be used occasionally or always with two hands should be placed in the bimanual working areas. The controls that are most frequently used and are most important should be placed within the normal working areas and preferably centrally located in front of and close to the body. All this is pretty obvious—so obvious that it hardly seems worth saying. Yet there are very few machines which actually meet these standards. Engineers too often forget these simple principles when they design the machines.

THE PATTERN OF PLACEMENT

Even if all this advice is followed, it tells us only in what general areas we must be sure to have controls. A more important problem, and one that is harder to solve, is the problem of the particular pattern of controls. Which control is placed next to which other control? Exactly how should they be laid out? To this there is also a general answer. Controls having a similar function should be grouped together. A control that is frequently used immediately after another control should be placed next to it (unless there is some reason to have both hands participate alternately or simultaneously in the sequence). That is a good general principle, but how does one put it into practice?

In some kinds of machines, particularly machines that are producing things, the sequence of control motions is standard. The operator always goes through exactly the same sequence of adjusting controls. When this is the case, the methods of motion-and-time engineering that we have already described are adequate. To apply them we should go through the following sequence: set up some kind of mock-up before we build the machine; have the operator go through the sequence and record the different motions made; redesign the motions to be most efficient; see what arrangement of controls that design calls for; and finally, arrange the controls on the machine to suit the best way of doing the task. That is all straightforward. All we have to do is study the operator's job, find out the best sequence of movements, lay out the controls according to that sequence, and give the layout to the design engineer.

But there are many jobs in the world that are not so cut and dried. Even driving a car is not a simple one-two-three proposition. Sometimes we push the clutch before the brake, and sometimes vice versa. Sometimes we step on the accelerator before we turn the wheel, and sometimes we slow down first. A man in the aircraft control tower does many different things, and he does not always do them in the same order. The same is true of the radar operator, the pilot of an aircraft, and operators in many other tasks which are not simply a matter of assembly-line production.

These unstandardized tasks need study just as much as the regular production tasks. And they can be made much more or less efficient and accurate, depending on the layout of controls. But the problem is to find some method of laying out controls scientifically even when the task is not standardized. Such methods are not encompassed in the bag of tricks of the motion-and-time engineer. Instead we must take a more statistical approach to the problem. In a standardized task, we can find out what the operator *always* does—he always operates control B just after control A. In the unstandardized task, we have to find out what the operator does, not all the time, but most of the time— at least more of the time than he does anything else. Thus, he may sometimes operate control C after control B, sometimes control A after control B. But which of these sequences does he follow the most, and how can we arrange the control to make the best compromise among the different things that he does?

To answer this question, we need to solve two problems, not just one. First we must find out what the operator does in carrying out his task, and, second, we must have some method of applying this information to the arrangement of a pattern of controls. We shall take up these problems in turn.

ANALYZING THE VARIABLE TASK

In order to analyze effectively what the operator is doing, even in a statistical way, we must know what we want to find out. In part, we want to know how often he uses each of the several controls available to him. But frequency of use of controls is not the important thing in the *pattern of arrangement*. What is important is the *sequence* of use of controls. After the operator has used control A, which one does he use next? And, after that one, which one is next? If the task is very complicated and if there are very many controls, this is a difficult problem.

The link. There is a notion, however, that helps a great deal in solving the problem. The notion is the *link*, which you may think of as any two controls used in sequence. If the operator uses control A first, and then control B, the link is AB. If he uses control C after control B, we have another link, BC, and so on. Links can be studied and counted just as the frequency of using particular controls, and our studying links gives us a breakdown of the task which can be used to obtain the best pattern of controls for the job.

Link frequency. With the concept of the link clearly in mind, we turn now to the task of finding out what links an operator uses in the variable unstandardized task. There are two ways to get this information: by direct observation of the task or by asking operators who are experienced in the task. If it is at all possible, it is certainly best to study the task directly, either on machines already in use or on machines mocked up for the purpose of the study. Needless to say, such a study should be a fair one. The operator—indeed, several operators —should be observed for reasonable periods of time and on repeated occasions. Every effort must be made to get a fair sample of the operator's job. In this matter, as in almost anything else in scientific work, our answer is no better than the sample of data we obtain.

If we assume that an extensive, fair, and representative sample of the operations is taken, there is little more to the study than to count the links in the operators' behavior. Any method of recording that gives a picture of which controls are used after each other is satisfactory. Perhaps tabulation on mimeographed sheets will do the job, or perhaps a more elaborate method is necessary. In any event, all we need to do is to count the number of links of various sorts. In Figure 174, you see the kind of result you will obtain. The numbers in that illustration are purely imaginary. We simply made them up, but they could apply to many complex situations. Each control is coded A, B, C, and so on. A scatter diagram is set up with each control heading a column and also a row. Each time a control link occurs, it is tallied. When the experiment is over, the tallies are totaled and converted into number scores for each link. That is what we want to know; it is a statistical summary of the sequences of controls used in the variable task.

Link importance. Before we go on to the methods of determining patterns of arrangements, let us point out that there is more to control sequences (links) than just the frequency of their use. Some links are more important than others, even though they may not be so frequently used. If it is a matter of life and death that a man be able to operate a control at the right time, we want to put it where he can get it and use it quickly when he needs it. Sometimes it is essential that two controls be used in sequence, whether or not they are used very often, and this must be considered in the arrangement of controls.

Control

	A	B	C	D	E	F	G	H	I	J	K	L
A		3	4	2	10	9	8		7			3
B	3		1	2		5		7		14	10	
C	4	1		4	20	12		15	3	4		15
D	2	2	4		7	16		10		5	9	
E	10		20	7		7	6	17	21	10	12	
F	9	5	12	16	7		8		13			20
G	8				6	8		3	8	20	9	
H		7	15	10	17		3			18	4	
I	7		3		21	13	8			5		
J		14	4	5	10		20	18	5			
K		10		9	12		9	4				
L	3		15			20						
	46	42	78	55	110	90	62	74	57	76	44	38

(Left axis label: Control)

Fig. 174. An example of the data we might get for link frequency in a task involving many controls. Each letter at the top and side stands for a particular control. The numbers in the blocks represent the relative number of times a particular link is used. Notice that all the numbers above the diagonal line are duplicates of those below it, just to make it easier to see the link frequencies of each control with every other control. This example is probably more complicated than most we will encounter in practical situations.

So, in addition to frequency, sometimes we must also have some idea of the relative importance of particular links.

This business of link importance is especially difficult because we cannot measure it simply by observing the behavior of the operator, no matter how hard we try. It is, in fact, solely a matter of knowledge and judgment. People who know how the machine is built and what each control is for are the only ones who can tell us the relative importance of various controls and the links between them. The problem then is to get the best possible quantitative judgment of those who know about the importance of links. There are some special questionnaire techniques for making such studies, and it is well to use them. Even experts differ on such matters, and, even if they do not, it takes some special devices to get their judgments in quantitative terms that we can use for making accurate calculations of the best way to arrange controls.

Psychologists know that people do not have very good memories and that they have different standards for their judgments. The best technique for getting around this difficulty is to employ "forced judgments." We give the man a list of controls and make him rank-order the controls in respect to their importance of use. He has to say that one control is number one, another is number two, and so on. Such a preferential rating scheme avoids all sorts of misunderstandings and misjudgments on the part of the operator, and it tends to give us a fairly correct idea of the relative importance of use of the various controls. If several different people, operating the same machines, agree well in their judgments, we can place fair reliance on the results of this method of getting at importance of controls and control links.

Link value. Assume that we now know the relative frequency of different links and also have some knowledge of their relative importance. Next we will have to find some way of combining relative frequency and relative importance, if these are at all different. That, like determining importance, is a matter of judgment. Perhaps the important links are so important that it does not matter how frequently they are used; we must give them the highest priority in our arrangement. Or, at the other extreme, the relative merit of a link may rest entirely on how frequently it is used; there may be no reason for distinguishing frequency from importance. We must decide what the situation is and give relative weightings to the two aspects of the links' uses.

For most situations, it is satisfactory to give frequency and importance equal weighting. That, at any rate, is the typical case, and we will assume it in order to explain the rest of the procedure. First, we convert link-frequency and link-importance values into standard scales. The numbers we have from our experiments or questionnaires may be of many different sorts: the time the link is in use, the frequency of use, number of votes cast for the importance of the link, or rank-order ratings. It does not matter. Whatever the form of the numbers, they should be put into some simple terms. For most purposes, a three-point scale will do. All links can be rated, 3, 2, or 1, according to their relative use or importance. The most used and most important links would be rated 3 on each scale, those used moderately often and of moderate importance would be rated 2. Those used infrequently and of slight importance would be rated 1. Then, to combine with equal weight, we simply multiply the numbers for each link. Actually, we can add them, if we wish, but multiplying them simply emphasizes the links that are most important and most frequently used. The result is an over-all link value which weights both frequency and importance.

THE DESIGN OF SYSTEMS

Before we explain how to use over-all link values to arrive at an arrangement of controls on a panel, it would be well to discuss another problem which can be attacked and solved in just about the same way as the problem of control arrangement. This is the business of systems arrangement—how to arrange men and machines in an effective system.

Systems arrangement is an important and often puzzling problem. Many engineering psychologists have already been called in many times to advise engineers how to design over-all systems of men and machines. In every case we find that existing methods are little better than those some persons use to arrange furniture at home. First they put the sofa along the front wall, an easy chair along the side wall and a radio next to it, and end up with no place for the bookcase. So they start over again. By endless shufflings and reshufflings of the furniture they finally decide on one arrangement they like best of all. In another week or two they may become unhappy with the arrangement, because the bookcase is too far from the radio.

In arranging machinery and men for production or other purposes, this trial-and-error method is certainly too primitive. If we do not arrange a machine shop in the best possible way, a lot of waste motion results, the flow of materials is slowed, the time required to get from one machine to another slows down production, and it costs a lot of money to move the machinery to new locations when we find out that the first arrangement was a bad one. There certainly ought to be a more scientific way, a less costly way of arranging men and machines. And there is.

In arranging man–machine systems, we do just what we do in planning the arrangement of controls. First we think about links. In this case the links are man-to-man, man-to-machine, and machine-to-machine. If one man must talk to another one or pass material to him, that is a link. If the information or material coming out of one machine must go to another one, that is a link. If a man must adjust first one machine and then another, or work with several machines in succession, as a machinist usually does in a machine shop, that is a man-to-machine link. To find out what these links are, how frequently they are used, and how important they are, we do just what we do in the operation of controls. We find out in the most careful way possible, either by conducting a systematic study of the operations or by getting competent ratings from a number of people who are supposed to know. And in the end, we come out with a set of link values for the different man–machine links in the system.

THE ARRANGEMENT PROCEDURE

Since we have just been talking about systems arrangement, let us use it to show how the link-value information may be used to arrive at an optimum arrangement. Remember, however, in all that we say now that the same procedures can be used in arranging anything, including the controls and indicators on a panel.

The mathematical problem. This business of finding the optimal arrangement is a complex affair. It is something about which people are seldom scientific or systematic; yet it is one of the most complicated mathematical problems one encounters. The proper placement for each man and machine in a system depends on the placement of every other man and machine. The problem is comparable to the solution of a myriad of simultaneous equations in each of which there are as many constants as there are men and machines in the system and in which the values of the constants are not simple linear values but rather vectors. No one, except the chronic mathematician, likes to get ensnarled in such problems, for he may never get out again.

The graphical solution. Fortunately, there is a rough graphical solution to the problem that is about as useful for most purposes as any precise mathematical solution. The steps in the graphical solution are easy. In fact, there are several rather simple ways to go about it, but we will suggest only one which will work. If we solve problems of this sort, we can work out variations to suit our problem and our preferences.

First, select for analysis only the important and major items about which you are concerned. Do not consider any small items such as telephones, switches, pencils, or such that must inevitably go wherever the man or the machine goes. Next, select only the men and machines (or the controls, if you have a control problem) that have some link values. A wall chart, for example, may be a major item, but, if it is not used in the main function of the system, in relation to some other man or machine in the system, leave it out of the problem. Now tabulate all link values. As a matter of convenience, you may use some sort of code for distinguishing men and machines, say, letters for machines and numerals for men. That is what we have done in the example we are going to use. The job is made still easier if all link values are put into a diagram or table, such as that in Figure 175.

In that figure you see a diagram similar in principle to the example in Figure 174. In Figure 174, however, we simply tabulated link frequency and made no distinction whether the links were between controls, between men, or between men and machines. In this diagram, we have taken a hypothetical man–machine problem. There are no links between machines, although there are links between men and

		Machines				Men			
		A	B	C	1	2	3	4	5
Men	1	2	1	6		9	9	2	
	2	1	6	4	9				
	3	6	2	4	9				
	4	4	4		2				
	5			2					

Fig. 175. A chart of the link values in a hypothetical man–machine system. The numbers in the blocks, representing the links, were obtained by multiplying link-frequency rating with link-importance rating. The ratings were made on a 3–2–1 scale. Though relatively simple in appearance, this chart actually has more link relationships than we will find in most practical problems.

between men and machines. Letters have been used for machines, numerals for men. Also in this diagram, you see overall link values, obtained by getting 3–2–1 rating-scale values for importance and frequency and multiplying the two together. There are many variants of this technique which we can always devise for our own purposes. Figure 175 is just an example of how such summaries look in general.

With the kind of data we have in this table, we are ready for the solution. The first part of the solution will look like the upper part of Figure 176. For convenience, we use circles for men and squares for machines. We draw and code the item that has the most links. That is man number one. Then we plot the item linked with the first one that has the highest link value; that is man number two. Then we plot the items that have the strongest connection with the items already plotted. When we finish this sequence, we start with the item still unplotted with the highest link value and continue until all items are on the graph. Then we draw in all remaining links between items on the chart. Using the data in Figure 175, we will come out with a graph like that in the upper part of Figure 176. This result may be a little confusing, but we can straighten it out by a little obvious rearrange-

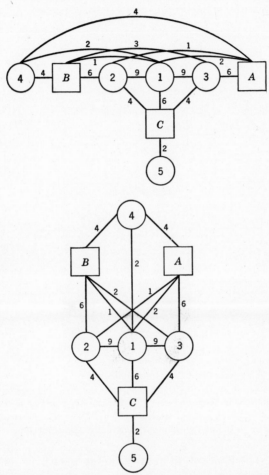

FIG. 176. The graphical solution of a systems-arrangement problem. The link values come from Figure 175. The upper part of the figure is the approximate solution, obtained by following directions in the text. The bottom part of the figure is the same as the upper part after it is simplified to make the link lines as short as possible.

ment to make the lines as short as possible. The bottom part of Figure 176 is the straightened-out version. It is the best pattern for our layout, and it has all the items in the correct relationship.

Applying the solution. Now, the thing to remember about this model is that it is made of rubber. You can twist it and bend it, make it rectangular or circular, swing items around their axes into mirror-image positions—all without destroying the essential pattern of the items in

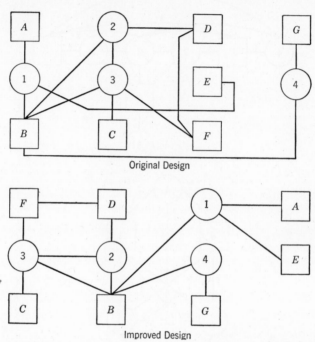

Original Design

Improved Design

Fig. 177. Link analysis applied to a communications center. The original design is a schematic diagram of the men and machines before the analysis. Notice the number of crossing links and long links. The improved design is the pattern of men and machines after graphical analysis. Notice how the pattern is simplified, the crossed links eliminated, and many links shortened.

your model. These elastic properties of the model, in fact, must be used to fit the solution to any particular space that is available.

A communications center. As an example of how this sort of approach works out, let us describe briefly one problem of systems arrangement we encountered in the last war. It concerned a certain type of room that was of considerable importance. In it were many men and many machines. A lot of information came into and went out of this room, and a number of things got controlled from the room. But the room was a problem, because nobody seemed to be where he ought to be at the right time, and some could not see or hear what they wanted to when they wanted to. We did not have an opportunity to study really carefully the relative frequency and importance of various links, but we could establish which links existed and were of any importance at all. Taking only the men and machines involved in these links, we could make a diagram of the existing arrangement of the room as they found it. Obviously, this was not the ideal arrangement. So we constructed a chart like the one in Figure 177. All this did was indicate which links were used and which were not. Then, by following the procedure outlined previously, we worked out a rubber model of the ideal arrangement of men and equipment. The final design appears in the lower half of Figure 177.

Described in this way, it looks very simple. Actually, it took only a few minutes after the facts about link values had been assembled. Before that, however, the problem looked so complicated that none of us could reach agreement on how to go about it. The same approach can be used for many different sorts of problems—in fact, any problem in which the sequence of action or pattern of arrangement is important. In the arrangement of controls and instruments in a large aircraft, for example, the sequence of action is important. Here, a link represents any sequence of use of two instruments or any sequence of action linking two operators. In other respects, the link analysis is unchanged.

SUMMARY

As we can see, there are a lot of angles to the arrangement of work. A better way can be found, if not the best way, to do almost everything.

To find it, we must pay attention to a lot of little details of the work and the work place. Can the operator do the job both sitting and standing? Is the seat designed for the greatest comfort? Are tools and controls within the maximum reach of the individual, and are the most important ones within the normal working area? Is the work distributed to the best advantage between the feet and hands and between the two hands? Are the motions of the hands natural and symmetrical? Are the controls placed in the right pattern for economical and errorless use? Is the sequence of movement the shortest and most effective? And, finally, in complex systems, involving many men and machines, are they placed in the optimal relationship to each other? Attention to these questions, one by one, in the long run, may make a great difference in the efficiency of the work, as well as the safety and comfort of the operator.

SELECTED REFERENCES

1. BARNES, R. M. *Motion and time study* (3rd Ed.). New York: John Wiley, 1949.

2. BARNES, R. M. *Work methods manual.* New York: John Wiley, 1944.

3. BEDALE, E. M. Comparison of the energy expenditure of a woman carrying loads in eight different positions. *Indust. Fat. Res. Bd. Rep.,* 1924, No. 29.

4. CHANNELL, R. C. An analysis of pilots' performances in multi-engine aircraft (R5D). Office of Naval Research, Special Devices Center, 1947.

5. HOOTON, E. A., *et al. A survey in seating.* Gardner, Mass.: Haywood-Wakefield, 1945.

6. LIPSCHULTZ, H. L., and SANDBERG, K. O. W. Maximum limits of working areas on vertical surfaces. Office of Naval Research, Special Devices Center, Report No. 166–I–8, 1947.

7. McFARLAND, R. A. *Human factors in air transport design.* New York: McGraw-Hill, 1946.

8. MOGENSEN, A. H. *Common sense applied to motion-and-time study.* New York: McGraw-Hill, 1932.

9. RANDALL, F. E., DAMON, A., BENTON, R. S., and PATT, D. I. Human body size in military aircraft and personal equipment. Air Materiel Command, Army Air Forces, Technical Report No. 5501, 1946.

13. Working and Resting

THE EFFICIENCY OF A HUMAN BEING AT WORK DEPENDS ON MANY FAC-
tors, some of which we have discussed in this book. His inherent
ability, the design of the instruments and machines he works with, the
design of the work itself, all contribute their bit to making man either
an efficient or an inefficient animal.

One of the biggest troubles with people, however, is that they get
tired. You cannot work all the time because you have to sleep now
and then. And you cannot even work all your waking hours, at least,
not if you want to work efficiently and live as long as most people manage to live. The problems of how long we can work without falling
over from exhaustion, of how much rest we should have, of how long
the working day should be are just as important as the problems of
equipment design. They are the problems we deal with in this chapter.

THE PROBLEM OF FATIGUE

Fatigue is important. In the last half-century, and even before,
probably no topic has received quite so much consistent attention as
the amount of work one man should be expected to do. There has
been a progressive shortening of the number of working hours in a
week, and there probably will be even more shortening in the future.
Some of this change has come about because of humanitarian interests,
some because of technical advances. There has also been, however,
increasing recognition that the efficiency of a worker depends on how
many hours a week he works, or how long he works without a rest
pause. We now realize that one worker can often produce more in 40
hours than he could if he were working 60 hours a week.

We know that fatigue is important, and most of us think we know
what fatigue is. At least we have a lot of words to describe the various
feelings and effects of fatigue. Words like weary, tired, exhausted,
spent, worn, all describe our feelings when we have various amounts
of fatigue. And yet the problem of fatigue has been, experimentally
at least, a very tough nut for psychologists to crack. When we do

experiments, we find things that act like fatigue when we think no fatigue should be there. Or we find no measurable effects of fatigue, when we know the effects ought to be there, because the subjects say that they feel tired.

Kinds of fatigue. These many difficulties have made people try to distinguish among various kinds of fatigue, as a way of straightening out some of the problems. The usual distinction is between mental and physical fatigue. Such a distinction, however, is probably more useful when applied to the work, rather than to the effects of work. It is true that you get different effects with different kinds of work, but all these effects *can* occur with all kinds of work. And there is the further complication that boredom, sometimes called psychological fatigue, gets treated as a kind of fatigue. Boredom is primarily a problem in social motivation, and we shall not discuss it here.

SOME SYMPTOMS OF FATIGUE

It is all very well to talk about fatigue, but if we want to do something about it, we must be able to measure it, for, if we cannot measure fatigue, how are we going to find out what causes it and how to prevent it? There are several ways of measuring fatigue. To be more precise, of course, what we really measure are the effects of fatigue, and these effects can be thought of as the symptoms. All these symptoms are changes in the behavior of the worker, changes due to continued work at one job.

Changes in performance. In many jobs, there are progressive changes in performance the longer a man works. By changes in performance we mean performance which is overt and directly related to the job. We shall see later that there are many different kinds of change in performance. As a man shovels coal, for example, he shovels less and less the longer he works. That is a change in performance. Or a typist may make more errors as the day goes on. In other jobs, the variability of work may change. A worker setting controls on an automatic machine, for example, may be less and less consistent in setting those controls as he continues work.

Greater energy expenditure. Many times, particularly with very strong motivation, a man may work at a hard job hour after hour without any noticeable decrease in output. He gets just as much work done at the end of the day as he did at the beginning. In keeping his performance up, however, he may be using more energy at the end than at the beginning.[6] Few of us ever work at the top of our real capacity, physiologically speaking. As we get more and more tired, we may work harder and harder in order to keep output the same. But working harder and harder takes more energy, and it is possible to get some measure of the extra energy used.

One study, for example, showed that a man uses about 20,000 cubic centimeters of oxygen per mile if he walks at a rate of 2 miles an hour.[20] At a rate of 5 miles an hour, he uses over 25,000 cubic centimeters of oxygen per mile. This is certainly much less efficient, because he uses more energy to get the same amount of work done. Likewise, we can expect that he will use even more oxygen to do the same amount of work after he has been walking several hours.

Physiological effects. It is hard to say exactly what we mean by physiological efficiency. There are many physiological changes that occur when we get tired or exhausted. These changes may indicate lowered efficiency, but we cannot always be sure. They may simply be by-products of a general fatigue effect. And, unfortunately, we often find no measurable change short of complete exhaustion.

The U. S. Public Health Service recently made a study of fatigue in almost 700 truck drivers.[13] This study showed that the average heart rate of the drivers was 83 beats per minute if they had done no driving for some length of time, but that it went down to 79 after 10 or more hours of continuous driving. The blood pressure also was slightly higher after long hours of driving, although this increase was much less consistent than the drop in heart rate. Most of the other physiological factors showed little or no effect even after 10 hours of driving. Physiological changes can be found, then, but we are not always sure that they are a good measure of fatigue.

Unnecessary motion. Another measurable effect of fatigue is the amount of waste motion a man makes—motions that do not help get the work done. Most of us have certainly noticed that we wriggle in our seat more at the end of an hour's lecture than at the beginning. After studying a long time, we want to get up and walk around. These extraneous unnecessary motions increase as we get fatigued, and they give a good indication of the presence of fatigue.

There have been several studies of eye fatigue, and most of them have not found any real change in capacity for performance on the job. But unnecessary movements increase, and the rate of eye blinking increases, the longer we work on a job.[8]

Subjective feelings. We must not forget, of course, that subjective feelings of fatigue, even though there is no change in performance, are important. In fact, most of us prefer to trust our feelings instead of some indirect measurement of our fatigue. If we feel tired, we probably are tired. Our feelings can be quantified by having us rate them with numbers. For example, if you feel real good, we could give you a fatigue score of 0. If you never felt worse, we could call that 10. And other feelings could be rated between these two extremes.

Studies that have measured subjective feelings are ambiguous. Sometimes subjective feelings agree well with performance. At other times, there seems to be no relation between them. Occasionally, the worse we feel, the more work we get done. When this happens, it usually means that our motivation has increased.

PROBLEMS OF MEASUREMENT

Direct measures. Depending on what we want to find out, any one or all of these measures of fatigue are useful. If we want to discover the underlying physiological basis of fatigue, measures of energy expenditure are very good. In most real situations, however, we are primarily interested in only one thing: Has the performance on the job changed as a result of longer working periods? Does production decrease? Does variability increase? Are more errors made? These are the questions and problems we are normally concerned with. A man's feelings may be important, but, from the purely practical point of view we have taken in this book, those feelings are not so important as what he does.

In this discussion, then, of the effects of fatigue, we shall concern ourselves almost entirely with changes in performance on the job.

Motivation. The problems of good scientific measurement are difficult. One of the biggest problems arises because we have trouble controlling the motivation of the subjects in our experiments. If we want to predict what will happen in a real situation, we would like motivation to be the same in our test situation as it will be in real life. Many times that is impossible. And actually there are times when it really is not desirable. In order to get the fullest understanding of fatigue, we want to isolate all the factors involved and study each of them by itself.

KINDS OF WORK

The effects of fatigue often depend on the kind of work done, and we have to look for different things on different jobs. Although it is impossible to make any hard and fast classification of kinds of work, the following groupings will probably help our later discussion.

Physical tasks. Some tasks are almost purely physical in nature. Very little perceptual skill is involved, and the fatigue effects are almost always muscular. Some physical tasks involve a rapid expenditure of energy, like running a foot race. Others are repetitive jobs, like using a handsaw. Still others involve postural restrictions, like standing at attention.

Psychomotor tasks. An intermediate class of work involves what we call psychomotor tasks. These tasks, in general, have both physical and motor or muscular aspects and are frequently problems of coordination. Coordinating the eyes and hands, for instance, in radar tracking is a psychomotor task. Driving a car or truck is another psychomotor job. There is also a large classification of work called skilled labor, which in most cases is really psychomotor work. Operating a lathe or other precision machinery involves both motor coordination and perceptual skill. All jobs that require a high degree of coordination between what we sense and what we do are psychomotor tasks.

Mental work. Still another type of work involves practically no real muscular effort. Reading a book, for instance, we can class as a mental job. Problem solving and tasks involving a great deal of judgment and decision can also be called mental. We are not trying to make an argument for the mental versus physical here, and we use the term mental only because it is a convenient classification.

FATIGUE AND PERFORMANCE

In this section we shall discuss some of the effects fatigue can have on performance. We shall see that some of these effects are found with almost any type of work; others are often found with limited kinds of work.

PRODUCTION RATE

Quantity. The first thing we usually expect when we talk about fatigue is that the production rate gets lower the longer a man works on the job. The quantity of work a man does becomes less. Either he gets less work done for each operation, or it takes him longer to complete a single piece of work.

Muscular work. Several years ago a series of experiments was done at Columbia University on the effects of continued work.[16, 30] These experiments were concerned with muscular work, and the experimenters used several kinds of muscular activity. They had their subjects lift weights with their fingers, with their hands, with their arms, and with their feet. They also used a laboratory kind of rowing, with the same kind of muscular effort we have to put forth in rowing a boat. Figure

178 shows the kind of work-output curve they obtained in most of these experiments. The longer a man worked, the less work he could do, until he could no longer move the weights at all.

The kind of work-output curves shown in Figure 178 is not very often found under real work conditions, because we rarely work so hard that eventually we cannot work at all. In the Columbia experiments, the motivation of the subjects was very high, and they could be asked to work very hard continuously. The curve shown here can be thought of

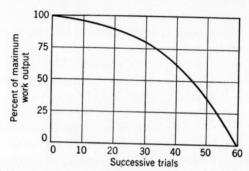

FIG. 178. The fatigue curve for continuous muscular work. This curve shows how work output drops from its maximum value as the work is continued. This type of work curve is found primarily with heavy muscular tasks. With lighter work, or perceptual-motor work, the work output does not drop off so rapidly and sometimes does not drop at all. Likewise, if the work were not continuous, output would hold up better.

as the basic fatigue curve for muscular work. If work is mixed with rest pauses, the curve will not fall so rapidly. If the rest pauses are long enough, of course, there will be no drop in output at all over very long periods of time.

Psychomotor work. A continued drop in production over a period of time is most often found with muscular work. Mental work and psychomotor work often do not call for real muscular effort, and, if we look for a drop in quantity of production, we sometimes cannot find it. Yet fatigue affects psychomotor work as well as muscular work. We have to look for different effects. Errors, accidents, slower reaction time, lack of precision and coordination, all occur as a result of fatigue on psychomotor tasks.

ERRORS

Another effect of fatigue can be found by analyzing errors made in production over a period of time. Frequently the number of errors will increase, even though there has been no serious drop in quantity of production. Such a rise in errors is an indication of fatigue just as much as a drop in production. We should perhaps emphasize the fact that fatigue can show itself in many ways other than a drop in production.

Typing errors. A good illustration of the increase in errors can be found in studies of typing In one experiment, subjects were required to type the letters *vbn* in sequence with three different fingers.[21] They

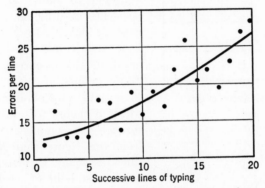

Fig. 179. The number of typing errors increases as greater and greater amounts of work are done. The data presented here were obtained by having men type the letters *vbn* in rotation with three different fingers. Since each line consisted of 50 letters, more than half the letters typed were wrong at the end of the work period. (After Robinson and Bills, 1926)

typed 50 letters on a line, and kept typing line after line. The average time for typing a single line increased at first, but later decreased toward the end of the work period. When errors were analyzed, however, it was found that they continued to increase throughout the whole work period, as shown in Figure 179. The change in total work done was very small compared to the increase in number of errors. In fact, toward the end of the work period, over half the letters typed were wrong.

We can expect errors to increase in many types of work. Any task that requires a worker constantly to set controls, or read dials, will probably show an increase in errors toward the end of a work period.

ACCIDENTS

Another measure of performance which is closely related to errors is the accident rate. Industry has found that an analysis of accident records is very valuable for many kinds of things. Workers can be selected for low accident rates, machines can be redesigned to lower accident rates, and we could mention many more. Right now, however, we are concerned with the problem of fatigue.

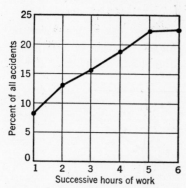

FIG. 180. This curve shows that the number of industrial accidents increases with a greater number of successive hours of work. The data for this curve were obtained from surveys in Germany, England, and the United States. (After Muscio, 1920)

Time of day. Some years ago, records on industrial accidents were compiled over a long period of time from Germany, England, and the United States. These records were analyzed to show the number of accidents at different hours of the working day.[18] In Figure 180 we have shown the percentage of all accidents that occurred during successive hours of work. Many of these data were obtained at a time when 6 hours of work straight through was common. You can see from this figure that nearly three times as many accidents happened in the last hour of work as in the first hour. About 45 percent of all accidents occurred in the last third of the work period.

These are very impressive figures and once again should remind us that the effects of fatigue can be found in many and varied places.

VARIABILITY OF PERFORMANCE

In Chapter 3 we saw that variability of work was an important problem. A lot of work has been done trying to reduce variability of performance in many different jobs. If a man has to make a lot of adjustments in a machine, we would like him to make all his adjustments the same. If he is consistent, then we can adjust the machine to take care of any constant error in his work. But if he is very inconsistent, our real problems begin.

Muscular work. Perhaps one of the best indicators of fatigue is the variability of a man's work. The more tired a man is, the less consistent he will be. This variability occurs in almost all kinds of work, although the kind of variability may be different with different jobs.

In heavy muscular work, the average amount of work done decreases as the worker gets fatigued. Along with this decrease in amount of work, there is usually an increase in variability, as shown in Figure

181. In that figure, we have shown relative variability. Now, since the average work done was less toward the end of the work period, the relative variability would increase if the absolute variability remained the same.

In one of the Columbia experiments mentioned previously, variability of work output was determined with various kinds of work.[30] The experimenters measured the trial-to-trial variability over short

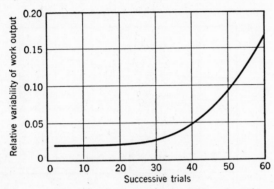

Fig. 181. This curve shows that the relative variability of work output increases with greater amounts of work. The ordinate is a measure of the variability of work output divided by the average work for a short period of time. This type of variability occurs with fatigue curves like that shown in Figure 178. With that type of fatigue curve, absolute variability tends to increase also, but relative variability increases considerably more.

periods of time and divided the variability by the average work done in that period. The curve of relative variability they obtained was very similar to that shown in Figure 181. In that same experiment, there was some increase in absolute variability as well, although that increase was quite small compared to the increase in relative variability. He can expect, then, that variability of work output will increase when the worker is fatigued, even when work output has decreased.

Psychomotor work. In many types of psychomotor work, very little muscular effort is called for. And frequently there is no evidence of fatigue over long periods of time, if we look only at the average work curve. If, however, we look at the variability of performance, we may find some surprising changes. Variability may increase very rapidly, even though the average performance has not changed. Such a situation is graphically illustrated in Figure 182. We recognize that here it does not matter whether we plot relative or absolute variability. Since the average performance does not change, relative and absolute variability are really the same thing.

Foxboro experiments. During the recent war, many experiments were done at the Foxboro Company on the problem of radar tracking.[1] In this kind of problem, the operator has to move a handwheel around to keep a small spot centered on a radar display scope. Not much muscular effort is required in this job, but a great deal of coordination

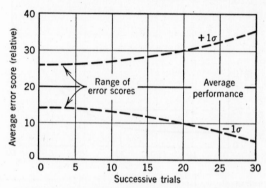

Fig. 182. In many types of psychomotor tasks, average performance (here shown as an error score) does not become worse as the work is continued. The variability of the performance increases, however, as shown by the range of error scores in this figure. In this situation, the only real evidence of fatigue is the increased variability of performance.

is necessary. In one of those experiments, radar operators were kept at work for as long as 3 hours continuously without a rest period. Over that length of time the records showed no decrease in average performance, as measured by an error score. But they did show that variability increased by over 50 percent. This is indeed an interesting finding. Remember that here the measure of performance was an error score—a score that indicated how consistently the spot was kept centered on the radar scope. In order for the variability to increase, some of the time the radar operators had to do better at the end than they did at the beginning. In a sense, they got both better and worse the longer they worked.

OTHER FATIGUE EFFECTS IN PSYCHOMOTOR WORK

So far, we have been talking about the direct effects of fatigue on the work itself. Our measurements have been in terms of quantity and quality of production, in terms of accidents or variability. In many kinds of psychomotor work, however, it is almost impossible to get a good direct measure of performance as the work goes on. In truck driving, for example, how do we determine how well a man is driving a truck? Although it is true that we can measure accident rates, or even total time to drive a certain distance, these would be very insensitive and unsatisfactory measures.

In jobs like driving a truck, we can study fatigue by studying the effects of continued work on psychomotor skills which themselves ought to have a direct effect on the job. As an example of this type of measurement, and its usefulness, we shall return to the study of truck drivers which we mentioned previously.[13] These truck drivers were tested at stations in Baltimore, Chicago, and Nashville, for many different psychomotor and physiological factors.

Hand steadiness. Hand steadiness certainly should have some bearing on how well a man can drive a truck. The tests on the truck drivers showed that hand steadiness decreases with continued hours of driving. Two kinds of steadiness measures were used. The drivers were asked to hold a metal stylus in a small hole for a short period of time. Every time the stylus touched the edge of the hole, the movement was recorded. The two measures used were (1) the smallest hole the drivers could hold the stylus in without touching the sides, and (2) the average number of contacts made with the sides.

The results showed that men who had done no driving after a long rest period could hold the stylus in a hole $\frac{11}{64}$ of an inch in diameter. Drivers who had been on the road for more than 10 hours touched the sides of the hole, on the average, whenever the diameter was less than $\frac{7}{32}$ of an inch. Likewise, men with no driving since rest made an average of 71 contacts with the sides; men who had been driving up to 10 hours touched the sides 79 times; and drivers with more than 10 hours of driving made contact an average of 84 times in the one-minute test period.

Reaction time. Other psychomotor tests showed clear effects of driving time. Both complex and simple reaction time increased with a greater number of hours on the road. In the complex reaction, the drivers had to reach for a pencil on a signal from the tester and move the pencil from one hole to another. The time required to do this was longer when the men were tired. Other measures were made of braking time in a simulated driving situation. The longer a man had been driving, the longer it took him to get his foot off the accelerator and onto the brake pedal.

The results of the simple reaction time tests are shown in Figure

183. In this test, the drivers had to turn a high-speed timer off as soon as it was turned on. The timer clock then showed how long it had taken the man to get the clock turned off. Figure 183 shows that the simple reaction time increased by a tenth of a second after the drivers had been on the road for 10 hours or more.

Speed of tapping. The drivers were also tested on tapping rates. In this test, they had to tap a metal plate with a metal stylus as fast as

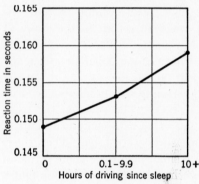

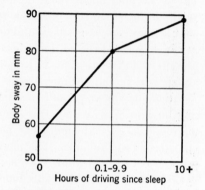

Fig. 183. Simple reaction time becomes longer after men have been driving trucks several hours. Reaction time was measured by having the truck drivers stop a clock as soon as possible after it was started. They pressed a button to stop the clock. (After Jones *et al.*, 1941)

Fig. 184. The amount of body sway increases after men have been driving trucks several hours. In this test, the drivers stood erect with their arms across their chests. The measurement shown on the ordinate is the total amount of head movement in a 1-minute interval. (After Jones *et al.*, 1941)

they could for a period of 45 seconds. Measurements of their rate of tapping were made at various times during the test period. At all times, speed of tapping was greater for those drivers who had not driven after a long sleep period. But the greatest difference of all was found in the last 5 seconds of tapping. This is interesting, because it shows that the longer a man has been driving, the more rapidly he becomes fatigued on a new job.

Body sway. Figure 184 shows the effects of driving time on body sway. In the sway tests, the men were required to stand erect with their feet straight and their hands folded across their chests. Strings fastened to the tops of their heads ran up over pulleys and measured the total amount of movement they made while trying to stand perfectly still. Figure 184 shows that the amount of sway increased over 50 percent after long hours of driving.

Eye factors. Still other tests showed that saccadic eye movements became slower and that recovery from glare was slower after many hours of driving a truck. Also, the longer the men had been driving, the more trouble they had telling a flickering light from a steady light. The flicker rate had to be slower for them to see that it was flickering.

Many other tests besides these were made, and most of the psychomotor tests showed some effects due to fatigue. It is silly, of course, to ask whether there was any "less driving." But we can still show that continued driving produced fatigue. And these fatigue effects undoubtedly lowered overall driving proficiency.

A LOWERED STANDARD

What is the basic nature of fatigue? Is it something that changes our capacity to work, or does it simply change our performance? Or, for that matter, can we ever really distinguish between capacity and performance? These questions are easy to answer for some types of work. Continued muscular work most certainly changes our capacity to do more work. Because it changes our capacity, it also changes our performance. In this case, then, we could measure a change in performance and assume that it means a change in ability or capacity— *if motivation has not changed.*

But what about the mental and psychomotor tasks? In many psychomotor tasks experiment after experiment has shown no measurable change in capacity or ability to do work. And yet many of these jobs, if not measured in a test situation, show changes in performance, that is, in the actual work done. What has happened, and how can we find out what has happened?

Cambridge studies. This problem concerned some psychologists working at Cambridge University, in England.[2, 3, 15] The particular task they were worried about was instrument flying in aircraft. They wanted to know what happened to pilots who had to spend long hours flying on instruments. The pilot must read dials all the time and must make judgments about alignments and misalignments of the indicators on the meters. There is little point in simply measuring the pilot's threshold of discrimination, because he has to respond not only to a misalignment, but also to the direction of it. Furthermore, he has to pick out the one misaligned meter from many.

When they made tests of the pilots' visual acuity in the laboratory, they found that the ability to make very fine discriminations did not change over long periods of work. And yet in some of the jobs calling primarily for a visual discrimination, they found that performance changed quite consistently over long periods of work.

These psychologists devised a task to determine what was happening. The observer had to watch a small needle, very much like the needle on instrument dials. Every once in a while at irregular inter-vals the needle would jump a small amount, and the pilot observers had to bring the needle back to zero. In this type of test, perform-ance became worse as the pilots continued their observations, as shown in Figure 185. But, if the observer was stopped and given a test to determine the smallest movement he could detect, they found that the ability to make this particular discrimination had not changed. The tired pilot, then, can see just as small a difference as the fresh pilot can, but he does not do anything about it until the differ-ence gets bigger.

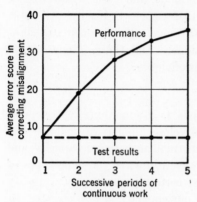

FIG. 185. In many kinds of psycho-motor work, performance becomes worse as the work is continued, al-though it can be shown that there is no real change in capacity. The test results shown here tell us that the observer's *ability* to detect the mis-alignments has not changed with time. But the performance curve indicates that the observer will not *report* such a small difference later as he would at the beginning of the run.

In other experiments, the Cam-bridge studies showed that perform-ance could be kept high if sufficient motivation were used, or if the observer had his attention brought back to the problem. In view of these results, these psychologists felt that the fatigue essentially lowers the pilot's standard of what he ought to do. His judgment about what the task requires has changed. He no longer feels that his best work is necessary and is willing to get along with a little less effort. We have to make a distinction between the pilot's threshold of discrimination and his threshold of worth. In some of these experiments, the threshold of discrimination (ability) was as good at the end of 2 hours' work as at the beginning, but the pilot's threshold of worth, as indicated by his performance, was three and four times its original value.

Laboratory experiments. There is a real significance in these results for laboratory experimenters. In the usual experiment, motivation is very high. In the laboratory, then, we usually measure capacity, since the subject literally does his best. But if we want to find out about fatigue, we must remember to distinguish between capacity and performance. What a man can do is one thing. What he will do is quite another matter.

CHARACTERISTICS OF THE WORK CURVE

Until now we have been talking more or less about the isolated effects of fatigue. As a man works through a period of time, certain changes occur in his performance. Because of the nature of these changes, we attribute them to fatigue. But many other effects occur as a man works over a period of time—effects that also represent changes through time. Some of them act like fatigue, but others do not. All of them, however, will together determine what any particular work curve looks like. When the work curve we get in an industrial setting does not look like a fatigue curve, we have to look for these other factors and attempt to isolate the fatigue effect.

Warming up. Several of the characteristics of a work curve are shown in Figure 186. The top curve indicates the warming-up effect, which is quite the opposite of the fatigue effect. With certain kinds of work, people start slowly and then gradually increase their rate of production. This gradual increase may be very short, or it may go on for several hours. In muscular work, for example, we may have to limber up our muscles before we can really start work, much the same as an athlete warms up before a game. In mental work, the warming up may be a matter of getting ourselves organized before we can settle down to continuous labor.

Beginning spurt. In other types of work, just the opposite effect may be true. We may start off with an initial enthusiasm which rapidly drops off as we settle down to the long grind. The beginning or initial spurt should be clearly separated from a fatigue effect. The beginning spurt is usually a purely psychological effect and has little relation to fatigue. It may, however, be closely related to boredom, in the sense that we have less enthusiasm for the work as time goes on. There are also other jobs where the steady grind does not call for full effort all the time. What often happens is that we start out at a high level and then realize that we cannot keep that level. So we slow down to an evener but lower rate.

End spurt. Just as we may start the day with a bang, so we often end the day with a burst of energy. This increased rate of production at the end of a work period we call an end spurt, and it can occur

with almost any kind of work. Sometimes this increase at the end
can completely offset the previous loss due to fatigue. That we are
able to increase our rate after a long period of time, of course, is one
of the best arguments that fatigue
changes our judgment of what we
should do more than it affects our
real capacity. If we always worked
at the top of our real capacity, an
end spurt would be impossible.

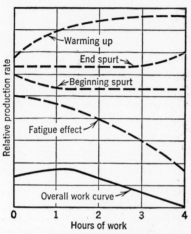

The end spurt, like the beginning
spurt, is probably due primarily
to motivational factors. Just as
we have an initial enthusiasm for
work, we can also become quite
enthusiastic about the prospects of
quitting. The seeing-of-the-end
has an important effect on the work
curve.

FIG. 186. This figure shows how various characteristics of the work curve
can combine to give an overall work
curve that shows effects other than
simple fatigue. The relative importance of the various work characteristics determines, of course, the shape
of the overall curve. With a greater
end spurt, for example, the work curve
may actually rise at the end of a
work period. Such a rise would not
necessarily mean that there was no
fatigue.

Overall work curve. We have
already discussed the fatigue effect
itself. The important things to remember are that an overall work
curve has all these factors in it and
that the particular shape of the
work curve depends on the relative
importance of the other factors.
With a small fatigue effect, and a
large warming up and end spurt,
the work curve could actually rise
throughout an entire morning.
Under other conditions, of course, the drop in work could be more
severe than we have shown here.

Almost any work curve has at least two or three of these factors in
it. Realizing this, we cannot say that a work curve as we find it in the
typical situation tells us about the amount of fatigue. There may be
fatigue when production does not drop, if the warm-up effect is strong,
and if we are motivated sufficiently. Likewise, an initial rise in work
followed by a later drop does not mean that there was no fatigue until
the drop occurred. It is even possible to have genuine fatigue even
though the over-all work curve rises steadily throughout a short work
period!

THE LENGTH OF THE WORK PERIOD

We are concerned with people working with machines. When we work for long periods of time, our efficiency drops because of fatigue. The problem of fatigue is universal, and this makes the problem of preventing fatigue just as universal. Fatigue lowers the efficiency of the worker, and we would like to prevent it if possible. The prevention of fatigue, of course, not only makes the worker more efficient, but also usually keeps him happier and healthier.

REST PERIODS

Probably the most straightforward way of attacking this problem is to ask how long a man should be expected to work. How long can one man stay on the same job before he becomes inefficient? If he has become fatigued, how long does it take for him to recover from that fatigue?

Recovery from fatigue. One of the experiments at Columbia University was concerned with the problem of recovery from fatigue due to muscular work.[16] In this experiment, the subjects were asked to do the various kinds of muscular work—lifting weights with their fingers, arms, and so on—until they were completely exhausted. For example, if the subjects were lifting weights with their arms, they continued to lift weights until they could no longer move their arms. Then the subjects were allowed to rest for various periods of time. After the rest period, they were tested again to see how high they could now lift the weights. The results of these tests are shown in Figure 187. At 0 minutes of rest, of course, they could not lift the weights at all. After 5 minutes of rest, they could lift the weights with about 80 percent of their previous ability, and, after 20 minutes, they were back to about 95 percent of their best work output.

This curve tells us that we recover from fatigue quite rapidly at first, but that there is a rather long slow period of recovery before we get back to where we started from. At the rate recovery is occurring in Figure 187, it would take nearly 40 minutes for complete recovery, which is a rather long time to wait. Normally, we would like to avoid having to take so long to recover from fatigue.

Intermittent rest and work. If the subjects in these experiments had not been so completely fatigued, it would not have taken so long to recover. The more fatigued we are, the longer it takes us to recover. Muscio has presented some interesting observations and calculations on this point.[18] And he has shown how short work periods can be more efficient than long work periods. The experiments he reports were concerned with weight lifting with the middle finger.

These are his conclusions. If we lift the weight one time after another, with no rest pauses in between, very soon we cannot lift the weight at all. This we have already seen. If we lift the weight 30 times continuously with no rest, it will be 2 hours before we will be back to normal efficiency. If we lift the weight 15 times running, then

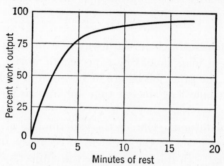

FIG. 187. Recovery from fatigue after various rest periods. Subjects lifted weights with their fingers until they could no longer move the weights. This curve shows how their ability to lift the weights recovered after various rest periods. One hundred percent work output is the amount of work they were able to do before any fatigue. Notice that recovery starts very rapidly but is not complete after 20 minutes of rest. (After Manzer, 1927)

recovery time is reduced to half an hour. In other words, cutting the work in half reduces recovery time to one fourth. But if we allow enough rest between each successive finger contraction, there will be no fatigue at all over long periods of time. With a rest interval as small as 10 seconds, for example, no noticeable fatigue will appear. The finger muscles have plenty of time to recover in this short time.

Now suppose we compare three different methods of working. In one method, we lift the weight 30 times, then rest 2 hours (which we have to, in order to keep on working). In another method, we lift the weight 15 times and then have to rest half an hour. In the third method, we lift the weight continuously, but with a 10-second rest period after *each* contraction. In an 8-hour day, we would lift the weight 120 times with the first method, 240 times with the second method, and 2,400 times with the third method. There is little question here as to which is the most efficient method.

A principle. This is only an illustration, of course, even though it is a true one. But it does emphasize one rather important principle of work: The best way to prevent fatigue is to take a rest period before fatigue sets in. Recovery from fatigue is very rapid with small amounts of fatigue but becomes very slow with larger amounts. Don't wait, then, until you are completely exhausted before you rest. You will get more benefit if you rest before you get tired.

Voluntary rest periods. Rest periods are an essential part of every working schedule. And, if rest periods are not scheduled, they get taken anyway. There are many studies showing that most workers quite consistently take unauthorized rest periods if they are not scheduled by the employer. The total amount of time spent in these rest periods varies with the type of work. In heavy work like building and roadmaking, for instance, as much as 20 percent of a worker's time is spent in rest. In lighter industry, such as shoemaking, the rest periods may take up only 5 percent of the total time. In general, fewer and shorter rest pauses are taken when the total number of hours worked is small. But the general point is that most work cannot be done without fairly reasonable rest pauses, and, if the rest pauses are not authorized, workers will take them anyway. They have to.

Scheduled rest periods. There are many studies showing that, if rest pauses are scheduled, production can increase anywhere up to 30 or 40 percent.[10, 20] Even though the scheduled rest period decreases the total working time, there is usually an increase in production, both per hour and per week. The hourly increase in production is more than enough to offset the time lost resting.

An illustration. We shall use a recent study as an illustration of the effects of rest pauses on production. This study, reported by Mc-Gehee and Owen,[17] involved routine office work. The 16 people working in this office worked a 7-hour day, with a 45-minute lunch period. Over a period of 2 weeks, these people were averaging about 21 minutes a day of unauthorized rest periods—time when they were actually away from their desks. During this time, there were no scheduled rest periods. Then they were given two 8-minute official rest periods, one in the morning and one in the afternoon, but they had to work 15 minutes longer each day to make up the time. After official rest periods were started, unscheduled rest dropped to an average of 8 minutes per day. When this is added to the official rest time, we see that they actually increased the total rest time by a very small amount—from 21 to 24 minutes a day.

Furthermore, the production records showed an increase in average production of 28 percent after the scheduled rest periods were started. In a sense, all that had happened was that scheduled rest periods were substituted for unauthorized rest, and yet production increased. Why?

The set for work. The answer to this "why" is a bit difficult, because it seems that the effect of the rest periods had to do with more than just fatigue. The answer, however, is probably this. Most of us manage to adjust our level of performance to the length of time we have to work, or the amount of work we have to do. For example, the runner starting out on a mile run does not run as fast as he can right away. He knows that he will not last long if he does. He adjusts his initial speed to the total amount of running he has to do.

If a man knows he has to work for only a minute, he will usually work harder than if he has to work for 10 minutes. To illustrate, suppose you ask a man to turn a crank as fast as he can for 10 seconds and for 5 minutes. He agrees and tries his best both times. Then measure how fast he was turning it the first 10 seconds. You will find that he did not crank nearly so fast (in the first 10 seconds) with the 5-minute job. In both instances he thought he was working as hard as he could, and yet the record shows that he was not.

It is quite likely that scheduled rest periods have this same effect. The scheduled rest period gives a shorter working objective. This anticipated shorter work period results in an increased level of performance.

The best rest periods. Everybody wants to know what the best scheduling of rest periods is. There is, unfortunately, no single rest schedule that is best for all kinds of work. Heavy work requires more frequent rest than light work. The longer the total work period, the more rest periods we need. In general, rest periods should be more frequent towards the end of the day. But these are just general principles.

If we want to schedule rest periods, probably the best thing to do is this. Get complete production records throughout the working period. Then look for the first drop in production. The first rest period should be given just *before* the drop occurs. Then get new production records. As soon as another drop in production starts, put in another rest period. The length of the rest period has to be pretty much a trial-and-error business. For most kinds of work, however, the best length is probably between 5 and 10 minutes.

HOURS OF WORK

For many years it was assumed that the best way to get a lot of production was for everybody to work long hours. The longer we worked, the more we got done. It was as simple as that. There has been, however, a progressive decrease in the number of hours worked in any one day or week. But when a war came along, the number of hours was increased again. It was still assumed that more hours meant more production.

Some illustrations. Muscio tells the story about some Tasmanian apple growers.[18] Two brothers each had large estates and maintained a group of apple packers. All the packers normally worked 8-hour days. But once a very large order came through, and one group of packers began to work 10 hours a day to cope with the unusual order. The other group continued to work only 8 hours, and they soon discovered that they were packing about 5 cases a day more than those who worked 10 hours. Since the workers were on piece rate, they were losing money by working more hours.

There is another report of a woman who worked as a yarn winder in England. The normal working day was 12 hours, but she refused to work more than 8. In addition, she occasionally took days off. She claimed that she could *not* do as much work in 12 hours as she could in 8, and a later check showed her to be right. She had gotten more work done in 160 hours than any of the other workers had in 237 hours throughout the same period.

These illustrations point out the basic problem. It is hard at first to believe that more work can be done in fewer hours. It is easy enough to see that production goes down after we have worked a while, but what is not recognized is the fact that production is down all day long if the hours are too long. There can be a total loss in efficiency that more than offsets extra hours.

Daily changes in production. First let us consider just how production changes in a normal day's work. Figure 188 shows the work curve for production in a plant working 8 hours a day.[11] The two different curves are for light and heavy hand work. For both types of work, production shows an initial rise (warming up) and then a drop. This drop continues through the morning, but there tends to be a slight rise after lunch. Then there is a period of little change, followed again by a drop in production. In general, there is more fatigue for the heavier work, but the curves are otherwise very similar.

The shape of the work curve differs from plant to plant, and from job to job. Most daily production curves look somewhat like this one, however, and so we call this the typical work curve.

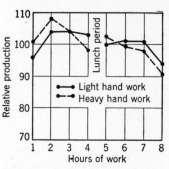

Ten-hour days. Figure 189 shows the work curves from a plant working 10 hours a day. These curves have the same general shape as those in Figure 188, with one big exception. In the morning the curves rise and then fall, but in the afternoon the drop in production during the last hour is much greater. There is much more evidence of fatigue in the 10-hour plant than in the 8-hour plant.

FIG. 188. Daily work curves for two kinds of work. These curves show relative production during various hours of the day for light and heavy hand work. The production scores shown on the ordinate are adjusted so that average production is 100. Notice that there is more fatigue effect with the heavier work. Curves like these are so frequently found in industry that they are called typical work curves. (After Goldmark *et al.*, 1920)

In each of these figures we have shown relative production, and we cannot compare the overall production of one against the other. It would be difficult because two different plants were involved. The average production in each figure is 100. But notice this about each curve. In the 10-hour plant the peak production is relatively higher than it is in the 8-hour plant. This means that average production in the 10-hour plant was not so close to peak production as it was in the 8-hour plant.

Hours per week. It has been shown many times that a reduction in hours produces an increase in total production, or at least in production per hour of work. Some results for different kinds of work are summarized in Table 12. These data were obtained when hours were still relatively long, and the effect of the shorter hours is somewhat more striking than we would expect. In heavy hand work, for example, reducing the hours of work per week from 66.7 to 55.5 resulted not only in an hourly increase in production, but also in a weekly increase of 19 percent.

In all the cases shown in Table 12, there was an increase in hourly production, although there was a slight decrease in weekly production for the lighter work. In general, this seems to be true: A reduction in number of working hours has more effect on total production with heavy work than with light work.

Another study compared work weeks of 36, 40, 44, and 48 hours.[19] It showed that maximum production per hour was obtained with the 40-hour week, although maximum production per week was obtained with the 48-hour week. In general, the many studies seem to agree that production per hour is greatest with approximately 36 to 44 hours of work per week, but that greatest production per week is obtained with work between 48 and 54 hours. Any increase in hours beyond that usually results in decreased production for the week.

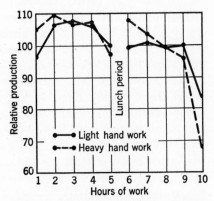

FIG. 189. Daily work curves for two kinds of work with a 10-hour day. These curves are of the same kind as those shown in Figure 188 but were obtained in a plant working 10 hours a day instead of 8. Notice the greater fatigue effect here. (After Goldmark *et al.*, 1920)

The machine or the worker? This difference in maximum production per week versus maximum production per hour points up another problem. If our aim is to get the maximum work per week from each worker, then a man on the average should work about 48 hours per week. Such a conclusion neglects, of course, any factors of mental well-being, general happiness, and so on.

TABLE 12. THE EFFECT OF NUMBER OF HOURS WORKED PER WEEK ON RELATIVE PRODUCTION

After Ghiselli and Brown, 1948

	Hours worked per week	Relative output	
		Per hour	Per week
Heavy hand work	66.7	100	100
	60.2	120	105
	55.5	137	119
Heavy work, hand and machine	74.5	100	100
	63.5	121	100
	55.3	156	113
Light work, hand and machine	71.8	100	100
	64.6	121	102
	57.3	133	97
Light work, machine	76.8	100	100
	60.1	121	93

But there is another point of view. Suppose our aim is to get the maximum production from each machine. Then, of course, we would want somewhat shorter hours. We would then want each man working at maximum hourly efficiency. Many times that is the correct point of view. In national emergencies, the machines are often as scarce as or scarcer than the workers. Real efficiency for an entire country, in those circumstances, would not call for more hours per individual, but for fewer hours.

Shift work. One way to get greater production per machine is to use shifts of work. Each worker works a relatively short day, but several workers take turns on the same machine. The most common type of shift work uses three 8-hour shifts per day. There has been much discussion of the advantages and disadvantages of the shift system. If it is not efficient for one worker to work more than 8 hours a day, then certainly we must use some sort of a shift if we need to keep the machine in operation.

But the objection has frequently been raised that night work or shift work is not efficient. The worker has his normal sleep schedule disrupted, and it is claimed that this is bad. Also, others feel that night work interferes with social life at home. Actually, these criticisms seem unfounded for the most part. There are great individual differences, to be sure, but many workers actually prefer night work, or at least alternating day and night work.

As far as the efficiency of shift work is concerned, the evidence, if anything, favors shift work. Vernon has reviewed many studies comparing the production of shift workers (people who alternate day and night work) with that of day workers.[26, 28] The data show a greater hourly output for the shift workers compared with that of the day workers. Actually, in all the cases he reviews, the shift workers had fewer hours of work per week; so some of the advantage might have been due to the shorter hours rather than the shift work. In any case, there is no good evidence that shift work (at least with the shorter hours) is bad for production.

When day work is compared to night work alone (not on shift), there is again no advantage for the day work. If a man stays on night work for a long time, however, his production seems to drop a little. The effects of the night work may be cumulative and thus are not noticed in short periods of time. If regular night work is planned, it probably is better to have workers change from day to night shifts at fairly frequent intervals. A change every two weeks seems to be satisfactory in most cases.

SLEEP

We have shown that man is a more efficient worker if he manages to get some rest now and then. But does it matter how he gets that rest? Is it all right if he just lies down? Obviously some of the time he has to sleep, and one of the big questions is concerned with this problem of sleep. How much does a man need? Does his efficiency decrease if he does not get enough sleep?

Loss of sleep. Many studies have been aimed at finding out what happens to a man's ability to work after various periods of time without sleep. A variety of tests have been used to measure performance —tests like tapping, mental arithmetic, maze learning, and performance. May Smith, for example, in an experiment on herself, slept 1½ hours the first night, 3½ hours the second night, and 5½ hours the third night.[24] She used a memory test and a tapping test. After the third night of subnormal sleep, she was, if anything, better on these tests than she had been before. After she went back to a normal night's sleep, she got worse again.

Psychomotor tests. These results are typical. Loss of sleep up to 100 hours does not seem to affect our *ability* in most motor and psychomotor tasks. And yet people feel fatigued if they do not get enough sleep. The answer to this dilemma is that the tests are not crucial. They do not measure the right things. It is quite likely that the subjects in these experiments have such a high level of motivation that we cannot measure any real change in performance. The tests are measuring real ability. As we have seen before, fatigue frequently affects performance without affecting ability.

Ability versus performance. Edwards, for example, reports the effects on 17 subjects of staying awake for 100 hours.[9] The psychomotor tests showed very little change due to the loss of sleep. But he reports that on a mental test the subjects were able to perform "with only the greatest effort." It is very likely, then, that performance would have dropped off much more rapidly if the subjects had not been in a laboratory test.

General effects of loss of sleep. Specific tests of ability, then, do not show much effect of the loss of sleep, although lack of sleep seems to affect our higher mental processes a bit more than muscular work.

In most reports, however, there is evidence of real personality changes after many hours without sleep. Subjects become irritable, have more daydreams and even hallucinations, and become more absent-minded. They forget simple things they ought to remember, and do not pay attention when they should. Cameron reports the case of a young man who managed to stay awake for nearly 10 days continuously in an experiment to see whether sleep was "just a bad habit." [7] At the end of that time, he became so irritable and emotionally unstable that the experiment had to be dropped. He had begun to accuse the research staff of interfering with him and had developed real delusions of persecution.

How much sleep. Unfortunately, we cannot say just how much sleep a working man needs. Prolonged loss of sleep is very bad, particularly for our personality. But just how much a man needs depends on the kind of work he is doing and on his individual needs. Some people seem to need about 10 hours sleep a night, whereas others seem to get along with as little as 3 or 4 hours.

SUMMARY

In this chapter we have discussed some of the problems of working and resting. The longer a man works, the more fatigued he becomes. This fatigue can show itself in many ways. The worker may show changes in performance, in efficiency, in useless motion, and in his own feelings. Even his changes in performance are not so simple as they sound. These changes may show up as decreased quantity of production, as increased errors and accidents, or as increased variability of performance. And we have to be careful to distinguish between changes in performance and capacity, because often fatigue does not change our ability, although our performance becomes worse.

The best way to prevent fatigue in industry is to use scheduled rest periods. These rest periods should come just before the effects of fatigue are noticed, not after. Also, man is not most efficient when he has to work long hours a week. Probably the best efficiency can be obtained with a work week of about 40 hours.

The loss of sleep over long periods has little effect on our capacity to work. The lack of sleep, however, may change our willingness to work and our standard about what is required. Furthermore, after long periods without sleep most of us become irritable, and we cannot get along with others very well.

SELECTED REFERENCES

1. ANONYMOUS. Accuracy of tracking by means of handwheel control. Foxboro Co., Foxboro, Mass., Report No. 2, 7 December 1942, OSRD Report No. 3452. (Available through the Publications Board, U. S. Department of Commerce, Washington, D. C.)

2. BARTLETT, F. C. Fatigue following highly skilled work. *Proc. Roy. Soc.*, 1943, B131, 247–257.

3. BARTLETT, F. C. The measurement of human skill. *Occup. Psychol.*, 1948, **22**, 31–38.

4. BARTLEY, S. H., and CHUTE, E. *Fatigue and impairment in man.* New York: McGraw-Hill, 1947.

5. BILLS, A. G. *The psychology of efficiency.* New York: Harper, 1943.

6. BITTERMAN, M. E. Fatigue defined as reduced efficiency. *Amer. J. Psychol.*, 1944, **57**, 569–573.

7. CAMERON, D. E. Job misfits. Work conditions. *Canadian Med. Assoc. J.*, 1944, **50**, 508.

8. CARPENTER, A. The rate of blinking during prolonged visual search. *J. Exp. Psychol.*, 1948, **38**, 587–591.

9. EDWARDS, A. S. Effects of the loss of one hundred hours of sleep. *Amer. J. Psychol.*, 1941, **54**, 80–91.

10. GHISELLI, E. E., and BROWN, C. W. *Personnel and industrial psychology.* New York: McGraw-Hill, 1948.

11. GOLDMARK, J., HOPKINS, M. D., and FLORENCE, P. S. Comparison of an eight-hour and a ten-hour plant. *Publ. Hlth. Bull.*, 1920, No. 106.

12. JOHNSON, H. M., SWAN, T. H., and WEIGAND, G. E. Sleep. *Psychol. Bull.*, 1926, **23**, 482–503.

13. JONES, B. F., *et al.* Fatigue and hours of service of interstate truck drivers. *Publ. Hlth. Bull.*, 1941, No. 265.

14. MAIER, N. R. F. *Psychology in industry.* Boston: Houghton Mifflin, 1946.

15. MACKWORTH, N. H. The breakdown of vigilance during prolonged visual search. *Quart. J. Exp. Psychol.*, 1948, **1**, 6–21.

16. MANZER, C. W. An experimental investigation of rest pauses. *Arch. Psychol.*, N. Y., 1927, No. 90.

17. McGEHEE, W., and OWEN, E. B. Authorized and unauthorized rest pauses in clerical work. *J. Appl. Psychol.*, 1940, **24**, 605–614.

18. MUSCIO, B. *Lectures on industrial psychology.* (2nd Ed.) London: Routledge, 1920.

19. MILES, G. H., and ANGLES, A. The influence of short time on speed of production. *J. Nat. Inst. Indus. Psychol.*, 1925, **2**, 300–302.

20. POFFENBERGER, A. T. *Principles of applied psychology.* New York: Appleton-Century, 1942.

21. ROBINSON, E. S., and BILLS, A. G. Two factors in the work decrement. *J. Exp. Psychol.*, 1926, **9**, 415–443.

22. RYAN, T. A. *Work and effort.* New York: Ronald Press, 1947.

23. SAYERS, R. R. Major studies of fatigue. *War Medicine*, 1942, **2**, 786–823.

24. SMITH, M. *Handbook of industrial psychology.* New York: Philosophical Library, 1944.

25. TIFFIN, J. *Industrial psychology.* (2nd Ed.) New York: Prentice-Hall, 1947.
26. VERNON, H. M. The speed of adaptation to altered hours of work. *Industr. Fat. Res. Bd.,* 1920, Report No. 6.
27. VERNON, H. M. *Industrial fatigue and efficiency.* New York: Dutton, 1921.
28. VERNON, H. M. *The shorter working week.* London: Routledge, 1934.
29. VITELES, M. S. *Industrial psychology.* New York: W. W. Norton, 1932.
30. WEINLAND, J. D. Variability of performance in the curve of work. *Arch. Psychol., N. Y.,* 1927, No. 87.

14. The Working Environment

SO FAR WE HAVE IGNORED ONE VERY IMPORTANT ASPECT OF MAN–MACHINE systems—where they work. Men and machines do not work in empty space; they work in environments of various sorts. The conditions of these environments may make a lot of difference in the efficiency of men, and it behooves us to list some of these factors and see how important they are.

Industrial applications. In recent years business and industrial concerns have spent millions of dollars trying to make factories and offices more comfortable, more attractive places in which to work. More, bigger, and better lighting fixtures flood our modern factories with light almost as good as natural daylight. Air-conditioning plants keep the work area at an even cool temperature the year around. Sound-absorbing materials keep down the noise levels. In some cases industrial noises have been replaced with other noises—commonly known as music—which are supposed to make work more pleasant. For each of these improvements one can find dozens of reports in engineering and trade journals pointing enthusiastically to increased production, decreased accident rates, and improved worker morale. If we are interested in engineering psychology we cannot ignore these developments. We ought to examine carefully the scientific studies that show the effects of these various environmental factors on human efficiency.

Military problems. The need for studying the work environment is even greater when we consider military systems. Many of us know from experience that most military systems are not located in very comfortable places. Riding inside a tank, for example, is something like being in a boiler factory built on a roller coaster. Modern aircraft hiss and roar through space so fast that sounds can just barely keep up with the plane. In the space of a few minutes a man may be whisked up to an altitude where the air is so thin that a match will not burn. And many of us can testify that a ship in a heavy sea succeeds, with astounding speed, in reducing our work efficiency to zero.

These unusual stresses that mechanized war places on man make the design of man–machine systems much more difficult.

Machine design. We have already seen that man is the weak sister in most man–machine combinations. If we put the man–machine combination in an environment unfavorable to the man we cannot expect to get as much out of the system. In many cases, the environment is so important—and so stressful—that we may have to design an entirely different kind of machine just so the man will be able to work with it. Let us cite one illustration. We all know that when it gets dark we cannot read small print. If, therefore, our system has to be located in an environment that must be kept fairly dim, then, obviously, the display part of the system, the dials and scales, have to be redesigned so that we can see them. But again, we should notice that it is necessary to redesign the machine, not because the machine will not function in darkness, but because man's eyes cannot.

EXPERIMENTAL PROBLEMS

Before cataloging some of the environmental conditions that affect human efficiency, we must introduce a note of caution. In Chapter 1 we described the method of science as being a method of *controlled* observation. The importance of controls in experimentation is probably nowhere better illustrated than in this field. If a production engineer goes into a factory, changes the lighting, and then finds that production goes up, the scientist is not satisfied. He wants to know, "How can we be sure that the lighting had anything to do with the increase in production?" Maybe the workers learned how to do the job better in the meantime. Maybe the new production engineer was popular, so that everybody spent less time grumbling. The scientist is not willing to accept the results of any factory experiments, no matter how enthusiastic its author may be, unless he is sure that other factors have been adequately controlled.

Production up. We can get some idea about how important these other factors can be from the results of an experiment done in the Hawthorne Works of the Western Electric Company.[12] This study extended over a period of 2 years, during which time various experimental conditions were tried out on a group of 5 women who were assembling telephone relays. One of the most important findings of this 2-year study was that production went up no matter what the experimenter did. He gave the girls two 5-minute rest periods—production went up. He gave them two 10-minute rest periods—production went up some more. He gave them six 5-minute rest periods—production went up still more. He gave them free lunches—production went up. He let them quit work a half-hour earlier every night—production still went up. And, even when he took away all rest periods and the free lunches, production was still much higher than it had been to start with.

The artifact—morale. What was happening here? Well, the 5 girls were in a separate room. They knew they were being experimented on. They knew that they were being given special consideration, and they so enjoyed having this attention that their morale reached a new high. Anything the experimenter did resulted in more production. It is this kind of evidence that should make us very skeptical about most factory experiments.

Hidden effects. There are still other things that we must keep in mind when we look at studies in this field. Few of them measure all the effects, or even the long-term effects, of repeated exposures to various kinds of environments. Let us see what this means. If we raise the temperature of a work room a little, there might be absolutely no change in the amount of work done there. But we could be fooled. There might be some hidden costs which do not show in the experiment—the workers might do a lot more grumbling and complaining, the labor turnover rate might go up, accidents might increase, and so on. In the long run, these other effects might really be serious. So we must be very careful in making up our minds about the results of experiments on the working environment. No experiment can ever measure everything, and we must always think about other possible effects which the experiment did not measure.

Cumulative effects. Then, too, it is possible that some effects will not show up in our experiments because a few exposures have no real effect. The real effect might not happen until a worker has been in a particular environment for a long time. Take coal mining, for example. The air in a coal mine has a lot of finely powdered coal dust in it. A healthy man may work in a coal mine for months or years without any apparent loss in efficiency. But after many years, he may have inhaled so much dust that he becomes a total loss physically. The same sort of thing may happen to people who work around radium or in very noisy places—boiler makers or weavers, for example. The point is that small doses might not have any real effect on a man's performance. But we have to remember that the effects of a bad working environment might add up over a long period of time. Few experiments have ever been done on these long-term effects.

On the other hand, these long-term effects sometimes work the other way. Take working at high altitudes, for example. If you have lived at low altitudes for a long time and then move to a mountain region, about 10,000 feet high, let us say, you will find that it is hard to work. You get out of breath easily, you get tired fast, and might even have a lot of trouble sleeping. But after a week or so, you will notice that you begin to get your pep back again. Your body makes certain automatic changes to the rarefied air. Your rate of breathing gradually changes, your blood gets more red blood cells, the oxygen-carrying ability of your blood increases, and so on. So it is possible that a new environment can have short-range effects that disappear after we have worked under the new conditions for a while.

All these things should make us realize that we cannot always take published results at their face value. If we look for really good experiments in this field, we find pitifully few of them. There are enough of them, however, for some good general conclusions to come through our screen of skepticism.

Other factors. One thing more. In this chapter we are going to look at the *physical* work environment. This does not mean that other things are not important, because they are. Morale, good leadership, letters from home, pay, and dozens of other psychological factors play an important role in the efficiency of the working man—no matter whether he is a sailor, soldier, or factory worker. But we have to draw the line somewhere. So we will stick to the physical environment.

ATMOSPHERIC EFFECTS

TEMPERATURE AND HUMIDITY

Almost all of us will agree that the temperature and humidity of the environment seem to affect our performance. In 1940, the British Industrial Health Research Board attempted, after considerable investigation, to set down the chief requirements for satisfactory heating and ventilation in the work space.

Feeling comfortable. They found very soon that people differed a lot in what they thought was a comfortable environment. After sampling a wide variety of opinions, however, they made some recommendations about temperatures and ventilation which seemed to suit the average person. Their recommendations are that in winter the best average temperature for very light work is about 65 degrees Fahrenheit, for active light work from 60 to 65 degrees Fahrenheit, and for work involving more muscular exertion from 55 to 60 degrees Fahrenheit. In hot weather they say that the temperature should be kept as low as possible by thorough ventilation. They further recommend that the supply of fresh air should not be less than about 1,000 cubic feet per person per hour and should preferably be greater. In winter, the rate of air movement should be about 20 to 40 feet per minute,

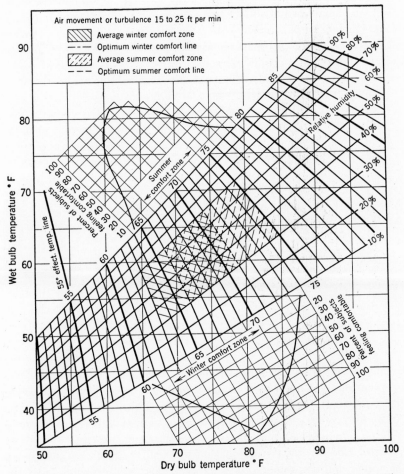

FIG. 190. Comfort zones for light work in winter and summer. For explanation see text. (Reprinted with permission from *Heating, ventilating, air conditioning guide,* 1948)

and in warm weather higher velocities are better. The relative humidity should not generally exceed 70 percent and should be less if possible.

The American Society of Heating and Ventilating Engineers has also published a comfort chart (Figure 190) which agrees pretty much with the British data. This chart gives summer and winter comfort zones which apply to people in the United States only. It is also limited to homes, offices, and similar environments where the amount of work done is normally light. There are two curves above and below the main chart which show the percentage of people who are comfortable at various summer and winter temperatures. The zones marked off in the center of the chart show the conditions under which 50 percent or more of the people are comfortable. Notice that most people are comfortable when the relative humidity is between 30 and 70 percent. In winter, most people feel comfortable when the effective temperature is between 63 and 71 degrees Fahrenheit; in summer, between 66 and 75 degrees Fahrenheit.

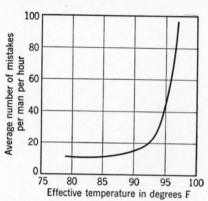

FIG. 191. Errors of wireless operators at different temperatures. We see that, above 92 degrees of temperature, mistakes increase markedly. (After Mackworth, 1946)

Temperature gradients. An important condition that also has a lot to do with the comfort of workers is the temperature gradient of the air. If the air at the floor is much cooler than the air at the head level—or if there is a lot more air movement near the floor—some workers are almost certain to experience extreme discomfort. The same is true for large temperature differences between different areas, for example, hallways and work rooms, especially for those workers who have to move around a lot.

Comfort versus efficiency. But we have to distinguish between comfortable temperatures and temperatures at which we *can* work, if we have to, without any loss in efficiency. The two are not necessarily the same, and, in general, rate of work does not drop off until the temperature is several degrees above the comfortable range.

Temperature and performance. During the war, a study [8] undertaken by the Applied Psychology Research Unit at the University of Cambridge, England, investigated the effects of heat on wireless telegraph operators who heard and recorded Morse messages for several hours at a clip. This study was undertaken primarily to discover how hot a room could get before the performance of wireless operators began to deteriorate. The experimenter had his subjects sit in a hot room at various temperatures—79, 85, 87½, 92, and 97 degrees Fahrenheit. The results of these experiments are shown in Figure 191. We see here the average number of mistakes made per man per hour during a 3-hour work period at the various room temperatures. It is clear from this study that, although the most comfortable working environment may be at a temperature of about 65 degrees, performance does not begin to deteriorate until temperatures of about 87½ or 92 degrees are reached. But at the worst temperature—97 degrees Fahrenheit —the number of mistakes increased nearly ten times.

Temperature and fatigue. It is also interesting to look at these data in another way. Shown in Figure 192 is the average number of mistakes per man per hour at the various room temperatures, with the data separated into the performance for the first hour and for the third hour. It is clear from these data that the performance of the wireless operators deteriorated markedly from the first to the third hours of work and that the amount of deterioration was worst at the extremely hot temperatures.

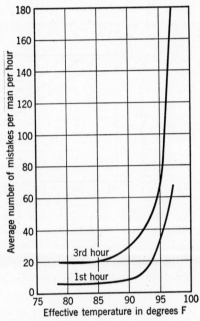

Fig. 192. Effect of temperature on mistakes of wireless operators during the first and the third hours of work. High temperatures cause a much greater breakdown in performance in the third hour than in the first hour of operation. (After Mackworth, 1946)

Humidity. Similar findings have been obtained in studies [6] performed in the Armored Medical Research Laboratory at Fort Knox. These data are a little more complete than Mackworth's, however, because they include one other factor—humidity. In this experiment the men were required to march for 4 hours at a rate of 3 miles per hour with a 20-pound pack. The results of this investigation, shown in Figure 193, prove what most people suspected all along: It is a lot harder to work well if the air is hot and sticky. Conversely, if the air is dry, a man can tolerate a much hotter temperature. Just to see how this works out, let us look at the figures for a temperature of 100 degrees Fahrenheit. At this temperature work becomes impossible when the humidity reaches about 86 percent. If the temperature goes up to 110 degrees Fahrenheit, then the humidity must be kept down to about 57 percent or less. It is important to point out that most

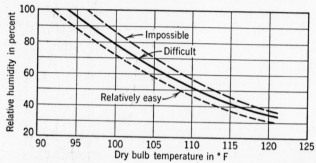

Fig. 193. How temperature and humidity are related in determining "easy," "difficult," and "impossible" environments to work in. (After Eichna *et al.*, 1945)

of the combinations of humidity and temperature tested do not occur in nature. But they do occur very frequently in many of the machines dreamed up by our engineers. One other thing that needs to be pointed out is that in both these studies the subjects were acclimatized; that is, they lived at these temperatures long enough to let their bodies get used to them. A person who had not been exposed previously to these temperatures would collapse under conditions which the acclimatized person could take with only moderate difficulty.

"Fresh air." The temperature of the air around us, however, has nothing to do with whether or not we consider it to be fresh or stale. There are probably a large number of factors that contribute to making the air around us feel and smell stale. Body odors, fumes, or exhalations from machinery, and moisture are probably large contributing factors. In most cases, rapid circulation of air in a room will remove the stagnant element. In an experiment conducted by the New York State Commission on Ventilation,[23] men were required to lift a 5-pound dumbbell a distance of 2½ feet. These men were tested under two temperatures, 68 and 75 degrees Fahrenheit, and with the air fresh and stagnant. The findings of this experiment are shown in Table 13. From these figures we can see that production, measured

TABLE 13. EFFECTS OF ATMOSPHERIC CONDITIONS ON PHYSICAL WORK

Data of the New York State Commission on Ventilation

Temperature, degrees Fahrenheit	Kind of air	Relative amount of work done, percent	Decrease in work done due to stagnant air	Decrease in work done due to increase in temperature
68	Fresh	100		
68	Stagnant	91.1	8.9	
75	Fresh	85.2		14.8
75	Stagnant	76.2	8.6	14.5

in terms of the number of times these men performed the operation, was at its highest level when the temperature was 68 degrees and the air was fresh. If the value for fresh air is used as the base line, stagnant air caused production to fall off approximately 9 percent under each of the two temperatures. Production dropped nearly 15 percent both with fresh and with stagnant air when the temperature rose from 68 to 75 degrees. Under the worst condition, namely that of stagnant air at 75 degrees Fahrenheit, production was nearly 24 percent below that of the most favorable condition.

Other related studies. The general findings reported here have been substantiated in a number of other types of industrial situations. The British Industrial Health Research Board [20] summarized the results of studies in heavy industry, for example, iron and steel mills, cotton weaving plants, laundries, pottery factories. Everywhere the pattern is the same. Production drops off, mistakes and accidents increase as the temperature and humidity rise above certain optimum limits. These optimum limits vary from 65 to 85 degrees Fahrenheit, depending on the nature of the work and the amount of physical exertion required of the worker.

Low temperatures. So far we have been discussing temperatures that are too high, and we ought to say just a word about temperatures that are too low. As one might expect, experiments show that manual dexterity—the ability to make precise neat movements with the hands and fingers—falls off slightly at temperatures of 55 degrees Fahrenheit, and markedly below 50 degrees Fahrenheit. In a study of munition workers, for example, it was found that the fewest accidents occurred at temperatures of 67 degrees Fahrenheit (see Figure 194). When the temperature dropped to 52 degrees Fahrenheit, the accident rate rose by 35 percent; when it rose to 77 degrees Fahrenheit, accidents increased by 23 percent.

The influence of incentives. It is generally assumed by designers of military equipment that high incentives may compensate for hot and humid work environments. The argument goes like this: The soldier and sailor under battle conditions is so strongly motivated that he will not suffer any loss in efficiency even though he may be working under adverse conditions. This sounds reasonable and, if true, should be something to take into account. There are few experimental data

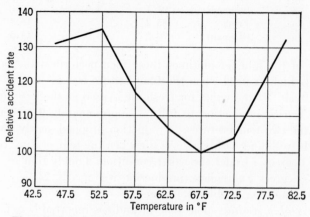

Fig. 194. The relative frequencies of minor accidents incurred by munition workers at different environmental temperatures. Accident rates are calculated as percentages of the minimum rate found at 67.5° F. Note that accidents increased whenever the temperature was much warmer or much colder. (After Vernon, 1936)

on this problem, but what has been done shows that this assumption is not true. Mackworth [9] tested 30 subjects at various room temperatures and with ordinary and high incentives. Under the ordinary incentive conditions, the subjects worked until they were exhausted. Under the high incentive conditions, Mackworth used the strongest psychological motivation he could create in the laboratory. He coaxed, pleaded, encouraged, and praised the subjects throughout the entire work period. High incentives got more work out of the men than did the ordinary incentives. That is to be expected. But here is the crux of the matter: Efficiency dropped off at the same temperatures and in the same amounts, regardless of the motivation. High incentives increased the overall amount of work done but did not have the slightest effect on the relative loss of efficiency at high temperatures.

This is a laboratory experiment which obviously cannot duplicate the extremely high motivation produced by battle. But it indicates that we must not assume that we can counteract the effects of poor working conditions by high incentives.

Physical versus mental work. It is interesting to note, however, that several studies seem to indicate that *mental* work, under such adverse conditions, does not deteriorate so rapidly as physical work. In the telegraph-operator study, for example, we remember that performance in receiving Morse messages did not begin to drop until temperatures of about 87 degrees were reached. In the New York study, where the men were doing some fairly heavy physical work, performance dropped off at 75 degrees. Men doing mental work show some tendency to take more frequent rest pauses under unfavorable conditions, but the surprising fact is that mental work is usually not affected until the conditions become extreme. The application of these findings to various man–machine systems should certainly be considered by design engineers.

Health. It is worth backtracking for a minute to consider an incidental finding in the Cambridge study [8] to which we referred earlier. During the course of this experiment two of the subjects developed severe head colds. The results of these two subjects in hearing and recording 9 consecutive code messages are shown in Figure 195. Each message took about 16 minutes.

The bottom curves in each instance represent the average performance of subjects when they were healthy, that is, not suffering from a head cold. When they had colds, the two subjects started out with very few errors, but, as the work period progressed into the second and third hours, the errors increased enormously. Although this finding is rather incidental to the general problem of the work environment, it gives us an indication that there are many bodily conditions of the man that may affect his performance greatly.

Temperature and health. A final consideration of importance in specifying the temperature of working environments is the influence of temperature on health. This is not entirely a psychological problem, but it is certainly one which relates to the ultimate efficiency of workers. Statistical analyses on this point are far from complete or conclusive, but there do appear to be some definite correlations between worker health and temperature. Sickness appears to occur more frequently among workers in environments which are hotter than optimum. This appears to be the result of rapid cooling and chilling of the workers after leaving work. In one study of coal miners, the sickness rate was decreased appreciably by providing them with a changing room and bath facilities.[20]   In this indirect way, therefore, temperature may have an important influence on efficiency.

Conclusion.   The general trend of all the studies of this sort is clear: Atmospheric conditions interfering with normal or constant body temperature reduce physical efficiency. Ventilation systems which move and filter the air and which control temperature and humidity are usually a sound investment from the point of view of efficient work. The point of all this, for our investigations on man–machine systems, is obvious: If the systems are to be used in environments that are hot and stuffy or too cold, we cannot expect the same kind of performance from the men operating the machines that we can when the environment is optimal.

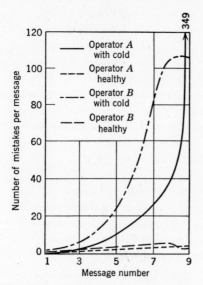

Fig. 195.   Number of mistakes made by two operators in recording nine consecutive Morse messages when they had head colds and when they were healthy.   (After Mackworth, 1946)

Oxygen Deficiency

Let us now turn to another aspect of the environment around us.   All of us work and play, live and die at the bottom of an ocean of air. Ordinarily we pay very little attention to the chemical composition of this medium.   Chemists tell us, however, that it consists of about one-fifth oxygen and four-fifths nitrogen, with a very small percentage of other rare gases.   The physicists tell us, too, that the pressure of this air around us at sea level amounts to about 15 pounds per square inch.   The chemical composition and the pressure of this air are pretty constant all over the face of the globe—as long as we keep at least one foot on the ground— and we ordinarily experience no difficulty in getting along in it.

Anoxia.   In some of the complex machines developed recently, however, man does not stay at the bottom of this ocean of air.   Our aircraft now are capable of flying as high as 40,000 to 45,000 feet, and, unless the supply of aviators is limitless, we had better know something about what happens to the human organism at these altitudes before we send any up there.   Physical experiments tell us that the pressure of air decreases markedly as we ascend to higher and higher altitudes. Although the composition of the air does not change, this means effectively that there is less pressure to force life-giving oxygen into the body at these altitudes. The condition that results when insufficient oxygen is fed into the body system is called *anoxia*. A considerable amount of work has been done on this problem during the war, and it is of some interest to review briefly the main findings of this research.

Anoxia and performance. As a result of experiments performed in the Andes Mountains, it is known now that the top limit at which men can work comfortably for prolonged periods of time is about 17,000 feet. Although there are individual records of men who have gone as high as 30,000 feet for short times and have lived to tell about it, the ordinary person can stay conscious for only 2 or 3 minutes at such an altitude. These are the top limits, however. We also know that at considerably lower altitudes the effects of anoxia may result in greatly impaired efficiency.

The sense of sight is an extremely sensitive indicator of the effects of anoxia, and Figure 196 shows the relative amount of light required for night vision at various altitudes. At an altitude of 14,000 feet, for example, a normal individual requires about twice as much light to see as he does at ground level. At an altitude of about 16,000 feet he requires nearly 2½ times more light. ·

Other effects of anoxia also have been very carefully studied and documented.[2] We know that, at altitudes of 16,000 feet, the average person begins to suffer from a dimming of vision even in daylight. Tremors of the hands appear, and it is difficult to move them with any precision. Exercise, even of the simplest type, becomes difficult, and a few deep knee bends may leave the individual panting and breathless. Worse than these effects, however, is the fact that thinking and memory become clouded and that serious errors of judgment are frequently made.

An especially dangerous aspect of anoxia is its insidiousness. It sneaks up on one. There are no warning signs that tell a person he is suffering from anoxia. There is no pain, and, as a matter of fact, people under the influence of anoxia tend to feel happy and gay. They may even want to call up a dear old aunt in Los Angeles. Pilots have fallen over unconscious before they ever suspected that anything was wrong with them.

Carbon monoxide. Obviously, our discussion of the effects of anoxia is primarily concerned with intricate systems such as aircraft that fly to altitudes where anoxia can occur. Of somewhat broader and more immediate concern to us are the noxious fumes and gases. The most important of these is carbon monoxide. Carbon monoxide poisoning produces anoxia in the body by destroying the red blood cells which carry oxygen to the various parts of the body. It is now known that anoxia due to carbon monoxide poisoning affects visual acuity, brightness discrimination, and dark adaptation just the same as the anoxia

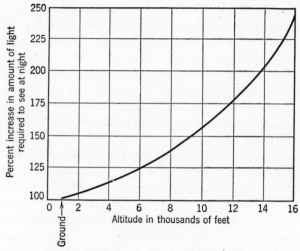

Fig. 196. How the amount of light for seeing must be increased at high altitudes to offset the effect of oxygen lack on vision. (After Pinson, 1941)

we suffer at high altitudes. For example, it has been shown that a 5 percent saturation of carbon monoxide in the blood has an effect on the visual threshold equal to that of an altitude of about 8,000 to 10,000 feet. Smoking three cigarettes [11] may cause a carbon monoxide saturation of 4 percent in the blood with an effect on visual sensitivity equal to that of an altitude of 8,000 feet.

Carbon monoxide is a serious problem in all environments where products of combustion, either of engines or machines or explosives, may contaminate the air. It is important because *very* small amounts of carbon monoxide in the atmosphere may affect efficiency enormously.[10] Thus, we know that a concentration of 1 part of carbon monoxide in 10,000 will produce no symptoms for about 2 hours. With a concentration of only 4 parts in 10,000, however, the air is safe for only 1 hour. If the concentration rises to 6 or 7 parts in 10,000, headache and unpleasant symptoms usually develop in less than an hour.

A carbon monoxide concentration of 10 to 12 parts in 10,000 is down-right dangerous if the exposure lasts 1 hour, and, if the concentration is as high as 35 parts in 10,000, it is usually fatal in less than 1 hour. The effects of carbon monoxide poisoning are a little more noticeable than those of anoxia. Some of the common symptoms are a tightness across the forehead, headache, throbbing in the temples, weakness, dizziness, dimness of vision, nausea and vomiting, and finally collapse.

AIR PRESSURE

So far, in talking about the ocean of air around us we have considered its temperature, its humidity, and the kinds of gases in it. For certain kinds of systems, however, it is important to consider another characteristic of the air, namely its pressure. Ordinarily we do not pay very much attention to the enormous weight of the column of air resting constantly on our shoulders and our bodies. However, we know from physical measurements that this pressure amounts to about 14 pounds per square inch, so that we carry a load of several tons of air on our shoulders at all times. So long as we stay at this same pressure, we experience no difficulty. However, the human body, if it is subjected to rapid changes in pressure, may suffer some serious effects.

Effects of pressure changes on the ear. If we change rapidly from low to high pressure, we may run the risk of damaging our ears.[2] The middle ear in man is a bony cavity inside the skull with two openings to outside atmospheric pressures. One of these is covered by the ear-drum which is flexible to some extent. If the pressure on one side of the eardrum is great, however, it may easily be damaged or broken. The other opening into the middle ear is by way of a thin tube, the Eustachian tube, which opens into the back of the mouth.

If we go from higher to lower atmospheric pressures, the air pressure increases inside the middle ear until a pressure difference of about 15 mm of mercury is built up between the air in the middle ear and the outside air. At this point the eardrum bulges out, and we cannot hear things quite as well as normally. If the pressure difference increases more than this, the air in the middle ear blows out through the Eustachian tube and balance is restored. Ordinarily this process is automatic, and the individual is aware only of a click as the air blows out.

In going from lesser to greater atmospheric pressures, however, the equalization process is not so easy. The Eustachian tube acts like a flutter valve which makes it difficult for the air to go from the mouth into the ear. Yawning, swallowing, or shouting help to open the tube for most people. But, if the membranes inside the mouth are inflamed or swollen because of a cold, or if the individual has some defect in the structure of the Eustachian tube opening, these devices may not work. In such cases, the eardrum bends inward owing to the increased pressure outside. If the air pressure outside becomes very much greater than the pressure in the middle ear, the eardrum may rupture and produce partial deafness.

"Bends." In going from greater pressures to lesser pressures, we may also experience serious symptoms that go under a variety of names—aeroembolism, aeroemphysema, caisson disease, or bends.[2] This kind of change is encountered in three types of occupational groups: caisson workers constructing bridges, docks, and so on, below the water; deep sea divers; and flying personnel. The symptoms develop when the change from a greater to a lesser atmosphere is too rapid, as, for example, a deep sea diver coming up too rapidly, or an aircraft ascending to high altitudes too rapidly. The worker experiences pain in and around the joints, which may be mild at the outset but very often becomes gnawing and boring in character and may become so severe that it is intolerable. These severe pains can cause loss of muscular power of the body member involved and, if the pain is allowed to continue, may result in total collapse.

Other symptoms go by the name of "chokes," which are a severe impairment of the breathing mechanism of the body. The individual suffers from a sensation of suffocation, and breathing becomes progressively more shallow and difficult, frequently resulting in collapse and unconsciousness. Skin symptoms also frequently develop, and finally there is a variety of neurological symptoms, effects on vision, other sensory disturbances, and loss of power of speech. A knowledge of these factors is obviously extremely important for certain kinds of working environments.

EFFECTS OF MOTION

Speed and Acceleration

If all of our man–machine systems were built on nice solid foundations, and did not show phenomenal proclivities for traversing such vast areas of geography, we would have a lot less to talk about in dealing with the general problem of the environment and its effect on the man who must work in it. Unfortunately, however, our modern man is not particularly happy to stay put anywhere. He moves—and rapidly. This business of getting from one place to another in the shortest possible time raises very serious problems in connection with engineering psychology.

Speed. Quite a lot of work has been done on the problems of speed and acceleration, particularly as they concern aircraft. At the present time, many of our modern aircraft have cruising speeds of around 200 and 300 miles per hour. We know that some special types of aircraft have attained speeds of about 550 miles per hour. There is considerable uncertainty about the ultimate speeds that will be attained by aircraft in the future, but it is anticipated that, when present difficulties with the compressibility factor are conquered, rocket flights may become a reality, and speeds of 25,000 miles per hour may eventually be reached. It is generally agreed that linear velocity *per se* has little or no effect on the body. But whether or not this general conclusion will be valid when we start shooting around the sky in rocket planes still is uncertain.

Human reaction time. From the standpoint of man–machine systems, the effect of speed, even though it does not appear to harm the body, raises some other problems. If an aircraft is flying at 600 miles an hour, for example, that means that it is making 10 miles a minute or about 300 yards per second. We know from studies of automobile drivers that it takes some drivers, even under the best conditions, about three quarters of a second to react to a red light by pressing on the brake pedal. If our pilot, therefore, suddenly decides to make a turn, he will have traveled several hundreds of yards before that nerve impulse can go from his brain down his leg, or his hand, to execute the decision. If, now, we add to this normal reaction time, delays arising from the fact that the pilot cannot see his instruments readily or that warning lights or signals are not detected immediately, it is very easy to imagine that a pilot will react a mile or more late.

Other problems of this sort arise too. We know from our experiences in World War II that in high-speed aircraft the pilot very frequently has only a second or two to line up his target in the gunsight. In short, as we increase the speed at which these various man–machine systems go hurtling through space, we encounter more and more the problem of the normal reaction time of the man who is operating the machine.

g forces. So much for the problems of speed as regards men and machines. Much more dramatic effects are experienced when we consider the problem of acceleration, that is, changes in speed of movement. In talking about problems of acceleration, the scientist uses a complicated equation derived from one of Newton's laws which states that the force is equal to the mass times the velocity squared divided by the radius of rotation. The force, in this case, is expressed in units of the force of gravity, called g, or the force exerted by gravity on a unit mass. If the acceleration occurs in a straight line, it is called linear acceleration; if there is also a change in direction, the acceleration is called centrifugal acceleration. Most studies have investigated the effects of centrifugal acceleration,[2] and these are the ones we shall describe here.

Positive g forces. In terms of their effects on the body, it is important to distinguish between positive and negative g forces. Positive g acts in the direction of the long axis of the body and from head to foot. It produces effects that vary with the magnitude of the acceleration, with the rate at which it is increased and decreased, and with the duration of its action. A force of $+1g$ is what we normally experience in the upright position. With a $+2g$ force, the principal sensation is an awareness that the body is exerting pressure on the bosom of the breeches and there is a heaviness of hands and feet. Plus $3g$ or $4g$ produces exaggeration of this sensation of heaviness, and movements are accomplished only with great effort. The skeletal musculature becomes tense, resisting the tendency for the body to be compressed in the vertical dimension. The trunk and head, unless well supported and maintained in a line parallel to the line of force, are held erect only with great difficulty.

At $+5g$ the body is beyond the control of the muscles except for slight movements of the arms and head, and for all practical purposes one is physically helpless. At this point, there is a distinct dragging sensation in the thorax, from the heavy traction of the intestines which normally float around loosely. The blood leaves the head and face, and in some cases there is a distinct diminution or complete loss of vision commonly known as "blacking out." The lower parts of the legs feel congested, and there may be cramping of the calf muscles. Breathing becomes difficult—probably due to the lowering of the diaphragm from the pull of the liver from below and the pressure of the heart and lungs from above. As acceleration increases the g forces from $+5$ to $+9$, there is no apparent exaggeration of these painful symptoms, possibly due to the anaesthetic effect on the brain by its loss of blood. Vision, however, is lost quite suddenly and is sometimes accompanied by spots or light flashes before the eyes. Coma or unconsciousness usually appears between $+5$ and $+8g$, depending on individual tolerances.

Negative g forces. Negative g forces, acting in the direction of feet to head, are not commonly experienced. They do occur, however, in certain kinds of acrobatic maneuvers in aircraft. At $-1g$, the sensation is equivalent to that of hanging head downward. If we experience $-1g$ in an upright position, there is a moderate upward displacement of the organs in the body and a moderate congestion of blood in the face. As the negative g forces increase, the feeling of congestion and distress about the head and face increases markedly. At between -2 and $-3g$, the face feels highly congested and there is a a throbbing pain throughout the head. At -3 to $-4\frac{1}{2}g$ the congested feeling becomes intense, there is a sensation of greatly increased intracranial pressure, and the skull feels as if it is about to burst. The eyes feel as though they were being shoved from their sockets and there is a dry gritty feeling in the eyelids. In most cases, objects in the field of vision at this point appear red and give rise to the phenomenon of red vision, seeing red, or "redding out." Up to about $-4\frac{1}{2}g$, which is the highest sustained negative g force that has been studied in the human being, consciousness is retained, but there is an increasing mental confusion. Following such an exposure this mental confusion persists for several hours and may be accompanied by a severe hangover-like headache. In this and the preceding paragraph, the g forces cited are for exposures lasting a second or more. Much higher forces can be tolerated if the exposure lasts less than a few tenths of a second.

Effects of mild g forces. It is possible to demonstrate the effects of moderate g forces on human reactions long before any severe effects are produced. One recent study [18] measured the ability of 34 rated military pilots in reading aircraft-instrument dials under the influence of $+1\frac{1}{2}$ and $+3g$. They made significantly more errors under the latter condition. As in anoxia, therefore, there appears to be a gradual reduction in human performance under the influence of increasing g forces until complete incapacity is finally produced.

Well, there is no reason to hammer the point home any further. In certain kinds of man–machine systems, speed or changes of speed of the work environment have to be considered by the designer and experimenter. The dimming and loss of vision, the loss of consciousness, and the greatly increased difficulty of making movements with the hands and feet all raise serious problems in the design of rapidly moving systems.

MOTION SICKNESS

Fortunately, the movements of our vehicles are not always quite so extreme as those we have been discussing so far. But, even if we are concerned with less rapid means of locomotion than aircraft, we very frequently encounter situations that affect men quite markedly. These are grouped under the general title of "Motion Sickness."

Kinds. Motion sickness includes a lot of different kinds of sickness, depending on the vehicle in which the person is riding. There is airsickness, seasickness, train sickness, car sickness, sickness on amusement park devices, sickness in parachute descents, and even sickness from riding animals—especially camels. All these types of sickness have pretty much the same general kind of symptoms. The victim experiences nausea, pallor, sweating, and vomiting, and all these experiences are produced by the same kind of stimulus—motion.

Causes. Several recent investigations have been concerned with clarifying and understanding the dynamics of motion sickness. In one of these experiments,[1] a vertical accelerator was used in which it was possible to control the wave form, acceleration, velocity, and amplitude of movement. As a result of experiments with this gadget, we know now that slow oscillations of large amplitude are more productive of sickness than faster waves of smaller amplitude. Thus, in one study 37 percent of the subjects became sick when they were stimulated with a wave frequency of 13 cycles per minute and an amplitude of 9 feet. But only 7 percent became sick with a wave frequency of 32 cycles per minute and an amplitude of 1 foot. It is also known that there is more to motion sickness than just motion. A number of psychological and physiological factors also contribute.[19] Fear, insecurity, inability to relax, and lack of confidence in the vehicle, for example, are some of the psychological factors which contribute enormously to motion sickness. Among the physiological factors are such things as temperature, ventilation, odors, fatigue, overindulgence in drinking, smoking, and digestive disturbances.

Consequences. Fortunately most people get used to motion of this sort after a number of exposures to it—they acclimatize. They do not get sick so often as they do when they are first exposed to the motion. Even so, as far as *work* is concerned, there can be no doubt that the efficiency of a man on a pitching, bucking, undulating, and rolling ship is not as good as the efficiency of the same man in a good steady environment. This factor is certainly one that has to be taken into consideration in the design and study of man–machine systems.

VIBRATION

There is still another kind of motion that needs to be considered, and that is the kind of motion usually called vibration. Vibration is a very high-frequency movement which may range anywhere from 20 to 140 cycles per second. It is also characterized by having a rather low amplitude.

Effects of vibration on the body. Not very much experimental work has been done on the effect of vibration on human efficiency. There is, however, one fairly extensive analysis of this problem made by a German scientist working at the Institut für Luftfahrtmedizin in Berlin. He had a specially built oscillating platform which was capable of vibrating through a frequency range of 15 to 1,000 cycles per second. His experimental room was damped acoustically so that noise would not affect the subjects. He gave all his subjects a series of tests before, during, and after a 2-hour exposure to vibrations of various known amplitudes and frequencies.

One of the most interesting findings of his research was that vibration greatly affected binocular visual acuity. The people could not see so well when they were being subjected to vibration. Two kinds of vibration were especially bad. One was at frequencies between 25 and 40 cycles per second, and the other between 60 and 90 cycles per second. Although it is not known exactly why these frequencies affect visual acuity in this way, some theories have been advanced to account for these findings. One is that the decreased visual acuity is due to the attempt on the part of the eyes to follow the movements of the vibrating instrument. Another possibility is that the eyeball may be set into resonance with the vibration as a result of the elasticity of the supporting muscles around the eyeball. Another interesting finding of this study on vibration was that certain reflex actions in the body were diminished and at certain frequencies and amplitudes were completely suppressed during vibration.

Although the effects of vibration on the body are still incompletely understood, these findings indicate that subjective complaints of tremor of the eyeball, changes in the muscle balance and depth perception, chronic headaches, and visual fatigue may all have their basis in fact. Those of us who have tried to read for any period of time on a jerky bouncing train will be able to confirm from our own experience the effects of vibration.

Other effects of vibration. So far we have considered the effects of vibration when the body is being vibrated. But there are other situations in which the machine may be vibrating and the operator not. What about efficiency in this situation? Here again we have only a few experimental data, but we do know that visual tasks may become very difficult when the object being looked at is vibrating. Recent studies [4] show that legibility of numerals may be seriously impaired if they are vibrating. These studies seem to indicate that high frequencies are worse than low frequencies, high amplitudes worse than low amplitudes, and rotary vibration worse than linear vibration. The vibration frequencies in these studies varied from 8 to 30.5 per second, and the amplitudes from 0.0079 to 0.11 inch.

NOISE

One characteristic of our working environment that deserves considerable attention is the problem of noise. One unfortunate aspect of our civilization is that, the more complex it gets, the noisier it gets. The problem of noise has attracted the attention of specialists in many professional fields. Physicians, public health authorities, architects, psychologists, otologists, physicists, sound and electrical engineers have all contributed to the literature in this field. Safety engineers and insurance companies are also interested in the problem because of the growing recognition of occupational deafness. Many large cities have undertaken extensive noise reduction campaigns, and in our general consideration of the work environment we certainly ought to know whether or not noise reduces human efficiency, because we find so much noise in modern industry.

Facts? Because of all this interest in the general problem of noise, we would expect to find a very large body of respectable scientific evidence pointing to the effects of noise on human beings. Strange as it may seem, however, there is no large group of accredited scientific facts in this field.[3] In part, this situation may be due to the confusion in the ordinary mind between the annoyance value of noise and the actual effects of noise as measured in terms of human efficiency. This distinction is very often overlooked. We know very little about what makes a noise irritating. We do know that the irritation produced by noise is not necessarily related to its loudness. The faint dripping of a kitchen faucet or the scraping of a fingernail along a blackboard may make a man's hair stand on end, and yet this same man may ride in a thundering airplane without the slightest inconvenience, even though the airplane may generate a hundred thousand times as much noise as the faucet or fingernail. This psychological effect of noise has been aptly summarized by the statement, "It ain't exactly what he hears; it's the nasty way he hears it!"

Annoying noises. Only one thing can be said with definite assurance regarding the relative annoyance value of different kinds of noises, and that is that high tones and extremely low tones are judged almost universally to be more irritating than those in the middle ranges. This general principle has been of considerable value in soundproofing aircraft, offices, and other work spaces. It has been found, for example, that the elimination of the very high frequencies in aircraft noise greatly reduces the annoyance value of the noise to the passengers in the aircraft, even though the overall intensity of the noise may be only slightly reduced. Another thing we know is that interrupted noise or discontinuous tones are most generally found to be much more annoying than steady noises. There seems to be some fairly clear-cut evidence, furthermore, that greater damage to the inner ear results in animals subjected to high intensities when the tones are interrupted.

There is also a large miscellaneous list of factors that probably influence the annoyance of noise. None of these, however, has been subjected to systematic investigation. Among these factors are the unexpectedness of the noise, the amount of reverberation, and the degree to which the noise is unnecessary or indicates malfunctioning of the equipment. It should be clear, therefore, that we need to know a lot more about this general subject. Another thing that needs to be systematically investigated is the general problem of the individual differences in noise tolerance; and we need to know, finally, what the limits of noise tolerance are for an average population.

Noise and deafness. If we look at those studies that have investigated the influence of noise on human efficiency, we find again that there is very little known about this problem. A few things, however, can be said with certainty. One of these is that noise greatly increases the difficulty of verbal or oral communication. This general problem of voice communication by radio or telephone in noisy environments has been treated systematically in another chapter, so that we shall not dwell on it here. Another fact which has been very definitely established is that exposure to extremely noisy environments greatly reduces the sensitivity of the ear. Although the results of all of the studies on this problem agree in showing that the hearing loss is temporary, it may extend over several days and is certainly a factor to be reckoned with in systems that contain a lot of noise. The degree of the temporary deafness may also be extremely impressive. In one series of investigations at the Psycho-Acoustic Laboratory at Harvard

University, it was discovered that the loss of hearing may amount to about 80 db with certain frequencies. Translated into terms of energy, this means that the victim needs a hundred million times the normal amount of energy to hear, following his exposure to the noisy environment. It is also important to point out, however, that, during 5 years of research at the Psycho-Acoustic Laboratory, all kinds of noise were used to produce an almost endless diversity of temporary impairment, and not one case turned out to be permanently hard of hearing.

The amount of temporary deafness that results from exposure to noises of various frequencies and intensities was worked out by a group of experimenters [5] during the war. They found that temporary deafness is almost always for tones higher in frequency than the tone to which the victim was exposed. They also found that higher tones were a lot worse in producing temporary deafness than were low tones of the same intensity. And, as we might expect, long exposures were worse than short exposures, although the relationship was not proportional—that is, a 10-minute exposure was not twice as bad as a 5-minute exposure. On the basis of their experiments, they have worked up tables of "equinoxious noises." These tables tell us what combinations of tones, intensities, and durations will produce temporary deafness which lasts less than 24 hours, about 24 hours, and more than 24 hours.

Noise and efficiency. If we turn to the general group of scientific studies concerned with the effect of noise on other aspects of human efficiency, we find a large mass of contradictory data. It is very difficult to interpret the results of those experiments that have been carried out in industrial concerns, because there are so many factors other than the noise that may affect performance. For one thing, it is difficult to control the factor of suggestion in these field studies. Workers may believe that, since the work environment has now been made quieter, they ought to be able to work faster, and so they do. This may or may not indicate any genuine effect of a noisy environment on performance.

Probably the most exhaustive study on the effects of noise was conducted by Stevens and his collaborators [14] early in the war at the Psycho-Acoustic Laboratory. Subjects were exposed day after day for as long as 8 hours at a time to extremely high intensities of airplane noise. They were given nearly 100 tests of intelligence and psychomotor efficiency. No significant effects could be detected in any of the test results, despite the fact that people subjected to this barrage of noise claimed that they did not like it, felt fatigued by it, and were less tolerant of their friends at the end of the day. Other less exhaustive studies performed in military establishments have given essentially the same results.

Research still needed. The final answer on this, however, has not been given. There is still some important research to be done. We need new methods to study the relation between noise and people. The studies to date have revealed nothing of significance; yet most people are quite emphatic about their dislike of noise. It is probable that this dislike in realistic situations has an effect on human performance if we could measure it. One subject in Stevens' experiment, for example, reported that after hearing and feeling his daily dose of noise he felt much more inclined to beat his wife. The experiment, however, did not measure such tendencies.

Even though these studies have shown no overall quantitative effect of noise on human performance, there is considerable evidence to indicate that subjects require more energy to perform the same kind of work in a noisy environment than in a quiet one. A number of studies have shown quite consistently that the basal metabolism of subjects working in a noisy environment is higher than those working in a quiet one. Since the basal metabolism measures the overall work output of the body in terms of the amount of oxygen consumed, this seems to indicate that subjects in a noisy environment perform about equally well but require more energy to do the same amount of work. This may account for the numerous reports of fatigue from workers in noisy environments.

LIGHT AND COLOR

Another aspect of the work environment we need to touch on is that of light and color. The basic relationships between visual acuity and illumination, brightness contrast of objects, time of exposure, and glare have all been so thoroughly explored that there is a special branch of engineering to handle the practical applications of these data. This is the branch of engineering known as "illuminating engineering." The data in this field are so extensive that it is possible to look into reference handbooks [22] and find the solution to many practical problems. Some of these basic relationships have already been discussed in Chapter 4. At this time we should like to summarize the lighting recommendations that are now generally accepted.

Lighting to suit the job. In most practical work environments, the job is a constant, and the problem is to find the kind of lighting that will permit the job to be done effectively. This is easy since the Illuminating Engineering Society has just issued an *IES lighting handbook* which gives recommended levels of illuminations for several hundred kinds of jobs. This handbook, incidentally, is an extremely valuable reference because it contains all sorts of useful information about light measurements, lighting installations, wiring diagrams, lighting fixtures, and other things that the illuminating engineer needs to know.

Because of the great diversity of jobs men do with their eyes, it is difficult to establish a single set of recommendations to cover all situations. In addition, the codes are subject to revision, and there is some recent evidence [15] that our present standards are a little high in some instances. The following is a rough guide compounded from the best available evidence:

One to 5 foot-candles are sufficient for seeing large objects and for illuminating hallways and stairs.

Five to 10 foot-candles are needed for visual work that is casual and more or less interrupted. This illumination is satisfactory for reception rooms, washrooms, warehouses, and storerooms.

Ten to 15 foot-candles are needed for visual tasks comparable to those of reading large-sized print (10 or 11 point) on paper of good quality.

Fifteen to 20 foot-candles should be used where handwriting and moderately fine detail must be discriminated. This is satisfactory for general office work, mail rooms, and file rooms.

Thirty to 40 foot-candles are required for difficult tasks comparable to the reading of 6-point type for long periods of time.

Forty to 50 foot-candles are needed for severe visual tasks, for example, drafting, which require the reading of fine scales over long periods of time.

Fifty to 100—and sometimes even more—foot-candles are needed for very severe visual tasks where the brightness contrasts are very low, for example, stitching on black cloth, manufacturing black shoes, and so on.

The job to suit the lighting. There are some work situations where the lighting cannot be manipulated at will to obtain maximum visibility. Dials used in aircraft are a case in point. If the illumination inside an aircraft is increased too much the pilot may be blinded and unable to see out of his cabin at night. Here the lighting is fixed, and the job must be made to suit the lighting. If we have only $\frac{1}{10}$ foot-candle of light in a certain work space and can use no more, the dials and symbols that must be read have to be twice as large as those in another room with 10 foot-candles of illumination. Other factors such as brightness contrast, the degree of blackness or lightness of various kinds of visual symbols, and their color must also be considered in the design of visual displays in these types of systems.

Color. However, we shall have to leave this interesting group of problems and conclude this chapter with a discussion of one more factor in the environment which has recently gained a lot of attention. Coming to the fore is the question of the color dynamics of the work environment. Does the use of color schemes for walls and machinery have anything to do with the efficiency of work? The Pittsburgh Plate Glass Company, which manufactures paints as well as glass, thinks so. They have put out a brochure reporting cases in which workers' comfort, morale, and production have been increased by painting walls in various pastel shades. It is hard to tell whether these cases mean what they seem to mean, because finding out whether this factor causes a jump in production is a difficult problem. But there is now a great deal of interest in it, and we may expect current and future research to give us some sort of an answer to it.

Contrast. One general consideration, related in a distant sort of way to this problem of color dynamics, is that of painting certain parts of machinery in lighter or darker colors so that they are more easily distinguished in the work environment. There seems to be no question that this factor does increase the efficiency of people operating machinery. This general principle does not seem to have been made use of as much as it should in complex systems such as radar rooms and aircraft, for example. The basic idea is simple. If the general background of the aircraft cockpit is painted a fairly dull color, the pilot's job can be made simpler if his important controls contrast with it markedly in color or in lightness. The same principle can be used in the design of radar; for example, if the background for the radar consoles is painted a dull color, then the important switches should be painted bright light colors to make them stand out so that they can be easily located and reached by the radar operator. In industry, main switches, fuse boxes, and important parts of machinery can be made to stand out in the same way.

CONCLUSION

So much then for a general consideration of the work environment. We have by no means exhausted this subject, but we have selected some typical material for discussion. To review briefly, in this chapter we have tried to advance the general thesis that machines do not work alone. They work in environments. And so do the men who operate them. We are forced to recognize that a great number of environmental factors in the work space affect the performance and efficiency of the man there. Our human requirements and our expectations of what a man can do in a system depend to a great extent on the kind of environment into which the system is thrown. If the temperature is excessively hot, if the environment is humid, if it vibrates excessively, if there is a lot of noise, and if the illumination is low, we cannot expect as much work or as efficient work from the man. Conversely, these various kinds of evidence give us some clues as to how we can increase the efficiency of men operating machines. Too little attention has been given to this problem in the past, and it seems almost certain that a considerable amount of improvement can be made by altering many characteristics of the environment in which men work.

SELECTED REFERENCES

1. ALEXANDER, S. J., COTZIN, M., KLEE, J. B., and WENDT, G. R. Studies of motion sickness: XVI. The effects upon sickness rates of waves of various frequencies but identical acceleration. *J. Exp. Psychol.*, 1947, **5**, 440–448.
2. ARMSTRONG, H. G. *Principles and practice of aviation medicine.* New York: Houghton Mifflin, 1946.
3. BERRIEN, F. K. The effects of noise. *Psychol. Bull.*, 1946, **43**, 143–158.
4. CROOK, M. N., HOFFMAN, A. C., WESSELL, N. Y., WULFECK, J. W., and KENNEDY, J. L. Effect of vibration on legibility of tabular numerical material: experiments 5 to 7. Research Laboratory of Sensory Psychology and Physiology, Tufts College, Report No. 4, August 1947.
5. DAVIS, H., MORGAN, C. T., HAWKINS, J. E., JR., GALAMBOS, R., and SMITH, F. W. Temporary deafness following exposure to loud tones and noise. Department of Physiology, Harvard Medical School, Report No. OEM cmr–194, September 30, 1943.
6. EICHNA, L. W., ASHE, W. F., BEAN, W. B., and SHELLEY, W. B. The upper limits of environmental heat and humidity tolerated by acclimatized men working in hot environments. *J. Industr. Hyg. and Toxicology*, 1945, **27**, 59–84.
7. LUCKIESH, M. *Light, vision and seeing.* New York: Van Nostrand, 1944.
8. MACKWORTH, N. H. Effects of heat on wireless telegraphy operators hearing and recording Morse messages. *Brit. J. Industr. Med.*, 1946, **3**, 143–158.
9. MACKWORTH, N. H. High incentives versus hot and humid atmospheres in a physical effort task. *Brit. J. Psychol.*, 1947, **38**, 90–102.
10. McFARLAND, R. A. *Human factors in air transport design.* New York: McGraw-Hill, 1946.

11. McFarland, R. A., Roughton, F. J. W., Halperin, M. H., and Niven, J. I. The effects of carbon monoxide and altitude on visual thresholds. *J. Aviat. Med.,* 1944, **15**, 381–394.
12. Pennock, G. A. Industrial research at Hawthorne. *Pers. J.,* 1930, **8**, 296–313.
13. Pinson, E. A. Effect of altitude on dark adaptation. Air Corps, Materiel Division, Experimental Engineering Section, Report No. EXP-M-54-653-63, 7 October 1941.
14. Stevens, S. S. The science of noise. *Atlantic Mon.,* 1946, **178**, 96–102.
15. Tinker, M. A. Illumination standards. *Am. J. Pub. Health,* 1946, **36**, 963–973.
16. Vernon, H. M. *Accidents and their prevention.* Cambridge: Cambridge University Press, 1936.
17. Viteles, M. S. *Industrial psychology.* New York: Norton, 1932.
18. Warrick, M. J., Nelson, R. E., and Lund, D. W. Effect of increased positive acceleration *(G)* on ability to read aircraft instrument dials. In Fitts, P. M. (Ed.) *Psychological research on equipment design.* U. S. Government Printing Office, 1947, 257–264.
19. Zwerling, I. Psychological factors in susceptibility to motion sickness. *J. Psychol.,* 1947, **23**, 219–239.
20. *Eighteenth Annual Report of the Industrial Health Research Board.* Medical Research Council, London, 1938.
21. *Heating, ventilating, air conditioning guide.* American Society of Heating and Ventilating Engineers, 51 Madison Avenue, New York, New York, 1948.
22. *IES lighting handbook: The standard lighting guide.* Illuminating Engineering Society, 51 Madison Avenue, New York, New York, 1947.
23. *Ventilation: Report of the New York State Commission on Ventilation.* New York: Dutton, 1923.

Index of Names

Adams, P. R., 187
Air Forces, 122–127, 131–133, 137–138, 155, 166, 188, 309, 312, 335
  see also Wright Field, Air Materiel Command
Air Materiel Command, 154, 155, 188, 295, 329, 421
  see also Wright Field, Army Air Forces
Alexander, S. J., 420
Alger, P. L., 44, 65
Angels, A., 391
Armstrong, H. G., 420
Army Air Forces, *see* Air Forces, Wright Field
Ashe, W. F., 420

Barnes, R. M., 13, 278–279, 295, 339, 341, 343, 346, 349, 364
Bartlett, F. C., 391
Bartlett, N. R., 117, 187
Bartley, S. H., 391
Bean, W. B., 420
Beard, A. P., 320–322, 329
Beck, C. S., 187
Bedale, E. M., 332–333, 364
Behar, M. F., 41–42, 44–45
Bell, Alexander Graham, 193
Bell Telephone Laboratories, 214, 218
Benton, R. S., 364
Berger, C., 177–179, 187
Berrien, F. K., 420
Biddulph, R., 211
Bills, A. G., 371, 391
Bitterman, M. E., 391
Blackwell, H. R., 85, 89, 116
Blondel, A., 87, 116
Bouma, P. J., 85, 116
Bouman, H. D., 296
Bray, C. W., 139–140, 155

Brown, C. W., 387, 391
Brown, J. S., 270–273, 278, 280–281, 283, 295
Buswell, G. T., 110, 116

Cambridge University, 155, 174, 188, 377, 398–399
Cameron, D. E., 390–391
Campbell, J. M., 18, 38
Carpenter, A., 391
Carter, L. F., 182, 188, 306, 329
Channel, R. C., 154, 351, 364
Chapanis, A., 42, 45–46, 51, 53, 55–56, 66, 83, 116, 135–136, 154, 164, 188
Chute, E., 319
Civil Aeronautics Board, 319–320
Clarke, H. H., 319, 329
Coakley, J. D., 39–40, 47–48, 66
Cobb, P. W., 103, 116
Columbia University, 369, 373, 381
Connell, S. C., 184, 188
Connor, J. P., 103, 116
Connor, M. B., 325–329
Cotzin, M., 420
Crook, M. N., 420
Croxton, F. E., 183, 188

Damon, A., 364
Davis, H., 208, 211, 241, 263, 420
Doughty, J. M., 257, 263
Duvoisin, G., 187

Edwards, A. S., 267, 295, 389, 391
Egan, J. P., 221, 241
Eichna, L. W., 400, 420
Ellson, D. G., 288–291, 295

Ferree, C. E., 102, 116
Fitts, P. M., 13, 122–124, 154–155, 275–276, 329

423

Subject Index